Mathematical Applications
in Accounting

Mathematical Applications
in Accounting

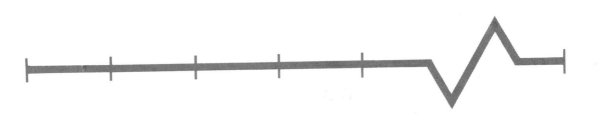

A. WAYNE CORCORAN, PhD, CPA
University of Massachusetts

Under the General Editorship of
ROBERT K. MAUTZ
University of Illinois

HARCOURT, BRACE & WORLD, INC.
New York | Chicago | San Francisco | Atlanta

6566

Preface

One need only glance at the current literature to see that accounting is moving toward the extensive adoption of applied mathematics. Instead of resisting the intrusion of mathematics, as was once the case, accountants are now using mathematical approaches. Many accountants have difficulty in applying mathematics to their daily work. I hope that this book will help them in their struggles.

Mathematical Applications in Accounting assumes a familiarity with the algebraic procedures necessary to solve $3x = 6$, and an acquaintance with algebraic factoring, the laws of exponents, and logarithms.

Chapter 0 has been written to refresh the reader's knowledge of high-school mathematics. The material in Chapter 1—compounding and discounting series of payments—has been chosen not only because of its importance in managerial and financial accounting, but because it enables the reader to review algebra, formulate mathematical models, manipulate logarithms, and obtain some notion of one of the important uses of finite and infinitesimal calculus. Chapter 2 also builds on algebra, so that by the time Chapter 3 (Calculus) is reached, the reader should be noting parameter positions in models and theorems and easily following algebraic procedures.

Although the book can be used as the nucleus of a separate course in mathematical accounting, it has been designed primarily as a supplement for the basic accounting courses (introductory, intermediate, advanced, cost, and managerial), or for courses in production management, managerial mathematics, industrial engineering, economics, finance, or operations research. Let me be more specific about its use in cost and managerial accounting courses.

Most good cost and managerial texts spend a great deal of time with the areas of planning and control and, in particular, with the subject of capital budgeting. Natural extensions of capital budgeting analysis are found in replacement theory, queuing theory, and inventory control theory. In fact, when to replace equipment, how many service channels to install, and what amount to invest in inventory are all capital budgeting questions. Similarly, planning and control are easily extended to embrace cost estimation as well as constrained and unconstrained optimization. With so many interesting mathematical topics available that are so closely related to cost and managerial accounting, it became very difficult to select "best" topics in organizing this book. Let us look at some of the topics that were selected as having especial importance in the cost and managerial accounting areas.

Chapter 1 develops compounding and discounting techniques, which are applied to capital budgeting problems in Chapters 2 and 4. Control charting is applied to cost control in Chapter 4. Chapter 5 and its problems discuss estimating production time via learning curves and studying the relationship of learning curves to cost estimation, standard costing, and make or buy decisions. It also develops inventory theory in deterministic and probabilistic situations under a variety of assumptions. Multiple regression analysis is presented in Chapter 6. Chapter 7 contains matrix approaches to process cost reports, secondary overhead allocation, and variance analysis; in addition, it discusses the processing structure common to many accounting areas and shows how simple matrix operations can clarify and unite accounting procedures. Chapter 8 concerns itself with linear programing and the selection of optimal production programs as well as the use of "shadow prices" in variance analysis. Chapter 9 deals with the transportation problem of linear programing and the minimizing of shipping costs.

The book, however, is not limited to cost and managerial accounting courses. Perhaps it would be wise to detail its possible use in other accounting courses.

Many intermediate courses consider time series mathematics (compounding and discounting) and its applications, which are the subjects of Chapters 1 and 2. The applications include mortgages, sinking funds, pensions, bond price determination, capital budgeting, and annuity and sinking fund methods of depreciation. A simple formula for treating the central issue of the chapter on statements from incomplete records appears in Chapter 0. Bonus and tax computations via matrix inversion are covered in Chapter 7. Advanced courses may not only use the compounding and discounting chapters, but should also find pertinent the matrix approach to statements of affairs and to the treatment of the elimination of intercompany profits in consolidated financial statements presented in terms of matrices in Chapter 7.

I owe a debt of gratitude to two wise and knowledgeable men, whose attitudes toward mathematics have significantly stimulated my own. My thanks, therefore, to Professors Edward L. Wallace and William W. Cooper.

The number of people who have helped directly or indirectly in the development of this book is indeed large. Many suggestions from Professors Robert Mautz, Nicholas Dopuch, and Bertrand Horwitz have been incorporated in the book and have resulted in substantial improvements. However, any errors remaining in the book are mine.

My choice of subject matter was influenced by fellow members of the Ford Foundation Seminar on Applied Mathematics and Computers held at the University of Chicago during the summer of 1965. Mr. Donald Stanhope, Manager of the Continuing Educational Program of the National Association of Accountants, and several of the accounting executives who have attended NAA mathematics seminars also helped in my selection of material.

Dr. Carl Dennler, chairman of the accounting department at the University of Massachusetts, helped me to keep the book's audience in clear focus.

Many students have helped in the development of problem material for the book. Three of them—Roy Ageloff, Dave Almond, and Wann Jong—were especially hard on me and deserve a special word of thanks.

Anyone who has ever done any mathematical writing knows what a blessing it is to find a good mathematical typist. Here is a job that calls for care, dedication, and patience. I was fortunate enough to secure the assistance of three experts—Mrs. Dian Doran, Miss Veronica Hosa, and Mrs. Vesta Powers.

Finally, I wish to thank my wife and my four boys for putting up with me, my eccentricities, and my work. Their blood as well as mine flows in this book, and to them it is affectionately dedicated.

A. WAYNE CORCORAN

Contents

Contents

Mathematical Applications
in Accounting

Attitudes and
Basic Mechanics

Introduction

As the field of accounting has expanded and the management services departments of leading CPA firms have grown, accounting literature has taken on a pronouncedly mathematical flavor. However, no texts have appeared that help the nonmathematical accountant understand and become operationally proficient at applying mathematics to his daily work. With such proficiency, the accountant is better able to

1. help management make complicated decisions whose analysis calls for sophisticated mathematical formulation,

2. revitalize approaches to traditional accounting areas,

3. converse fluently with other management consultants who use math terms in their daily discussions, and

4. understand better the language and uses of computers.

The goal of this text is to sell mathematics—not for its own sake, but rather to bridge the gap between it and its application to accounting problems. This is a difficult objective. Rather than assuming some level of mathematical conversance, this chapter is devoted to summarizing the basics of algebraic factoring, laws of exponents, logarithms, graphs, and sigma notation.

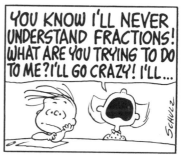

Notation

To overcome any fear of notation you may have, "symbolize" as many accounting relationships as you can. For instance, straight-line depreciation may be symbolized as follows:

$$D = \frac{C - S}{N}$$

KEY D = depreciation
C = cost
S = salvage value
N = number of years of life

Observe that the notation has been chosen mnemonically; that is, D for depreciation, C for cost, etc. Generally, the notation in this book will be so chosen. For example, in Chapter 1, the symbol p will be used for present and f for future. However, where the literature has developed standard notation and there is no way of improving it, standard notation will be employed. In this way, if you consult some of the suggested readings, you will already be familiar with the notation.

You could try to make up formulas for other methods of depreciation, or for inventory pricing, or for statement preparation, or for anything that has a set relationship. In this way, you will find out that notation is helpful and that English is often cumbersome and inadequate. Whole chapters in accounting texts may reduce to an equation, which is easily comprehended, even though the verbal descriptions are extremely difficult. One such chapter is that dealing with dollar-value-LIFO-retail inventories. Another chapter is that describing the preparation of statements from incomplete records, which reduces to the following equation:

$$T_c = T_a + \Delta PT - \Delta AT$$

T_c = revenue (let $T = R$ for revenues in formula) or expenses (let $T = E$ **KEY** for expenses) on a cash basis

T_a = revenues ($T = R$) or expenses ($T = E$) on an accrual basis

ΔPT = change in prepaid T (i.e., ending balance of prepaid T, minus the beginning balance)

ΔAT = change in accrued T (i.e., ending balance of accrued T, minus the beginning balance)

Note the use of mnemonics again: a for accrual, c for cash, P for prepaid, and A for accrued. Since we are here dealing with revenue and expense accounts, the so-called "temporary" accounts, T is used to stand for the general name of any such account. Unfortunately, Δ has no basis in mnemonics but rather is a widely used mathematical symbol meaning "change in" or "difference."

What are some standard notations? The letters x, y, and z are usually reserved for variables (intuitively, a variable is something that can take on many values) and the letters a, b, and c for parameters (i.e., coefficients, exponents, and constants). For example, you might see

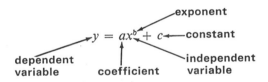

Here, independent and dependent are used in the usual, colloquial sense. One variable is free to take on any value, but the value of the other variable (y) depends on the value taken by the independent variable (x). The equation is in general form. Another general form would be

$$y = f(x)$$

This may be translated as "y is some function of x." We would be getting more specific if we wrote the values for a, b, and c (here arbitrarily chosen):

$$y = 3x^2 - 5,$$

where $a = 3$
$b = 2$
$c = -5$

To the uninitiated, such insertion of numbers in place of letters is very welcome. Unfortunately, however, when this is done, generality is abandoned, and rules and theorems (intuitively, statements) can be neither formulated nor proven.

In mathematics, it is important to be able to follow the manipulation of parameters in theorems and algebraic presentations. For example, one calculus theorem states

If $y = ax^b$,

then $\qquad \dfrac{d(y)}{dx} = \dfrac{d(ax^b)}{dx} = abx^{b-1}$

Ignoring $d(\ )/dx$, concentrate on how ax^b becomes abx^{b-1}.

Try to solve the following problem.[1]

$$y = 3x^4$$

$$\frac{dy}{dx} = ?$$

A Review of Algebraic Factoring

Suppose we wish to reduce

$$\frac{x^3 - 6x^2 - 16x}{8 - x}$$

to its simplest terms. We could begin by factoring out an x from the numerator.

$$\frac{x(x^2 - 6x - 16)}{8 - x}$$

Next, we could factor the expression within parentheses. To do this, we set up the expression

$$(x \qquad)(x \qquad)$$

and ask ourselves what two numbers (1) generate -16 when multiplied together, and (2) generate $-6x$ when individually multiplied by x and the

---

[1] If you get

$$\frac{dy}{dx} = 3(4)x^{4-1} = 12x^3$$

you are able to follow parameter positions. For those who have not been exposed to calculus before, you have now taken your first derivative.

Chapter 0: Attitudes and Basic Mechanics

separate products added. The numbers in question are -8 and 2, and the expression becomes

$$\frac{x(x - 8)(x + 2)}{8 - x}$$

Suppose, however, we did not see that -8 and 2 were the desired numbers. How would we proceed?

The quadratic formula was designed to accomplish factoring of second-degree polynomials.

A second-degree polynomial is one wherein the highest power of x is 2.   **NOTE**

The quadratic formula is based on the expression $ax^2 + bx + c = 0$. The roots (solution) of this expression can be obtained by applying the quadratic formula:

QUADRATIC FORMULA   ◀

$$\frac{-b \pm \sqrt{b^2 - 4ac}}{2a}$$

To illustrate, return to our numerator expression, $x^2 - 6x - 16$. To see what the letters a, b, and c are, recall that $x^2 = 1x^2$, and place the general expression above our expression as follows:

General expression: $ax^2 + bx + c$

Our expression: $x^2 - 6x - 16$

Substituting for a, b, and c in the quadratic formula yields

$$\frac{-(-6) \pm \sqrt{(-6)^2 - 4(1)(-16)}}{2(1)} = \frac{6 \pm \sqrt{36 + 64}}{2} = \frac{6 \pm 10}{2} = 8, -2$$

Note that the signs are reversed (we had $-8, 2$ before), because the general expression is set equal to zero and the actual solutions to the resulting equation are found. Our expression, on the other hand, is not an equation; hence, we cannot set individual factors equal to zero (e.g., $x - 8 = 0$) and must change the signs of the quadratic formula results.

Let us return now to our example. At this stage, we have

$$\frac{x(x - 8)(x + 2)}{8 - x}$$

It is now possible to do what is known as "-1 cancelation." Note that the numerator has a factor, $x - 8$, and the denominator has a factor, $8 - x$. If we multiply either factor by -1 and rearrange the resulting terms, we find

A Review of Algebraic Factoring   **5** that one factor is the same as the other. For example, multiply the denominator factor by -1:

$$(-1)(8 - x) = -8 + x$$
$$= x - 8$$

which is a numerator factor. Our last step then becomes

$$\frac{x(x - 8)(x + 2)}{8 - x} = \frac{x(x - 8)(x + 2)}{-(x - 8)} = -x(x + 2)$$

An alternative approach to the problem is to perform long division:

$$
\begin{array}{r}
-x^2 \quad -2x \\
-x + 8 \overline{)\, x^3 \, -6x^2 \, -16x} \\
\underline{-(x^3 \, -8x^2)} \\
2x^2 \, -16x \\
\underline{-(2x^2 \, -16x)} \\
0
\end{array}
$$

NOTE 1. The denominator terms were interchanged.

2. The quotient may be factored to our previous results, $-x(x + 2)$.

Laws of Exponents

Much of algebra and its applications involves the manipulation of exponents. Some rules that will help us are

   1. If x^i is multiplied by x^j, the answer is x^{i+j}.

EXAMPLE _____

$$x^2 x^3 = (x \cdot x)(x \cdot x \cdot x) = x^5$$

   2. If x^i is raised to the jth power, the answer is x^{ij}.

EXAMPLE _____

$$(x^2)^3 = (x \cdot x)(x \cdot x)(x \cdot x) = x^{2(3)} = x^6.$$

   3. If x^i is divided by x^j, the answer is x^{i-j}.

$$\frac{x^3}{x^2} = \frac{(x \cdot x \cdot x)}{(x \cdot x)} = x^{3-2} = x$$

There are different ways of writing exponents (exponents are also known as powers). We will use the symbol $\equiv$ to mean that the expression on the left of the symbol is identical to the one on the right in any case; that is, the expression on the left is defined as shown by the expression on the right. The $\equiv$ sign should be distinguished from the $=$ sign, which is weaker. Thus, in a given problem, $y^3 = x^2 + 3$ may be true. However, $y^3 \equiv y \cdot y \cdot y$ is always true. Some examples of different ways of writing exponents are

$$1^n \equiv 1$$

One raised to any power is still 1.

$$3x \equiv 3x^1$$
$$1 \equiv x^0$$

Anything other than zero raised to the zeroth power is 1.

$$\frac{1}{(1+r)^3} \equiv \left(\frac{1}{1+r}\right)^3 \equiv (1+r)^{-3}$$

Some people are puzzled by the middle expression. Recall that $1^n \equiv 1$ and consider an intermediate step

$$\frac{1^3}{(1+r)^3} \equiv \left(\frac{1}{1+r}\right)^3$$

Logarithms

Logarithms are needed in obtaining numerical solutions to problems. Before we consider logarithms (hereafter, simply called "logs"), we should specify the base of the logs. Two bases are in popular use: (1) common or base 10 logs, and (2) natural or base e logs. We shall employ only common logs in this book.

A log is an exponent. For example, $10^3 = 1,000$ states that $\log_{10} 1,000 = 3$. Here the subscript 10 indicates the base; however, if no number is shown as base, base 10 is usually assumed.

A log has two parts: a characteristic and a mantissa. Table A.5 contains mantissas for numbers, and characteristics may be determined by using scientific notation. Table 1 lists some numbers and their characteristics.

Table 1

Number	Number in Scientific Notation	Characteristic
1,000	10^3	3
100	10^2	2
10	10^1	1
1	10^0	0
0.1	10^{-1} (i.e., $\frac{1}{10}$)	-1
0.01	10^{-2} (i.e., $\frac{1}{100}$)	-2
0.001	10^{-3} (i.e., $\frac{1}{1000}$)	-3

Two rules for determining the characteristic of a log are

1. If the number (n) is greater than one (usual notation, $n > 1$), the characteristic is positive and is one less than the number of digits to the left of the decimal point.

2. If the number is less than one ($n < 1$), the characteristic is negative and is one more than the number of zeros immediately following the decimal point.

(You may want to copy Table A.5 to follow the rest of this section.) To find a log, first determine its characteristic. Then look up the first two digits (from the left) of the number in Table A.5 under column N and move along the column until you come to the third digit (from the left).

EXAMPLE

---

log   325 = 2.5119
log   18 = 1.2553
log   971 = 2.9872
log 0.325 = .5119 − 1 = −.4881
log 0.052 = .7160 − 2 = −1.2840

Note the alternative way of expressing the logs of 0.325 and 0.052. For instance, for log 0.325, we took the characteristic, − 1, and added the mantissa, 5119, to it to get the figure −.4881. The log of 0.325 could also be written as 9.5119 − 10, or, for that matter, as 84.5119 − 85. The log of 325 could be written as 12.5119 − 10, or any other arrangement that gives 2.5119.

Interpolation   Suppose we need the log of a four-digit number whose last digit is not a zero. Since Table A.5 lists logs only for three-digit numbers, we need to *interpolate* in the table. This is done by taking the last (fourth) digit, dividing it by ten, subtracting the mantissas of the immediately adjacent numbers containing our original number, multiplying the result by the fourth digit divided by ten, and adding this result to the lower of the adjacent mantissas.

Determine the log of 42.68.

Characteristic is 1. Mantissa is obtained by

mantissa of 427	= .6304
mantissa of 426	= .6294
difference	.0010
(difference) $\frac{8}{10}$ = (0.001 × 0.8)	= .0008
mantissa of 426	= .6294
mantissa of 4268	.6302

Therefore, the log of 42.68 = 1.6302

When multiplication of numbers is required, their logs are added. When division of numbers is required, their logs are subtracted.

Multiplication and Division

Multiply 25 by 36; divide 25 by 36.

$25(36) = $ antilog (log 25 + log 36)

$\dfrac{25}{36} = $ antilog (log 25 − log 36)

Many problems cannot be left in log form. To convert them from log form to ordinary numbers, the antilog of the log is taken. This is done by looking up the mantissa (*note: mantissa only*) of the log in Table A.5 and finding the number associated with that mantissa. Then take the characteristic of the log and reverse the rules for determining the characteristic of a number (for instance, if the log has a characteristic of 2, the antilog will be a number with three digits before the decimal).

Antilogs

Multiply 25 by 36 using logs.

$$25(36) = \text{antilog} (\log 25 + \log 36)$$
$$= \text{antilog} (1.3979 + 1.5563)$$
$$= \text{antilog} (2.9542)$$
$$= 900$$

The mantissa of 0.9542 corresponds to 900. The characteristic is 2; therefore, there are three digits.

Occasionally, we have to find the antilog of a log that is not in correct form (i.e., the log is a negative decimal). We may change this by adding and subtracting 1 to the log.

EXAMPLE

Find the antilog of $-.4559$.

$$\text{antilog} (-.4559) = \text{antilog} (1 - .4559 - 1)$$
$$= \text{antilog} (.5441 - 1)$$
$$= 0.35$$

Treatment of Exponents in a Number

An exponent of a number is treated as a coefficient of the log of the number.

EXAMPLE

(a) Find the square root of 0.003654 using logs.

$$\sqrt{0.003654} = 0.003654^{1/2} = \text{antilog} (\tfrac{1}{2} \log 0.003654)$$
$$= \text{antilog} (\tfrac{1}{2}(7.5628 - 10))$$
$$= \text{antilog} (\tfrac{1}{2}(17.5628 - 20))$$
$$= \text{antilog} (8.7814 - 10)$$
$$= \text{antilog} (.7814 - 2)$$
$$= .06045$$

(b) Find $(0.3)^{-1/3}$ using logs.

$$(0.3)^{-1/3} = \text{antilog} (-\tfrac{1}{3} \log 0.3)$$
$$= \text{antilog} (-\tfrac{1}{3}(.4771 - 1))$$
$$= \text{antilog} (-\tfrac{1}{3}(-.5229))$$
$$= \text{antilog} (0.1743)$$
$$= 1.494$$

Check by alternate procedure:

$$(0.3)^{-1/3} = \frac{1}{0.3^{1/3}}$$

$$
\begin{aligned}
\text{antilog} \left(\log 1 - \tfrac{1}{3} \log (0.3) \right) &= \text{antilog} \left(0 - \tfrac{1}{3}(9.4771 - 10) \right) \\
&= \text{antilog} \left(-\tfrac{1}{3}(29.4771 - 30) \right) \\
&= \text{antilog} \left(-(9.8257 - 10) \right) \\
&= \text{antilog} \left(-9.8257 + 10 \right) \\
&= \text{antilog} (0.1743) \\
&= 1.494
\end{aligned}
$$

(c) Determine $60(400)^{0.5}/0.72$ using logs.

$$
\begin{aligned}
\frac{60(400)^{0.5}}{0.72} &= \text{antilog} (\log 60 + 0.5 \log 400 - \log 0.72) \\
&= \text{antilog} (1.7782 + 0.5(2.6021) - (9.8573 - 10)) \\
&= (1.7782 + 1.3010) - (9.8573 - 10) \\
&= (13.0792 - 10) - (9.8573 - 10) \\
&= \text{antilog } 3.2219 \\
&= 1666.8
\end{aligned}
$$

Note that expressing the log 0.72 in an alternate form saves a few steps; to wit,

$$
\begin{aligned}
&= \text{antilog} (1.7782 + 0.5(2.6021) - (-.1427)) \\
&= 1.7782 + 1.3010 + .1427 \\
&= \text{antilog } 3.2219 \\
&= 1666.8
\end{aligned}
$$

The results can easily be checked because

$$400^{0.5} = \sqrt{400} = 20$$

$$\frac{60(20)}{0.72} = \frac{1200}{0.72} = \frac{100}{0.06} = 1666.7$$

(The slight difference is due to using only four-place log tables.)

COMMENT

Sometimes it is convenient to work with natural logs. Since the appendix to this book contains a table of common logs, it is useful to have a formula for converting to natural logs. The formula is

$$\log_a x = \log_a b (\log_b x)$$

Specifically,

$$\log_e x = \log_e 10 (\log_{10} x) = 2.30259 (\log_{10} x)$$

Converting Base 10 (Common) Logs to Base *e* (Natural) Logs

$$\log_e 4.5 = 2.30259(\log_{10} 4.5)$$
$$= 2.30259(.6532)$$
$$= 1.5041$$

$$\log_e 0.24 = 2.30259(\log_{10} 0.24)$$
$$= 2.30259(-.6189)$$
$$= -1.4271$$

Subscripted Variables and Sigma ($\sum$) Notation

Many problems dealt with in making managerial decisions involve more than the three ordinary variables x, y, and z. Therefore, it is convenient to be able to express a large number of variables in a simple way. This can be done by appending a subscript to the letter x and letting this subscript have a different value for each variable.

EXAMPLE

x_1, x_2, x_3, x_4, x_5 are five different variables that could be referred to by x_i, provided we specify that $i = 1, 2, \ldots, 5$.

We easily see that this device can represent thousands of variables merely by letting the subscript continue on from 5.

COMMENT It often happens that we need to add the values of several variables; for example,

$$x_1 + x_2 + x_3 + x_4 + x_5 + \cdots + x_{50}$$

To avoid the above cumbersome notation, the Greek letter sigma ($\sum$) is introduced as follows:

$$\sum_{i=1}^{50} x_i$$

Here the subscript i is called the index of summation, and the range of summation starts with whatever i equals under the $\sum$ sign and changes by 1 until the number on top of the $\sum$ sign is reached. This enables you to segregate certain variables for summation. For example,

$$\sum_{i=5}^{8} x_i = x_5 + x_6 + x_7 + x_8$$

Where no misunderstanding can result, it is customary to abbreviate the summing process even further:

$$\sum_{i=1}^{50} x_i = \sum x$$

When this is done, it is preferable to specify in a key to notation that $i = 1, 2, \ldots, 50$.

Another property of $\sum$ is brought out in the following example.

EXAMPLE

$$a_1 x_1 + a_2 x_2 + a_3 x_3 + \cdots + a_n x_n = \sum_{i=1}^{n} a_i x_i$$

where a_i is the coefficient of the ith variable, x_i. If $a_1 = a_2 = \cdots = a_n$, we also have

$$\sum_{i=1}^{n} a_i x_i = a \sum x$$

Here, the a has been factored out. For example,

$$3x_1 + 3x_2 + 3x_3 = \sum 3x_i = 3(x_1 + x_2 + x_3) = 3 \sum x$$

Graphing Straight Lines

A straight line is graphed as shown in Figure 1. We observe that the point at which the line cuts the vertical axis is known as the "y intercept" and has a value of a. In accounting, where many straight lines are fit to determine cost behavior, a would equal fixed costs, and the variable rate b times the volume x would equal the variable costs. The sum of the fixed costs and the variable costs would then equal the total cost y.

Suppose we did not know the formula for the line but had, say, nine observations of x and its corresponding y values. How could we determine the best straight-line formula? The best line would be an average line that

Figure 1

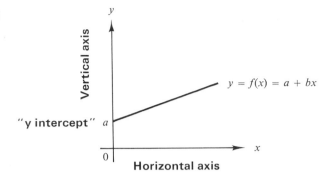

minimized the sum of the squares of the vertical distances from the actual costs to the costs that would be predicted by the line if we knew the formula for the line. To find this minimum sum, we have to use calculus. Calculus will not be discussed until Chapter 3. However, we will deal here with the equations that would have resulted if we had applied calculus.

An easy way to remember the least-square equations is

1. Start with the formula for a straight line, $y = a + bx$.
2. Multiply the formula through by $\sum$:

$$\sum y = \sum a + b \sum x$$

Because there are n such equations, there will be n times that a appears: so we see that $\sum a \equiv na$. We substitute this into the above formula to obtain

$$\sum y = na + b \sum x$$

3. Multiply the straight-line formula by $\sum x$:

$$\sum xy = a \sum x + b \sum x^2$$

4. Substitute values for $\sum y$, $\sum x$, $\sum xy$, and $\sum x^2$ into the last two equations and solve for a and b.
5. Put the calculated values of a and b into the straight-line formula. This line then expresses the desired relationship.

EXAMPLE

The total costs observed by a company during the past six months were

	Costs	Production Volume
January	$45,000	5,000
February	62,000	8,000
March	51,000	6,000
April	64,000	9,000
May	34,000	3,000
June	72,000	10,000

Find the formula relating costs to volume.   **Solution**

Let $M = 1,000$.

x	x^2	y	xy
$\$\ 5M$	$\$\ 25M^2$	$\$\ 45M$	$\$\ 225M^2$
$8M$	$64M^2$	$62M$	$496M^2$
$6M$	$36M^2$	$51M$	$306M^2$
$9M$	$81M^2$	$64M$	$576M^2$
$3M$	$9M^2$	$34M$	$102M^2$
$10M$	$100M^2$	$72M$	$720M^2$
$\sum x = \$41M$	$\sum x^2 = \$315M^2$	$\sum y = \$328M$	$\sum xy = \$2,425M^2$

Least-square equations: $\sum y = na + b \sum x$
$$\sum xy = a \sum x + b \sum x^2$$

Substituting the above values and observing that $n = 6$, we obtain

$$\$328,000 = \$6a + \$41,000b$$
$$\$2,425,000,000 = \$41,000a + \$315,000,000b$$

There are many ways in which to solve these equations. We shall use the ordinary algebraic approach of substituting the value of a from one equation into the other.

$$\$328,000 = 6a + \$41,000b$$
$$a = \frac{\$328,000 - \$41,000b}{6}$$

We substitute this value for a in the other equation.

$$\$2,425,000,000 = \frac{\$41,000(\$328,000 - \$41,000b)}{6} + \$315,000,000b$$

We obtain a common denominator:

$$\$2,425,000,000 = \frac{\$13,448,000,000 - \$1,681,000,000b + \$1,890,000,000b}{6}$$

$$\$14,550,000,000 - \$13,448,000,000 = \$209,000,000b$$

$$b = \frac{\$1,102,000,000}{\$209,000,000}$$

$$b = \$5.\overline{27}$$

NOTE The bar above the 27 indicates that 27 is repeated ad infinitum, that is, 27 27 27 $\cdots$ 27.

We now solve for a by using either of the original equations and substituting the value for b.

$$\$328,000 = 6a + \$41,000(\$5.\overline{27})$$

$$\$328,000 = 6a + \$216,182$$

$$a = \frac{\$328,000 - \$216,182}{6}$$

$$a = \$18,636$$

Our cost equation is

$$y = f(x) = \$18,636 + \$5.\overline{27}x$$

We can check a few values to see if the equation yields figures near past observed costs (since the line averages past observations, we cannot expect exact agreement):

$$f(\$5,000) = \$18,636 + \$5.\overline{27}(5,000) = \$45,000$$

$$f(\$8,000) = \$18,636 + \$5.\overline{27}(8,000) = \$60,818$$

$$f(\$9,000) = \$18,636 + \$5.\overline{27}(9,000) = \$66,090$$

Another formula for obtaining straight lines is explained in Problem 7, page 155.

Chapter 0: Attitudes and Basic Mechanics

Time Series Mathematics

Much of financial analysis involves manipulation of money flows that occur at different points in time. It must be realized that money changes in value with the passage of time. Not only is the purchasing power of the monetary unit likely to change, but a change always occurs equal to the interest the money earns during the specified time span. Sometimes the interest rate is stipulated contractually; at other times, it is implied in the circumstances, even though no cash is actually received. In any case, a sophisticated analysis in which there is a significant span of time must reflect the interest factor.

Where several time periods are involved, interest is earned on previous interest earnings, or, in other words, interest is compounded. This leads to a consideration of what constitutes a time period. Is a time period a year? A month? A second? When the period is as short as a second, interest may be said to be compounded continuously, and the infinitesimal calculus is used. When the period is a year or a month, interest is compounded discretely, and algebra is employed.

Discrete Compounding and Discounting

Let us consider a man with principal to invest. We wish to know how much he will have after a number of years with the assumption that the money will earn   **Single Sums** a certain percentage of interest compounded every year.[1] The situation is portrayed symbolically below.

KEY p = original principal
$f_{\overline{i}\rceil r\%}$ = future worth of principal after i years of compounding interest at $r\%$
r = rate of interest
$f_{\overline{1}\rceil r\%} = p + rp = p(1 + r)$
$f_{\overline{2}\rceil r\%} = p + rp + r(p + rp) = p + 2rp + r^2p = p(1 + r)^2$
$f_{\overline{3}\rceil r\%} = p + 2rp + r^2p + r(p + 2rp + r^2p) = p(1 + 3r + 3r^2 + r^3) = p(1 + r)^3$
$\vdots$
$f_{\overline{n}\rceil r\%} = p(1 + r)^n$ \hfill (1)

For a numerical example, suppose a man puts $5,000 in a savings account that pays 4% interest compounded annually, and he wants to know what his balance will be five years from now. The calculation could proceed by employing the binomial theorem as follows:[2]

$5,000 $f_{\overline{5}\rceil 4\%}$
$= \$5,000(1 + 0.04)^5$
$= \$5,000[\binom{5}{5}1^5(0.04)^0 + \binom{5}{4}1^4(0.04)^1 + \binom{5}{3}1^3(0.04)^2 + \binom{5}{2}1^2(0.04)^3 + \binom{5}{1}1^1(0.04)^4 + \binom{5}{0}1^0(0.04)^5]$
$= \$5,000[1 + 5(0.04) + 10(0.04)^2 + 10(0.04)^3 + 5(0.04)^4 + (0.04)^5]$
$= \$5,000[1 + 5(0.04) + 10(0.0016) + 10(0.000064) + 5(0.00000256) + 0.0000001024]$
$= \$5,000(1.216652904)$
$= \$6,083.26$

We have shown the above method purposely to discourage the pursuit of such an approach. Mathematical tables that make the task of computation considerably easier are available.

---

[1] The use of simple interest, that is, a situation where interest is earned only on principal and not on principal plus accumulated interest, will not receive attention in this chapter beyond the following example. In this example, simple interest is added to the face value of a note to obtain its maturity value, from which simple discount is deducted at the bank's rate to determine proceeds. A bank discounts a $10,000, 90-day, 4% note after it is 30 days old. If the discount rate is 6%, what sum of money is given to the customer?

Maturity value = ($10,000 × $\frac{90}{360}$ × 4%) + $10,000 = $10,100
Proceeds = maturity value − discount = $10,100 − ($10,100 × $\frac{60}{360}$ × 6%)
= $9,999

[2] Rather than use Pascal's triangle in the binomial expansion, we will employ the more useful combinatorial notation. This is defined as follows:

$$_nC_k = \binom{n}{k} = \frac{n!}{k!(n-k)!} = \frac{n(n-1)\cdots(n-k+1)}{1\cdot 2\cdot 3\cdots k}$$

and

$$\binom{5}{3} = \frac{5 \times 4 \times 3 \times 2 \times 1}{(1 \times 2 \times 3)(1 \times 2)} = \frac{5 \times 4 \times 3}{1 \times 2 \times 3} = 10$$

Also,
$0! = 1! = 1$

If we let p equal unity in (1), we have

$$f_{\overline{n}|r\%} = (1 + r)^n \tag{2}$$

This is the formula used in calculating the figures in the Appendix, Table A.1. By using this table, the numerical example reduces to

$$\$5,000 f_{\overline{5}|4\%} = \$5,000(1.2167) = \$6,083.50$$

The $0.24 difference ($6,083.50 − $6,083.26) is attributable solely to the fact that the tables in the Appendix are only four-place tables. Had six- or eight-place tables been used, there would be no difference. The eight-place figure for $f_{\overline{5}|4\%}$ is 1.21665290, and $6,083.26 [i.e., $5,000(1.21665290)] is obtained using this reading. It will improve intuitions if an accumulation table such as Table 2 is constructed for this problem.

Year	Balance[a]	Interest
1	$5,000.00	4%($5,000.00) = $200.00
2	5,200.00	4%(5,200.00) = 208.00
3	5,408.00	4%(5,408.00) = 216.32
4	5,624.32	4%(5,624.32) = 224.97
5	5,849.29	4%(5,849.29) = 244.97
	6,083.26	

Table 2
Accumulation Table

[a] The balance column equals principal ($5,000) plus accumulated interest.

We see that the amount accumulated after five years is equal to the amount calculated using tables.

Now consider the reverse situation. If someone owed you a sum of money due several years from now, would you be willing to take a smaller sum if you were to receive it right away? Of course you would. In the intervening years you could certainly earn additional money by investing the sum you received. And, since the history of modern-day America has been one of almost uninterrupted inflation, the purchasing power of the money presently received would probably be greater than that of the money received several years from now. Finally, there is always the risk that the debtor would die in the meantime, or for one reason or another could not pay the debt when it became due.[3]

---

[3] Actually, to consider inflation and the risk of death of the debtor, it would be more proper to refine the analysis. Rather than employ the rough method of using $\gamma\%$ [where $\gamma\% = \alpha\%$ (for earnings) + $\beta\%$ (for inflation) + $\delta\%$ (for risk of nonpayment)], it would be a sounder theory to introduce an estimated lesser amount of the debt to cope with the purchasing power issue and to consult mortality tables (which are based on probability theory) to recognize the risk of nonpayment. Such refinements really add little to the main object of the chapter, but the illustrative problem that follows should be of interest to those who are curious.

To determine the present value of a sum due in the future requires a discounting rather than a compounding process. The result of a procedure similar to that used in obtaining (1) is as follows:

p = present value of f_n [corresponding to principal in Eq. (1)]

f_n = future amount of money due to be paid n periods hence

r = rate of interest

$p_{\overline{n}|r\%}$ = discounting factor of n periods at $r\%$

$$p = \frac{f_n}{(1 + r)^n} = f_n p_{\overline{n}|r\%} \tag{3}$$

If we let f_n equal unity in (3), we obtain the formula used to calculate the figures in Table A.2 in the Appendix. This formula, after modification, is

$$p_{\overline{n}|r\%} = \frac{1}{(1 + r)^n} = \left(\frac{1}{1 + r}\right)^n = (1 + r)^{-n} \tag{4}$$

All the above notations are seen in the finance literature. For a numerical example, let us consider the reverse of our previous example. A man owes $6,083.50 due five years from now, and we want to know its present value given an interest rate of 4%. The solution is as follows (let p = present value):

$$p = \$6,083.50 \, p_{\overline{5}|4\%}$$
$$= \$6.083.50(0.8219) = \$5,000.03$$

Once again, the inexactness of four-place tables is apparent—but, as before, the difference ($5,000.03 — $5,000 = $0.03) is trifling. An important relationship should now be clear.

$$1 = f_{\overline{n}|r\%} p_{\overline{n}|r\%} = (1 + r)^n \left(\frac{1}{1 + r}\right)^n = \frac{(1 + r)^n}{(1 + r)^n}$$

To determine a future value of an initial amount after n periods, we *multiply* by $(1 + r)^n$; conversely, if there is a future value n periods from now and we wish to determine its present worth, we *divide* by $(1 + r)^n$ (or we multiply by its reciprocal, given in Table A.2).

Before continuing, we will introduce an antidifference formula from numerical analysis. This formula, which will prove most useful in the work that follows, is presented here without proof.

---

[3] *Continued*

Money due one year hence	$1,000
Earnings rate	$\alpha\%$
Estimated purchasing power of money one year hence	0.97
Probability of collection	0.9
Present sum accepted in lieu of $1,000	p

$$p(1 + \alpha\%) = \$1,000(0.97)(0.9)$$

$$p = \frac{\$873}{1 + \alpha\%}$$

Chapter 1: Time Series Mathematics

$$\sum_{x=c}^{n} a^x = \Delta^{-1} a^x \Big]_c^{n+1} = \frac{a^x}{a-1} \Big]_c^{n+1} = \frac{a^{n+1} - a^c}{a-1} \tag{5}$$

where a = some number
        x = a varying power of the number
       Δ^{-1} = antidifference symbol (similar in meaning to an integral sign
           in the infinitesimal calculus)

Note that the upper limit changes from n to $n + 1$.

With formula (5) available, we can now treat the situation where there is a **Annuities** series of equal, adjacent payments (i.e., an annuity), rather than a single figure. Suppose, for example, f dollars were owed not just at the end of period n as before, but also at the ends of periods $1, 2, 3, \ldots, n - 1$. As before, assume we wish to know the present value, but this time of the series of n payments of f dollars each. Using (3) and recalling that $f_1 = f_2 = \cdots = f_n = f$, we might proceed as follows:

$$p = \frac{f_1}{(1+r)^1} + \frac{f_2}{(1+r)^2} + \frac{f_3}{(1+r)^3} + \cdots + \frac{f_n}{(1+r)^n} = \sum_{x=1}^{n} f\left(\frac{1}{1+r}\right)^x = f \sum_{x=1}^{n} \left(\frac{1}{1+r}\right)^x \tag{6}$$

Let $f = \$1$ (or 1 deutschemarke—it doesn't matter), recall formula (5), and let

$$a = \frac{1}{1+r}$$

Then (6) becomes

$$\sum_{x=1}^{n} a^x = \Delta^{-1} a^x \Big]_1^{n+1} = \frac{a^{n+1} - a^1}{a-1} \tag{7}$$

Resubstitute $a = 1/(1 + r)$, and (7) becomes

$$\frac{\left(\frac{1}{1+r}\right)^{n+1} - \left(\frac{1}{1+r}\right)}{\frac{1}{1+r} - 1} = \frac{\left(\frac{1}{1+r}\right)\left[\left(\frac{1}{1+r}\right)^n - 1\right]}{\frac{1 - (1+r)}{1+r}} = \frac{\left[\left(\frac{1}{1+r}\right)^n - 1\right]}{-r} = \frac{1 - (1+r)^{-n}}{r} \tag{8}$$

In finance, (8) is frequently indicated as

$$P_{\overline{n}|r\%} = \frac{1 - (1+r)^{-n}}{r} \tag{9}$$

Equation (9) is the formula used to calculate the figures in Table A.4.

Discrete Compounding and Discounting   **21**

The relationship

$$P_{\overline{n}|r\%} = \sum_{x=1}^{n} p_{\overline{x}|r\%}$$ (10)

should be emphasized. In other words, Table A.4 adds up the values of Table A.2 (with the possible exception of rounding in the fourth decimal place). For example,

$p_{\overline{1}|6\%} = 0.9434$
$p_{\overline{2}|6\%} = 0.8900$
$p_{\overline{3}|6\%} = 0.8396$
$p_{\overline{4}|6\%} = 0.7921$
$P_{\overline{4}|6\%} = \overline{3.4651}$

If a man owed \$5,000.00 at the end of each of the next four years and it was desired to know the present value of this annuity when discounted at 6% per year, we would calculate as follows:

$p = \$5,000 P_{\overline{4}|6\%} = \$5,000(3.4651) = \$17,325.50$

Intuitions will be well served if we construct a reduction table such as Table 3 for this problem.

Table 3
Reduction
Table

Year	Balance[a]	Interest Earned		Payment
1	\$17,325.50	6%(\$17,325.50) =	\$1,039.53	\$5,000.00
2	13,365.03	6%(13,365.03) =	801.90	5,000.00
3	9,166.93	6%(9,166.93) =	550.02	5,000.00
4	4,716.95	6%(4,716.95) =	283.02	5,000.00

[a] (0.03) → (three cents difference due to using four-place tables instead of eight-place tables).

Note that the balance column is equal to the original present value of the debt (\$17,325.50), plus the interest earned, and minus the yearly payment. Year 2 balance, for instance, was determined as follows:

Year 1 balance	\$17,325.50
Year 1 interest	1,039.53
	\$18,365.03
Year 1 payment	5,000.00
Year 2 balance	\$13,365.03

Table A.3 has purposely been disregarded until now, since it has a peculiarity. Thus,

$$F_{\overline{n}\rvert r\%} \neq \sum_{x=1}^{n} f_{\overline{x}\rvert r\%}$$

$$F_{\overline{n}\rvert r\%} = \sum_{x=0}^{n-1} (1 + r)^x = \sum_{x=0}^{n-1} f_{\overline{x}\rvert r\%} \qquad (11)$$

Just what are we saying in (11)? Equation (11) states that the future value $(F_{\overline{n}\rvert r\%})$ of an annuity (series of equal payments) equals the sum of $n - 1$ readings from the future value of a single sum $(f_{\overline{n}\rvert r\%})$ table plus 1.000 (which represents an amount that falls on the last day of the nth period and hence does not earn any interest). For example,

$$F_{\overline{3}\rvert 3\%} = \sum_{x=0}^{2} f_{\overline{x}\rvert 3\%}$$

$$3.0909 = 1.0000 + 1.0300 + 1.0609$$

NOTE $f_{\overline{0}\rvert 3\%}$ [i.e., $(1.03)^0 = 1.0000$] does not appear in Table 1, which starts with $f_{\overline{1}\rvert 3\%}$ [i.e., $(1.03)^1 = 1.0300$].

The foregoing attempts to make clear that Table A.3 lags one interest period as compared to the other three tables. Said another way, the index n in Table A.3 stands for n payments and $n - 1$ interest periods. By applying antidifferences, the formula for the table could be proved to be

$$F_{\overline{n}\rvert r\%} = \frac{(1 + r)^n - 1}{r} \qquad (12)$$

Some of the symbols needed in the discussions ahead are

$f_{\overline{n}\rvert r\%}$ = Table A.1 = future value of a single figure
$p_{\overline{n}\rvert r\%}$ = Table A.2 = present value of a single figure
$F_{\overline{n}\rvert r\%}$ = Table A.3 = future value of an annuity
$P_{\overline{n}\rvert r\%}$ = Table A.4 = present value of an annuity

Now let us see how these symbols may be used.
Consider the following example.

EXAMPLE

A father wishes to provide his son with a small varying annual income beginning when the son is 23 and ending when he is 46. To provide this income, the father has agreed to make five equal, annual deposits into a fund beginning when his son is 16. The established fund earns varying rates of interest during the term of the contract. The schedule of withdrawals and the rates applicable are as follows:

Birthdays	Yearly withdrawal
23rd through 25th	$ 300
26th	500
27th through 46th	1,000

	Birthdays	Rate
INTEREST RATE SCHEDULE	From 16th through 25th	5%
	From 25th through 26th	10%
	From 26th through 46th	15%

How much will each of the deposits be?

Solution   Before attempting to solve the above problem, you should understand the following rules for manipulating *annuities*.

1. Draw a continuum,[4] and label it carefully with the facts of the problem.
2. Count the number of payments (deposits) and the number of interest periods.
   (a) If the number of payments $= n =$ the number of interest periods,
      (i) Look up $P_{\overline{n}|r\%}$ if present value is involved; or
      (ii) Look up $F_{\overline{n+1}|r\%}$, and subtract 1.0000 if future value is desired.
   (b) If the number of payments $= n$ and the number of interest periods $= n - 1$,
      (i) Look up $P_{\overline{n-1}|r\%}$, and add 1.0000 if present value is called for; or
      (ii) Look up $F_{\overline{n}|r\%}$ if future value is desired.
3. Do not use deferred annuity techniques where interest rates change during the pertinent period.[5]

The continuum for this example would appear as follows:

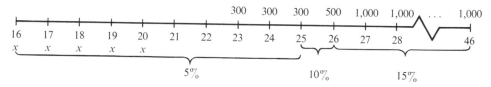

If the deposit and the withdrawal streams are equated on the son's 20th birthday, the result obtained by counting payments and periods is

$xF_{\overline{5}|5\%} = \$1{,}000P_{\overline{20}|15\%}P_{\overline{1}|10\%}P_{\overline{5}|5\%} + \$500P_{\overline{1}|10\%}P_{\overline{5}|5\%} + \$300P_{\overline{3}|5\%}P_{\overline{2}|5\%}$
$5.5256x = \$1{,}000(6.2593)(.9091)(.7835) + \$500(.9091)(.7835) + \$300(2.7232)(.9070)$
$5.5256x = \$5{,}555.49$
$\quad\quad x = \$1{,}005.40$

---

[4] A time period graph, |——+——+——+——+——+——+——|

[5] This rule and its terminology will be explained presently.

Chapter 1 : Time Series Mathematics

The last term, $\$300P_{\overline{3}|5\%}p_{\overline{2}|5\%}$, could be calculated more expeditiously by employing a deferred annuity technique. Thus,

$$P_{\overline{3}|5\%}p_{\overline{2}|5\%} = P_{\overline{5}|5\%} - P_{\overline{2}|5\%}$$
$$(2.7232)(.9070) = 4.3295 - 1.8594$$
$$2.4699424 = 2.4701$$

The difference is due to using four-place tables. A long multiplication process can be replaced by a simple subtraction *where the interest rate does not change* over the period from the equating point to the last payment in the particular series of equal payments. The deferred technique for present values involves counting the number of *periods* from the equating point to the last payment in the series to obtain the greater subscript number ($P_{\overline{5}|5\%}$ in this case), and then counting the number of equal payments in the series (three in this case), so as to select as the lower subscript ($P_{\overline{2}|5\%}$ in this case), that number which, when subtracted from the greater subscript, will yield the number of payments.[6] Look at the term $\$1,000P_{\overline{20}|15\%}p_{\overline{1}|10\%}p_{\overline{5}|5\%}$. Observe that at age 27 there are 19 periods (46 − 27) and 20 payments of $1,000 (19 payments corresponding to 46 − 27 plus the payment occurring at 27), but if we consider age 26, we have 20 payments and 20 periods (temporarily ignore the $500 payment at 26). Now since the interest rate does not change until 26, we can obtain the present value of the 20 payments by $\$1,000P_{\overline{20}|15\%}$ [rule 2(a)(i) on page 24]. Convince yourself that once this multiplication is performed, there is really a new figure at 26 ($\$1,000P_{\overline{20}|15\%} = \$6,259.30$) in addition to the $500. To discount the $6,259.30 (or, if desired, the $6,759.30) to the next interest change requires the present value of a single sum for one period at 10%; consequently, we multiply by $p_{\overline{1}|10\%}$, and our new figure then stands at 25. From 25 to 20 (age where streams were equated), there are five periods, so that we multiply by the present value of a single sum for five periods at 5% ($p_{\overline{5}|5\%}$). The result is $\$1,000P_{\overline{20}|15\%}p_{\overline{1}|10\%}p_{\overline{5}|5\%}$. The other terms being discounted are treated similarly.

Consider the term $xF_{\overline{5}|5\%}$. Observe that there are five payments of x and four interest periods, and recall rule 2(b)(ii) on page 24. Since we wish to find

---

[6] The deferred annuity technique for future values involves counting the number of *points* on the continuum from the beginning point of the series to and including the chosen terminal point to obtain the greater subscript and then counting the number of payments to obtain, by subtraction from the greater subscript, the lower subscript. Consider this illustration: A man intends to deposit $800 now and at the end of each of the next two years; what future value will he have in the fund at the end of six years if interest is compounded annually at 10% per year?

$x = \$800[F_{\overline{7}|10\%} - F_{\overline{4}|10\%}] = \$800(9.4782 - 4.6410) = \$800(4.8462) = \$3,876.96$

An alternate, difficult way:

$x = \$800F_{\overline{3}|10\%}\,f_{\overline{4}|10\%} = \$800(3.3100)(1.4641) = \$800(4.8462) = \$3,876.96$

Discrete Compounding and Discounting

the future value of this deposit stream at age 20, we merely multiply x by $F_{\overline{5}|5\%}$.

Actually, we could equate the input and output streams at any of the 31 birthdays. To illustrate, we will work the problem at several other points.

Equating at age 16 [this illustrates rule 2(b)(i) in connection with the deposit stream]:

$$x(P_{\overline{4}|5\%} + 1.0000) = \$1,000 P_{\overline{20}|15\%} p_{\overline{1}|10\%} p_{\overline{9}|5\%} + \$500 p_{\overline{1}|10\%} p_{\overline{9}|5\%} + \$300(P_{\overline{9}|5\%} - P_{\overline{6}|5\%})$$
$$4.5460x = \$1,000(6.2593)(.9091)(.6446) + \$500(.9091)(.6446) + \$300(7.1078 - 5.0757)$$
$$x = \$1,005.41$$

Equating at age 21 [this illustrates rule 2(a)(ii) in connection with the deposit stream]:

$$x(F_{\overline{6}|5\%} - 1.0000) = \$1,000 P_{\overline{20}|15\%} p_{\overline{1}|10\%} p_{\overline{4}|5\%} + \$500 p_{\overline{1}|10\%} p_{\overline{4}|5\%} + \$300(P_{\overline{4}|5\%} - P_{\overline{1}|5\%})$$
$$5.8019x = [\$1,000(6.2593) + \$500](.9091)(.8227) + \$300(3.5460 - .9524)$$
$$x = \$1,005.44$$

COMMENT $F_{\overline{6}|5\%}$ yields six payments and five periods; hence, because we have only five and five, we subtract 1.0000 to eliminate the excess, nonexistent payment. We can achieve the same result by $xF_{\overline{5}|5\%} f_{\overline{1}|5\%}$.

Equating at age 46 (this illustrates rule 3 for a future value situation):

$$x(F_{\overline{10}|5\%} - F_{\overline{5}|5\%}) f_{\overline{1}|10\%} f_{\overline{20}|15\%} = \$300 F_{\overline{3}|5\%} f_{\overline{1}|10\%} f_{\overline{20}|15\%} + \$500 f_{\overline{20}|15\%} + \$1,000 F_{\overline{20}|15\%}$$
$$x(12.5779 - 5.5256)(1.1000)(16.367) = \$300(3.1525)(1.1000)(16.367) + \$1,000(102.443)$$
$$x = \$1,005.38$$

The minute differences in the answers obtained are due, of course, to using four-place tables.

Limited Tables   The available interest tables may have neither enough periods nor the proper rate of interest. For single sum tables (Tables A.1 and A.2), all that is necessary is to remember the laws of exponents, for instance, $(1 + r)^{40} = (1 + r)^{30}(1 + r)^{10}$. That is, add the exponents, but multiply the factors. For example, Table A.1 shows $f_{\overline{40}|5\%} = 7.0400$, $f_{\overline{30}|5\%} = 4.3219$, and $f_{\overline{10}|5\%} = 1.6289$. $7.0400 = f_{\overline{40}|5\%} = f_{\overline{30}|5\%} f_{\overline{10}|5\%} \cong 4.3219(1.6289)$; hence, the technique works. Thus, $f_{\overline{60}|6\%} = f_{\overline{40}|6\%} f_{\overline{20}|6\%} = 10.2857(3.2071) \cong 32.9873$. The technique is not applicable to annuity tables (Tables A.3 and A.4), because they involve addition as well as multiplication. If the technique were attempted, some undesirable cross-product terms would result.

If you wish to obtain values for *annuities* beyond the periods in the tables or for any interest rates not contained in tables, you will need formula (5) and log tables. The next section contains an illustrative problem.

Frequently, problems are stated at a rate of $r\%$ per year compounded quarterly (or semiannually or monthly). The institution then compounds interest using $r/4$ as a quarterly percentage; because interest is compounded four times a year, the effective interest rate for the year is higher than $r\%$. $r\%$ is, therefore, referred to as the nominal rate. The following formula aids in the computation of one rate when given the other.

$r\%$ = nominal interest rate
$s\%$ = effective interest rate
n = frequency of compounding

$$1 + s\% = \left(1 + \frac{r\%}{n}\right)^n \tag{13}$$

From (13) it is clear that if the nominal rate is given, $f_{\overline{n}|r\%/n}$ is looked up, and 1 is subtracted from it to obtain the effective rate.

In the following example, we determine an effective rate and use anti-differences and logs[7] because payments are made every other six-month period. Of course, it is possible to use a single sum table for thirty-one factors that would then be added.

EXAMPLE

A man approached his accountant with an idea he had to provide for his retirement. He wanted to know how much he would have 30 years from now if he deposited $10,000 beginning immediately and a like sum each year thereafter, including the 30th anniversary of the plan. He will receive 6% annual interest, but it will be computed semiannually.

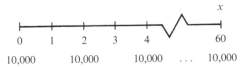

Using (13),

Solution

$$1 + s\% = \left(1 + \frac{6\%}{2}\right)^2 = (1.03)^2 = 1.0609$$

$$s\% = 1.0609 - 1 = 6.09\%$$

$$x = \$10,000 \sum_{k=0}^{30} (1.0609)^k = \$10,000\, \Delta^{-1}(1.0609)^k \Big]_0^{31} = \$10,000\left(\frac{1.0609^{31} - 1}{.0609}\right)$$

---

[7] Techniques can be applied to avoid use of antidifferences and logs, but these techniques are not as useful generally and will not be discussed in this book.

Using five-place log tables and interpolating where necessary, we obtain

$$31 \log 1.0609 = 31(.025679) = .79605$$
$$\text{antilog } .79605 = 6.25243$$

Therefore,

$$\$10,000 \left(\frac{1.0609^{31} - 1}{.0609} \right) = \$10,000 \left(\frac{6.25243 - 1}{.0609} \right) = \$10,000(86.2468) = \$862,468$$

Continuous Compounding and Discounting

We have been concerned only with situations where payments fall on specified dates. But how would this suit a business? Are profits, for example, earned only at the end of the year, or do they take place every second in small amounts, which are then compounded every instant? Most probably the profits are made in small amounts every instant. This suggests that interest should be compounded or discounted on a continuous rather than on a discrete basis.

Looking at (13), what we want is

$$1 + s\% = \lim_{n \to \infty} \left(1 + \frac{r\%}{n} \right)^n \tag{14}$$

NOTE $\lim_{n \to \infty}$ is read, "Take the limit as n approaches infinity." Loosely translated, it means, "Let n equal infinity."

But,[8]

$$\lim_{n \to \infty} \left(1 + \frac{r\%}{n} \right)^n = e^{r\%} \tag{15}$$

If we let $e^{r\%}$ become e^x, we may find values for e^x (and e^{-x}) in Table A.6.

Therefore, the effective interest under continuous compounding can be expressed as

$$s\% = e^{r\%} - 1 \tag{16}$$

Compounding   When compounding a single sum to obtain its future value, we have the following situation:

---

[8] The number e is the basis of natural logarithms. Some readers will be more familiar with the Taylor expansion of e^x:

$$e^x = 1 + \frac{x}{1!} + \frac{x^2}{2!} + \frac{x^3}{3!} + \cdots$$

In the limit, however, the two definitions for e^x are the same.

$x = \$ae^{r\%n}$

When a series of equal payments is involved and the payments occur *uniformly over each period* (i.e., each period's total payment is comprised of many uniform smaller payments spread evenly over the entire period), the situation is as follows:

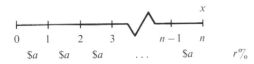

$$x = \int_0^n ae^{r\%t}\,dt = \frac{a}{r\%}(e^{r\%n} - 1) \qquad \text{Recall that } e^0 = 1.$$

Note that if the original period is broken down into z subperiods, both the original rate and payment must be divided by z.

_____ **EXAMPLE**

Determine x, given that \$1,200 is earned uniformly each year for three years and compounding is done continuously at 12% per year.

$$x = \int_0^3 \$1,200e^{0.12t}\,dt = \frac{\$1,200}{0.12}(e^{0.36} - 1) = \$4,333$$

Now suppose that \$100 is earned each month and all other facts are as before.

$$x = \int_0^{36} \$100e^{0.01t}\,dt = \frac{\$100}{0.01}(e^{0.36} - 1) = \$4,333$$

Also observe that if the money is received at a specific date and interest is compounded continuously, antidifferencing is used instead of integration. For example,

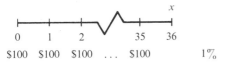

Continuous Compounding and Discounting   **29**

$$x = \sum_{t=0}^{36} \$100 e^{.01t} = \$100\,\Delta^{-1} e^{.01t}\Big]_0^{37} = \$100\left[\frac{e^{.01t}}{e^{.01}-1}\right]_0^{37}$$

$$x = \$100\left[\frac{e^{.37}-1}{e^{.01}-1}\right] = \$100\left[\frac{1.4477-1}{1.0101-1}\right] = \$4,432.67$$

The analyst must be very careful in translating the situation being modeled; "spread uniformly" calls for integration, while "specific time" calls for antidifferencing.

NOTE From integral calculus, the integral of e^{ct} over a given domain is defined:

$$\int_a^b e^{ct}\,dt = \frac{1}{c}\,[e^{cb} - e^{ca}]$$

Graphically, the area under the curve shown in Figure 2 is being calculated between the limits a and b.

Figure 2

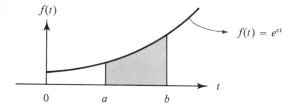

Chapter 4 will develop these concepts at length.

Discounting When discounting a single sum to obtain its present value, the continuum below pertains:

$$x = ae^{-r\%n}$$

When an annuity is involved, the continuum becomes

Chapter 1: Time Series Mathematics

$$x = \int_0^n ae^{-r\%t}\, dt = -\frac{a}{r\%}(e^{-r\%n} - 1)$$

A man wished to know what monthly sales volume his business must achieve to earn a 12% annual return on his investment of $60,000, given that monthly costs are $900 and that the investment will have a six-year life with no residual value.

Let x = monthly sales.

Solution

$$\$60,000 = \int_0^{72} (x - \$900)e^{-0.01t}\, dt = -\left(\frac{x - 900}{0.01}\right)(e^{-0.72} - 1)$$

Continuous Approach

$$\$60,000 = (100x - \$90,000)(1 - .48675) = 51.325x - \$46,192.50$$
$$x = \$2,069.02$$

$$\$60,000 = (x - \$900)P_{\overline{72}|1\%} = (x - \$900)\Delta^{-1}(.9901)^k \Big]_1^{73}$$

Discrete Approach

$$73 \log .9901 = 73(9.99565 - 10); \text{ antilog } (9.68245 - 10) = .4814$$

$$\$60,000 = (x - \$900)\left(\frac{.4814 - .9901}{-.0099}\right) = (x - \$900)51.3838$$
$$x = \$2,067.68$$

Discounting in Perpetuity

For some purposes in finance, it is assumed that some sum of money will be forthcoming each year and forever into the future, and the problem is posed: How much is this stream of payments presently worth? The solution to this problem is shown below for both discrete and continuous discounting.

S = sum of an infinite series of present values

KEY

r = discount rate

$$S = \lim_{n \to \infty} \sum_{t=1}^n \left(\frac{1}{1 + r}\right)^t = \lim_{n \to \infty} \sum_{t=1}^n a^t,$$

where $a = \dfrac{1}{1 + r}$

(17)

$$\lim_{n \to \infty} \sum_{t=1}^{n} a^t = \lim_{n \to \infty} \Delta^{-1} a^t \Big]_1^{n+1} = \lim_{n \to \infty} \frac{a^t}{a-1} \Big]_1^{n+1}$$

$$= \lim_{n \to \infty} \left[\frac{a^{n+1}}{a-1} - \frac{a}{a-1} \right] \tag{18}$$

$$\lim_{n \to \infty} \left(\frac{a^{n+1} - a}{a-1} \right) = \lim_{n \to \infty} \frac{a}{a-1} (a^n - 1) \tag{19}$$

Resubstituting, we have

$$\lim_{n \to \infty} \frac{1/(1+r)}{[1/(1+r)] - 1} \left[\left(\frac{1}{1+r} \right)^n - 1 \right] = \lim_{n \to \infty} -\frac{1}{r} \left[\left(\frac{1}{1+r} \right)^n - 1 \right] \tag{20}$$

Taking the limit, that is, letting n approach infinity,

$$S = \frac{1}{r} \tag{21}$$

The same result is generated in the case of continuous discounting:

$$S = \int_0^\infty e^{-rt} \, dt = -\frac{1}{r} e^{-rt} \Big]_0^\infty = \frac{1}{r} \tag{22}$$

Conclusion   The present value in perpetuity of an annuity is equal to the annuity payment multiplied by $1/r$.

Problems

Future amount   1. To what amount will $1,000 accumulate if interest is compounded at 6% annually and five years go by?

Answer: $1,338

Present value of annuity   2. A debtor is scheduled to pay $2,000 at the end of each of the next five years (first payment due one year hence). If the person to whom the debt is owed agrees to its being settled immediately at a 4% discount rate, how much money must the debtor pay?

Answer: $8,904

Deferred annuity   3. Solve for x:

Chapter 1: Time Series Mathematics

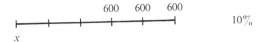

600   600   600

10%

x

Answer: $1,233

Problem 3

4. If interest is calculated semiannually at a 6% nominal, annual rate, what is the effective annual rate?   *Effective rate*

5. If a business is expected to earn $50,000 in perpetuity, what is the value of the business, assuming that value may be established by discounting at a 10% rate?   *Discounting in perpetuity*

6. (a) A woman puts $500 in the bank on January 1, 1971. If interest is 4% and is compounded quarterly on the first day of each quarter, how much will she have on deposit on January 1, 1972?   *Future amount, effective interest, accumulation table*

   (b) What effective interest rate will the woman receive?

   (c) Suppose the woman deposits $500 on January 1, 1971, and again on April 1, July 1, and October 1. How much will she have on January 1, 1972, (1) if she does not make another $500 deposit on January 1, 1972, and (2) if she does make another $500 deposit on January 1, 1972? Use Table A.3 to arrive at your answer, and then construct an accumulation table to prove your answer to (1).

7. Mr. Dorfman wishes to establish a fund that will enable his son Stephen to withdraw $25,000 each year starting January 1, 1980, to and including January 1, 2010. To provide this fund, Mr. Dorfman intends to make equal contributions on January 1 of each of the years 1960 to 1974. Assuming the fund earns 5% annually, what contributions must Mr. Dorfman make?   *Annuity*

8. A father wishes to provide an annuity for his son in varying amounts. The contract provides for different rates of interest and a series of five equal payments into a fund beginning with the son's 19th birthday. The son is to receive $5,000 on each of his 25th and 26th birthdays and $10,000 on each of his subsequent birthdays to and including his 40th birthday. The interest rates are specified as follows: *Annuity*

   19th through 26th birthdays = 2%
   26th through 28th birthdays = 4%
   28th through 40th birthdays = 6%

How much are each of the five payments made by the father?

9. A father wishes to provide his son with a small, varying annual income beginning when the son is 27 and ending when he is 50. To provide this income, the father has agreed to make four equal deposits into a fund beginning when the son is 20. The fund established earns varying rates of interest during the term of the contract. The schedule of withdrawals and the rates applicable are as follows: *Annuity*

Problems

33

	Birthdays	Yearly withdrawal
	27th through 29th	$6,000
	30th	8,000
	31st through 50th	9,000

	Birthdays	Rate
INTEREST RATE SCHEDULE	20th through 29th	6%
	29th through 30th	8%
	30th through 50th	10%

Streams are to be equated at age 24. How much is each of the four payments made by the father?

Continuous and discrete discounting

10. A woman wishes to know what quarterly sales volume her dress shop must achieve to earn an 8% annual return on her investment of $41,212.50, given that quarterly costs are $2,500 and that the investment will have a five-year life with no residual value. Your answer should assume (a) continuous discounting and (b) discrete compounding with all flows taking place on the last day of the quarter.

Answers: (a) $5,000.00
(b) $5,020.49

11. A real estate agent is negotiating a monthly rental charge for a new office building. He has invested $800,000 in constructing the building and anticipates holding the building for five years and then disposing of it for $600,000. He has estimated that maintenance, insurance, and tax costs will amount to $2,000 per month. If the real estate agent requires an 18% annual return on his investment, what monthly rental should he bargain for? Use continuous discounting.

12. Roy Thompson wishes to provide for his retirement in style. He wants to know how much he will have 20 years from now if he deposits $20,000 immediately and a like sum each year thereafter, including the 20th anniversary of the plan. He will receive 8% annual interest, but it will be computed semiannually. How much will these deposits amount to?

13. An investor is trying to evaluate a stock by discounting his estimate of its annual earning, $50,000, in perpetuity at a rate of 10%. He wishes to assume that these earnings occur in the middle of the year. What figure will he arrive at?

Answer: $\dfrac{50,000\sqrt{1.10}}{0.10} = \$524,400$

Hint

$$\lim_{n \to \infty} \sum_{i=1}^{n} \$50,000\left(\frac{1}{1.10}\right)^{(2i-1)/2} = \lim_{n \to \infty} \$50,000\sqrt{1.10} \sum_{i=1}^{n}\left(\frac{1}{1.10}\right)^{i}$$

2

Applications of
Time Series Mathematics

Chapter 1 dealt with the mathematical manipulations involved in compounding and discounting cash flows. This chapter will be concerned with further specific applications of time series mathematics.

Applications of time series mathematics are ubiquitous. One of the most frequently encountered applications, that is, the calculation of mortgage payments, is also one of the simplest, technically speaking. Here, annuity tables are used to compute that single amount which, when regularly remitted, will repay both the principal of an indebtedness and the interest due on it. Homes, automobiles, equipment, furnishings, and, in general, everything that involves "easy credit terms" are all acquired on the basis of some form of mortgage contract.

Other problems that may require the use of annuity tables are the calculation of bond prices and bond sinking fund contributions, the determination of pension fund liabilities, the computation of depreciation, and many of the calculations of capital budgeting.

In addition to discussing compounding and discounting, Chapter 1 gave the reader the opportunity to construct mathematical models and to review algebra. The book refers to compounding and discounting as time series mathematics precisely because a *series* of money payments must be moved through *time*. Chapter 2 concentrates on further specific applications of these techniques.

Simple Mortgage

A man purchased a home for \$61,229.60. He paid \$15,000 down and agreed to pay the remainder in 40 equal, semiannual installments (beginning six months after the purchase date) at an annual rate of 6% interest. How much were his payments?

Solution   46,229.60
$$46,229.60 = xP_{\overline{40}|3\%}$$
$$46,229.60 = 23.1148x$$
$$2,000 = x$$

Sinking Fund (Lump sum bond redemption)

A bond indenture provides for the creation of a sinking fund. Accordingly, bonds in the amount of \$100,000 must be redeemed 20 years from now. If the fund earns 4% compounded annually, how much money must be transferred to the fund each year? First deposits occur one year from now. Give the entry for the second year.

Solution $$xF_{\overline{20}|4\%} = \$100,000$$
$$29.7781x = \$100,000$$
$$x = \$3,358.17$$

	Balance in Fund	Interest Earned	Deposit
1	0	0	\$3,358.17
2	\$3,358.17	\$134.33	3,358.17

Sinking Fund	3,492.50	
Interest Earned		134.33
Cash		3,358.17

Sinking Fund (Serial bond redemption)

A bond indenture provides for the retirement of bonds on a serial basis at the rate of $20,000 per year beginning 16 years from now. If the total bond issue is $100,000 and the sinking fund is to earn 4% compounded annually, how much must be deposited at the end of each of the 20 years of the original issue's life?

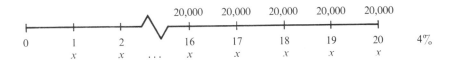

$$xP_{\overline{20}|4\%} = \$20,000(P_{\overline{20}|4\%} - P_{\overline{15}|4\%})$$
$$13.5903x = \$20,000(13.5903 - 11.1184)$$
$$x = \$3,637.74$$

The entry to record the initial payment into the fund would be

Sinking Fund Cash	$3,637.74	
Cash		$3,637.74

The entry at the end of the second year would be

Sinking Fund Cash		3,783.25	
Interest Income	(4% × $3,637.74)		145.51
Cash			3,637.74

Let us consider the entries that take place at the end of the 16th year. First it is necessary to determine the interest earned for the 16th year. The interest would be equal to 4% of the balance in the fund at the end of the 15th year. The amount of annuity table would enable us to compute either the balance in the fund at the end of 15 years or the interest for the 16th year directly. The computation would be as follows:

Let i = the interest for the 16th year
$$i = \$3,637.74(F_{\overline{15}|4\%} f_{\overline{1}|4\%} - F_{\overline{15}|4\%})$$
$$= \$3,637.74 F_{\overline{15}|4\%}(f_{\overline{1}|4\%} - 1)$$
$$= \$3,637.74(20.0236)(1.0400 - 1)$$
$$= \$2,913.63$$

The entries at the end of the 16th year would be

Sinking Fund Cash $ 6,551.37
     Interest Income $ 2,913.63
     Cash   3,637.74
To record increase in sinking fund.
Bonds Payable   20,000.00
     Sinking Fund Cash   20,000.00
To record redemption of bonds.

Sale of Bonds

EXAMPLE

The Hope Company sells a $100,000, 5%, 20-year bond issue on a 6% basis (i.e., the coupon rate is 5% but the bonds are to yield an effective interest of 6%). If the interest coupons are semiannual and the bonds are to be floated on an interest date, what will the proceeds of the issue be to the company? What entries will be made by the company during the first year?

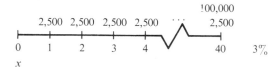

Solution

$$x = \$2,500 P_{\overline{40}|3\%} + \$100,000 p_{\overline{40}|3\%}$$
$$x = \$2,500(23.1148) + \$100,000(0.3066)$$
$$x = \$88,447.00$$

Amortization Table

	Balance	Interest		Amortization
		Coupon (2.5%)	Yield (3%)	
1	$88,447.00	$2,500.00	$2,653.41	$153.41
2	88,600.41	2,500.00	2,658.01	158.01
		$5,000.00	$5,311.42	$311.42

ENTRIES

Cash $88,447.00
Unamortized Bond Discount   11,553.00
     Bonds Payable $100,000.00
To record issuance.

Interest Expense	5,311.42	
Unamortized Bond Discount		311.42
Cash		5,000.00

To record payment of coupon interest (actually, this entry would be split up and written twice during the year at the interest dates).

COMMENT

There is a strong argument for recording bonds at their proceeds valuation and then accruing the amortization as time progresses. Thus, the entries would be

Cash	$88,447.00	
Bonds Payable		$88,447.00
Interest Expense	5,311.42	
Bonds Payable		311.42
Cash		5,000.00

Reasoning

At the date of issue, does the company have a liability for $100,000? Just what is this asset, Unamortized Bond Discount? In what sense is it an asset? What are the asset's future benefits? The situation is similar to the discounting of a note at a bank wherein the bank actually loans less than the maturity value of the note. For example, suppose a $40,000, six-month note is transacted at the bank using a 6% interest rate; the bank would loan $38,800. The interest charge is greater than 6% because the borrower has the use of only $38,800; hence, since the interest is both a function of the amount borrowed and of the time involved, it cannot be said that interest was prepaid—every dollar of discount reduces the amount actually loaned, and the interest is paid at the time of repaying the loan.

Sale of Bonds Subject to a Call Feature

Bonds are frequently sold on the basis that the issuing company may redeem them before maturity but after a specified date and after paying a price in excess of maturity value. This excess is known as a *call premium*, and it is intended to reimburse the bond holder for having to reenter the bond market when yields will probably be low. If yields were not low, there would be little reason for calling the bonds.

EXAMPLE

Assume the same facts as in the preceding example, except that the bonds may be called at the company's option at the end of 15 years or thereafter, at a price of $110,000. The problem on the 15-year basis appears:

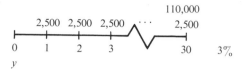

$$y = \$2,500P_{\overline{30}|3\%} + \$110,000p_{\overline{30}|3\%}$$
$$= \$2,500(19.6004) + \$110,000(.4120)$$
$$= \$94,321$$

y is greater than x, the previous price. According to established procedure, the bond holder pays the lower price, $88,447, and the discount, $11,553, is amortized over the 15-year life. The straight-line method is used to amortize $385.10 (i.e., $11,553/30) each six months.

Amortization Tables

EXAMPLE

Assume a 5%, four-year, $100,000 bond issue is sold to yield 4%. Interest coupons are annual, and the bond issue is sold on an interest date.

$$x = \$5,000P_{\overline{4}|4\%} + \$100,000p_{\overline{4}|4\%} = \$5,000(3.6299) + \$100,000(.8548) = \$103,629.50$$

Amortization Table	Year	Balance	Interest		Amortization
			Coupon	Yield	
	1	$103,629.50	$5,000.00	$4,145.18	$854.82
	2	102,774.68	5,000.00	4,110.99	889.01
	3	101,885.67	5,000.00	4,075.43	924.57
	4	100,961.10	5,000.00	4,038.44	961.56[a]

[a] Should be 961.10; $0.46 error due to four-place tables. Note that the balance at any time equals the price that would have to be paid to buy the bonds at that time, given the same rates. (If eight-place tables were used, price would exactly equal balance).

Chapter 2: Applications of Time Series Mathematics

To illustrate another use of amortization tables other than bonds, consider the adoption of a pension plan. When such a plan is adopted, existing employees will frequently have vested interests in the plan based on their past services. It often happens that the insurance company permits the business to settle the initial liability in installments over a period of a few years.

EXAMPLE

Assume that a company must pay $20,000 now and at the end of each year for the next four years. Also assume that the market rate of interest hovers around 5%.

Let x = the present value of the debt
$x = \$20,000(P_{\overline{4}|5\%} + 1.0000)$
$x = \$20,000(4.5460)$
$x = \$90,920$

The liability to the insurance company should then be recorded as below:

Prepaid Pension Costs	$90,920	
Pension Costs Payable		$70,920
Cash		20,000
To record past-service liability.		

NOTE

"Prepaid Pension Costs" are often called "Deferred Past Service Costs," but since this latter title is anomalous (when translated it would mean something paid in advance for a past service), "Prepaid Pension Costs" has been used.

Amortization Table

Year	Liability Balance	5% Interest	Payment	Liability Amortization
0	$90,920.00	$ 0	$20,000.00	$20,000.00
1	70,920.00	3,546.00	20,000.00	16,454.00
2	54,466.00	2,723.30	20,000.00	17,276.70
3	37,189.30	1,859.47	20,000.00	18,140.53
4	19,048.77	951.23[a]	20,000.00	19,048.77

[a] Decreased by $1.21 due to use of four-place tables.

Once again it is interesting to observe that the liability balance at any time equals the present value at that time of the remaining liability payments. For instance,

$$\$37,189.30 = \$20,000 P_{\overline{2}|5\%} \cong \$20,000(1.8594)$$

Because of income tax regulations, it is customary to charge the original discounted liability off over a period of ten years. If a straight-line method is employed, the following entry might be made at the end of the third year:

Pension Cost Payable	$18,140.53	
Pension (or Past-Service) Expense	10,951.47	
Prepaid Pension Costs ($90,920/10)		$ 9,092.00
Cash		20,000.00

Sale of Bonds Between Interest Periods

EXAMPLE

On September 1, 1962, the Crosby Company issued $100,000 of 5% bonds due July 1, 1964. Interest is payable semiannually on January 1 and July 1. Compute the proceeds of the issue on an effective rate basis assuming a yield rate of 4% per year. Also, give the necessary journal entries for 1962 and prepare an amortization table.

Solution There are several approaches that might be followed. We shall calculate a price at January 1, 1963, and then discount it back to September 1, 1962. This is in keeping with the concepts previously presented whereby the price of a bond issue is the present value of its par and coupons as of the date of sale.

Observe that, as of September 1, 1962, two months have passed since the last interest period. We seek a discount factor that yields an *effective* rate of 2% for a four-month period; consequently, we cannot simply divide 0.02 by 6 (months) and then multiply it by 4 (months). This latter procedure would be an example of linear interpolation in nonlinear circumstances, and nominal interest would result.

Recall that

$$\left[\left(\frac{1}{1.02} \right)^{1/3} \right]^3 = \frac{1}{1.02} = .98039216$$

Chapter 2: Applications of Time Series Mathematics

Since a four-month period constitutes an exponent of $\frac{2}{3}$, we need a discounting factor equal to $.98039216^{2/3}$.

$\frac{2}{3} \log .98039216 = \frac{2}{3}(.99139 - 1) = \frac{2}{3}(-.00861) = -.00574$

$\text{antilog}(-.00574) = \text{antilog}[(1 - .00574) - 1] = \text{antilog}(.99426 - 1) = .986875$

With these thoughts in mind, the astute reader might observe that saying 4% effective (or yield) interest is actually a misuse of the term "effective." If one really wanted effective interest, he would discount throughout by powers of

$$\left(\frac{1}{1.04}\right) \text{ not } \left(\frac{1}{1.02}\right)$$

We continue with our computation of price.

$\begin{aligned} x_2 &= .986875 \, [\$2,500(P_{\overline{3}|2\%} + 1.000) + \$100,000 p_{\overline{3}|2\%}] \\ &= .986875 \, [\$2,500(2.88388327 + 1.00000000) + \$100,000(.94232233)] \\ &= \$102,577.70 \end{aligned}$

To obtain an accurate amortization table, extra decimal places have been carried in the above calculations. **NOTE**

Balance (B)	Interest		Amortization	
	Coupon (C)	Yield (Y)		
102,577.70	2,500.00	1,364.23	− 1,135.77	
101,441.93	2,500.00	2,028.84	− 471.16	
100,970.77	2,500.00	2,019.42	− 480.58	
100,490.19	2,500.00	2,009.81	− 490.19	
100,000.00				

Amortization Table

1. The first yield figure was determined by *compounding* at the effective rate **COMMENT** of 2% for four months. This is the reciprocal of the discount factor (i.e., $1/.986875$ or 1.0132995) less 1.

2. Y = yield rate; C = coupon rate

3. $A = Y - C$

4. $B \rightarrow B + A$ ($\rightarrow$ means "is replaced by")

5. The formulas for Y, A, and B hold whether premium or discount is involved.

ENTRIES

September 1

Cash	$102,577.70	
Bonds Payable		$100,000.00
Interest Payable ($2,500 $\times$ $\frac{1}{3}$)		833.33
Bond Premium		1,744.37

December 31

Interest Expense	1,364.23	
Bond Premium	302.44	
Interest Payable ($2,500 × $\frac{2}{3}$)		1,666.67

(Note that the amortization table was set up as having $2,577.70 premium although only $1,744.37 of this was actually premium while $833.33 was really accrued interest. After this entry, the premium balance, $1,441.93 (i.e., $1,744.37 − $302.44), will agree with the balance in row 2 of the amortization table.)

January 1

Interest Payable	2,500.00	
Cash		2,500.00

A popular approximation of the above procedures is to determine price at the preceding interest period (July 1, 1964) and add to it two months' interest at the effective rate. For example,

$$x_1 = \$2,500 P_{\overline{4}|2\%} + \$100,000 p_{\overline{4}|2\%}$$

$x_1 = \$2,500 P_{\overline{4}|2\%} + \$100,000 p_{\overline{4}|2\%}$	$101,903.86
Two months' interest: $\frac{2}{6}(\$101,903.86 \times 0.02)$	679.36
	102,583.22

The difference between the two prices is due to the reliance on linear interpolation in the approximation method.

Capital Budgeting

EXAMPLE

The data for two mutually exclusive (i.e., the acceptance of one necessitates the rejection of the other) proposals are listed below. The investments in each proposal are to be depreciated on a sum-of-the-years'-digits basis with 20% residual values being estimated for the end of the fourth year. Income taxes amount to 60%, and required return is 10% after taxes.

Time	Net Cash Earnings Before Taxes (E)	
	Proposal A	Proposal B
t_1	$32,000	$ 5,110
t_2	24,000	7,270
t_3	10,000	9,430
t_4	6,500	21,715
Investment (I)	40,000	18,000

(a) Compute time adjusted rate of return for each proposal.
(b) Compute net present value for each proposal.
(c) Compute profitability indexes for each proposal.
(d) Decide which proposal is better via an incremental approach.
(e) What other factors should be considered before a final decision is made?

$$D_i = (C - R)\left[\frac{n - i + 1}{n(n + 1)/2}\right]$$

Depreciation
Calculations

($40,000 − $8,000) 0.4 =	$12,800	($18,000 − $3,600) 0.4 =	$5,760
0.3 =	9,600	0.3 =	4,320
0.2 =	6,400	0.2 =	2,880
0.1 =	3,200	0.1 =	1,440
	$32,000		$14,400

Tax Calculations

	Proposal A				Proposal B		
E	D_i	*Net*	*Taxes* @ 60%	*E*	D_i	*Net*	*Taxes* @ 60%
32,000	12,800	19,200	11,520	5,110	5,760	(650)	(390)
24,000	9,600	14,400	8,640	7,270	4,320	2,950	1,770
10,000	6,400	3,600	2,160	9,430	2,880	6,550	3,930
6,500	3,200	3,300	1,980	21,715	1,440	20,275	12,165

Continuums

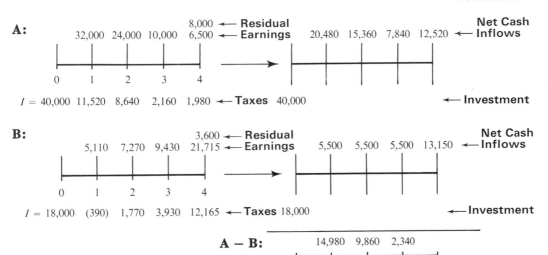

A:
8,000 ← Residual
32,000 24,000 10,000 6,500 ← Earnings

Net Cash
20,480 15,360 7,840 12,520 ← Inflows

0   1   2   3   4

I = 40,000 11,520 8,640 2,160 1,980 ← Taxes 40,000 ← Investment

B:
3,600 ← Residual
5,110 7,270 9,430 21,715 ← Earnings

Net Cash
5,500 5,500 5,500 13,150 ← Inflows

0   1   2   3   4

I = 18,000 (390) 1,770 3,930 12,165 ← Taxes 18,000 ← Investment

A − B:
14,980 9,860 2,340

22,000   630

(a) Time adjusted rate of return (TAR). This requires finding the rate of return that equates the net cash inflows of each proposal with its investment. By trial-and-error use of the interest tables, the following rates were determined:

A: $\$40,000 \approx \$20,480 p_{\overline{1}|16\%} + \$15,360 p_{\overline{2}|16\%} + \$7,840 p_{\overline{3}|16\%} + \$12,520 p_{\overline{4}|16\%}$
B: $\$18,000 \approx \$5,500 P_{\overline{3}|20\%} + \$13,150 p_{\overline{4}|20\%}$

Consequently, if TAR were the ranking method, proposal B would be chosen.

(b) Net present value (NPV) for each proposal. Net present value calls for the discounted cash inflows (DCI) of each proposal, minus its investment. The required rate of return is used in discounting.

A: $\$20,480 p_{\overline{1}|10\%} + \$15,360 p_{\overline{2}|10\%} + \$7,840 p_{\overline{3}|10\%} + \$12,520 p_{\overline{4}|10\%} = DCI = \$45,753$
   $NPV = DCI - I = \$45,753 - \$40,000 = \$5,753$

B: $\$5,500 P_{\overline{3}|10\%} + \$13,150 p_{\overline{4}|20\%} = DCI = \$22,659$
   $NPV = DCI - I = \$22,659 - \$18,000 = \$4,659$

Consequently, if NPV were the ranking method, proposal A would be chosen.

(c) Profitability indices. Profitability indices are gotten by dividing DCI by I. When the required rate of return is used in discounting, it is assumed that it reflects the expected earnings rate of future proposals. If its index exceeds 1, a proposal is acceptable; furthermore, the greater the excess, the more attractive the proposal.

A: $\dfrac{DCI}{I} = \dfrac{\$45,753}{40,000} = 1.14$

B: $\dfrac{DCI}{I} = \dfrac{\$22,659}{18,000} = 1.26$

Consequently, if profitability index is the ranking method, proposal B would be chosen.

(d) Incremental analysis. In incremental analysis, the required rate of return is used to decide whether the additional earnings of one proposal merit the additional investment in that proposal. This assumes that the acceptability of proposal B has been tested; otherwise, we might risk accepting proposal A because it is relatively better than B although A itself might not be absolutely good. Relatively better does not always mean absolutely good. We use the $\mathbf{A} - \mathbf{B}$ continuum previously presented:

$\$22,000 \overset{?}{\leq} \$14,980 p_{\overline{1}|10\%} + \$9,860 p_{\overline{2}|10\%} + \$2,340 p_{\overline{3}|10\%} - \$630 p_{\overline{4}|10\%} = \$23,095$

Consequently, if incremental analysis is the ranking method, proposal A would be chosen.

Chapter 2: Applications of Time Series Mathematics

(e) At this point in the decision process, two ranking methods prefer A and two prefer B. If the decision maker's best friend sells one of the machines, the controversy is ended; however, what happens if no such rigidity comes to our rescue? If there is greater uncertainty about the earnings or life estimates of one proposal than there is for the other, probability theory and, perhaps, utility theory can help in the decision. (These approaches will be presented in a later chapter.) And if there is some other employment of the incremental investment that, when combined with B, yields better earnings than A, then this seeking of the optimal combination would resolve the problem.

Depreciation and Time Series Mathematics

The annuity method of depreciation attempts to recognize that funds are tied up in plant and equipment items and that depreciation charges ought to be increased by the interest earnings that have been forsaken. The net effect of this approach is that interest charges find their way into the production costs of a manufacturer. Once all production has been sold, however, the effect on net profit is zero.

Annuity Method of Depreciation

C = cost of depreciable asset
S = salvage or residual value of asset
r = interest rate assumed to reflect forsaken interest earnings on money invested in plant and equipment items
n = number of years of estimated life of asset
x = annual depreciation charge

KEY

ANNUITY METHOD FORMULA

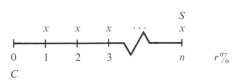

$C = xP_{\overline{n}|r\%} + Sp_{\overline{n}|r\%}$
$x = (C - Sp_{\overline{n}|r\%}) \div P_{\overline{n}|r\%}$

EXAMPLE

A machine that costs \$30,000 and that has an estimated useful life of four years is to be depreciated using the annuity method. The residual value of the machine at the end of its useful life is estimated to be \$5,000. It is thought that 8% could have been earned in the next best employment of the funds invested.

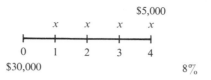

$5,000

$30,000   8%

Solution
$30,000 = $xP_{\overline{4}|8\%}$ + $5,000p_{\overline{4}|8\%}$
$30,000 = $x(3.3121)$ + $5,000(.7350)$
        x = $7,948.13

A reduction table for this problem appears as follows:

Reduction Table

Year	Book Value	Interest Earned (8%)	Depreciation	Accumulated Depreciation
1	$30,000.00	$2,400.00	$7,948.13	$5,548.13
2	24,451.87	1,956.15	7,948.13	5,991.98
3	18,459.89	1,476.79	7,948.13	6,471.34
4	11,988.55	959.08	7,948.13	6,989.05
				4,999.50[a]

[a] The $0.50 error in residual value has resulted from the use of four-place rather than eight-place tables.

The journal entry for the third year would be

Depreciation	$7,948.13	
Imputed Interest		$1,476.79
Accumulated Depreciation		6,471.34

Observe that although total depreciation taken is in excess of cost, the accumulated depreciation eventually results in the familiar cost minus salvage figure. Also note that, in theory, the investment in the asset is being constantly reduced by the accumulated depreciation amounts. This reduction is similar to the withdrawal of cash from a savings account or the receipt of a payment under an annuity contract.

Sinking-Fund Method of Depreciation

Suppose it is desirable to set aside funds regularly in order to have money on hand with which to replace an asset at the end of its useful life. To accomplish this goal, the sinking-fund method of depreciation may be employed. The presentation that follows employs the symbols and the example discussed in the section dealing with the annuity method of depreciation. Here, however, x is the payment into a fund, which, when accumulated and added to the residual value of the present asset, will be sufficient to replace the present asset—assuming that cost of the replacement asset is the same as present cost.

SINKING-FUND METHOD FORMULA ◀

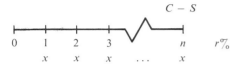

$$xF_{\overline{n}|r\%} = C - S$$

$$x = \frac{C - S}{F_{\overline{n}|r\%}}$$

EXAMPLE

$$xF_{\overline{4}|8\%} = \$30,000 - \$5,000$$
$$x(4.5061) = \$25,000$$
$$x = \$5,548.03$$

An accumulation table appears as follows:

Year	Deposit	Interest	Balance
1	$5,548.03	0	$ 5,548.03
2	5,548.03	$ 443.83	11,539.89
3	5,548.03	923.19	18,011.11
4	5,548.03	1,440.89	25,000.03

Accumulation
Table

The journal entries for the third year would be

Sinking Fund	$6,471.22	
Interest Income		$ 923.19
Cash		5,548.03
Depreciation	6,471.22	
Accumulated Depreciation		6,471.22

The sinking-fund method may be employed without actually creating the fund. If this is the case, then only the depreciation entry would be made.

Problems

Mortgage 1. Howard Stoll purchased a home for $61,229.60. He paid $15,000 down and agreed to pay the remainder in 40 equal, semiannual installments (beginning six months after the purchase date) at an annual rate of 6% interest. How much were his payments?

Mortgage 2. Mr. Wargo purchased a Rolls Royce on June 30, 1962, for $14,281.50. He paid $3,000 down and agreed to pay the balance in 24 equal monthly installments with interest payable at 6% per year. How much was each installment?

Sale of bonds 3. On June 1, 1972, a company issues $200,000 of 6% bonds due in ten years. Interest is payable semiannually on March 1 and September 1. Compute the proceeds of the issue on a 4% yield basis, and write all journal entries connected with these bonds from date of issue through December 31, 1972 (the date the annual financial statements are prepared).

Sale of bonds 4. (a) Rocketships, Inc., wishes to float a 4%, $500,000, 20-year bond issue to finance its diverse operations. If the coupons are paid semiannually, and if the current market yield to investors is 5%, how much will the issue bring when it is sold?

(b) What entry should be made for the third interest payment to record the total interest expense for that period?

(c) The bond indenture provides for establishing a sinking fund for the serial retirement of the issue at the rate of $100,000 a year beginning 16 years from date of issue. If the fund earns 3% compounded annually, how much must be deposited at the end of each of the 20 years? Give all entries for year 17.

Sales of bonds subject to a call feature 5. The Wargo Construction Company sold a $500,000, 4%, 25-year bond issue on a 6% basis. If the bonds were callable after 20 years at a price of 108, what price was received for them? Assume that the coupons are semiannual and that the bonds were sold on an interest date, January 1, 1968. Give the journal entries for the issuance of the bonds and for the payment of the sixth coupon.

Pension fund 6. Stoll Company has adopted a pension program and has incurred a liability for past services in so doing. The insurance company has offered to accept $10,000 now and at the end of each of the next seven years in settlement of the past service liability. Assuming that the market rate of interest is 6%, give the entries

(a) to record the initial liability, and

(b) to record the payment to the insurance company at the end of the sixth year and the past service expense for that year. Assume a ten-year amortization of the past service cost.

7. Management must decide between two proposals. The investments in each proposal are to be depreciated on a sum-of-the-years'-digits basis with 10% residual values and three-year lives. Income taxes are 60% and the required rate of return is 12%. *Capital budgeting*

	Time	Proposal A	Proposal B
Investment	t_0	$80,000	$100,000
Net Cash	t_1	$95,400	$ 35,000
Earnings	t_2	39,000	57,500
Before Taxes	t_3	12,000	80,000

Decide which proposal should be preferred based on

(a) time adjusted return,

(b) net present value,

(c) profitability index, and

(d) incremental approach.

8.

Asset cost	$40,000	*Sinking fund and annuity depreciation*
Estimated salvage value	$5,000	
Economic life	10 years	
Sinking-fund interest rate	6%	

Give the entries to record both depreciation and transfer of cash for the second year under the sinking-fund and annuity methods of depreciation.

3

Calculus

Calculus deals with change in variables and, in particular, with their rate of change. When this rate of change is zero, we know that the corresponding value of the variable is at a local maximum (think of the top of a hill) or minimum (think of the bottom of a valley) point. And if we can ascertain the maximum or minimum of a function, we simultaneously learn corresponding values of the controllable variable (known in calculus as the independent variable). With knowledge of these values of the controllable variable, we are able to optimize the associated function.

Accounting, and especially managerial accounting, is concerned with optimization. Stated in other terms, accounting is interested in profit maximization and cost minimization and in knowing what best performance is in order to establish budgets and standards.[1]

Another aspect of optimization that has always concerned accountants is the detection and elimination of waste. For one example, the accountant traditionally takes great pain to see that property, plant, and equipment

---

[1] There is redundancy here, since knowing what best performance is constitutes one step in both profit maximization and cost minimization.

53

items that are not in use are segregated in the other asset category on the balance sheet; he may even go so far as to provide a reserve for contingency for the possible loss on disposal of such idle assets. By extension of this concept, we see that the accountant is interested in "idle" cash and "idle" inventory, as well as other "idle" assets. But how does one determine idleness? One approach is to calculate the optimal quantity of an asset, given reasonable managerial policies, and then to treat as "idle" any quantity in excess of the optimal quantity. This process invokes either calculus or linear and nonlinear programing.[2]

In this chapter, we will be concerned with two basic calculus operations: differentiation and integration. A brief exposure such as this cannot hope to develop more than an understanding of some mechanics of calculus; to acquire an intuitive appreciation, you would be well advised to take formal courses. Although several examples of various operations will be presented, the use of letters (this process is usually referred to as "use of general notation") will be employed to state the basic rules (i.e., theorems). Take particular note of the *labels* of parameters (i.e., letters used to designate coefficients, constants, and exponents) *and their positions*.

Functions

A function expresses the interrelationship of two or more variables. Thus, we may have the function $y = ax^b + c$, where y is a dependent variable, x is an independent variable, a is a coefficient, b is an exponent, and c is some constant or, better, some number. We can become more specific by assigning numerical values to the parameters: $y = 6x^{-4} + 200$. By assigning values to x (the independent variable) we can determine values for y (the dependent variable).[3] If we wish to speak generally rather than specifically about a function, we write $y = f(x)$, where $f(x)$ is read "f of x," or simply "y is some function of x."

Functions are useful in many ways because

1. They describe behavior of phenomena.

---

[2] See Chapters 8 and 9 for a discussion of linear programing.

[3] The inverse function switches the roles of the dependent and independent variables by means of algebra. Thus, we have as the inverse of

$$y = ax^b + c$$

the following:

$$x = \sqrt[b]{\frac{y - c}{a}}$$

that is, the bth root of $(y - c)$ divided by a.

Chapter 3: Calculus

2. Their peaks (maximums) and troughs (minimums) may be readily determined by differentiation.[4]

3. The area under the function may be calculated by integration.

4. The reading along the curve (i.e., the value of y) may be determined by inserting the appropriate value for the independent variable. For example,

$$y = f(x) = 6x^{-4} + 200$$
$$y = f(2) = 6(2)^{-4} + 200$$
$$= \frac{6}{2^4} + 200$$
$$= 200\tfrac{3}{8}$$

Derivatives

The derivative of a function is the rate of change or slope of the function. In the straight-line case, we are reminded of the roof of a building when discussing slope (see Figure 3):

Figure 3

$$\textbf{Slope} = \frac{\textbf{rise}}{\textbf{run}} = \textbf{tangent of angle } a$$

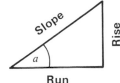

Now, if a true curve, rather than a straight line, is involved, the slope of the curve differs from point to point. The slope, therefore, is not a constant as in the case of a straight line, but rather a function of x itself (see Figure 4).

Figure 4

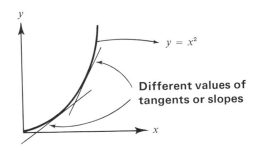

$y = x^2$

Different values of tangents or slopes

---

[4] Differentiation is permitted only where a given function is continuous. Strictly speaking, if a function is valid only where changes between adjacent points are discrete and fixed in size (intuitively, the changes are one unit rather than very small fractions of one unit), infinitesimal calculus and differentiation should be replaced by finite calculus and differencing. However, if the quantities of x are large, the results of infinitesimal calculus closely approximate the results of finite calculus. For our studies, we will assume continuity.

Suppose $y = x^2$. Then the formula for the slope of y is

$$y' = f'(x) = \frac{dy}{dx} = 2x$$

Here, y', $f'(x)$, and dy/dx have all been used as general notations for the first derivative of y, and $2x$ represents the specific formula itself. Thus, if we wanted to know the slope at, say, $x = 8$, we would insert 8 in the slope (or rate-of-change) formula: $f'(8) = 2(8) = 16$.

The Limit Approach Let us see how the slope formula, $f'(x) = 2x$, could have been obtained. We continue with our definition for slope:

$$\text{Slope} = \frac{\text{rise}}{\text{run}} = f'(x) = \lim_{\Delta x \to 0} \frac{\Delta y}{\Delta x}$$

Δy is the change in y from one point to the next, that is, $y_1 - y_0$. Δx is the corresponding change in x, that is, $x_1 - x_0$. By the expression $\lim_{\Delta x \to 0}$, we mean that the change in x will approach zero (or no change) in the limit. In other words, we shall make the change in the run value so small that there is almost no change.

We substitute for Δy to get our expression entirely in terms of x:

$$f'(x) = \lim_{\Delta x \to 0} \frac{\Delta y}{\Delta x}$$

$$= \lim_{\Delta x \to 0} \frac{y_1 - y_0}{\Delta x}$$

$$= \lim_{\Delta x \to 0} \frac{(x + \Delta x)^2 - x^2}{\Delta x}$$

We now perform some algebra:

$$f'(x) = \lim_{\Delta x \to 0} \frac{(x^2 + 2x \, \Delta x + (\Delta x)^2) - x^2}{\Delta x}$$

$$= \lim_{\Delta x \to 0} \frac{\Delta x \, (2x + \Delta x)}{\Delta x}$$

$$= \lim_{\Delta x \to 0} 2x + \Delta x$$

Now we take the limit; that is, we let $\Delta x = 0$: $f'(x) = 2x$, which is the formula we wished to obtain.

The limit approach has been presented because it permits some intuitive understanding that a derivative is the rate at which the values of a curve change, given an almost imperceptible change (i.e., a change that is zero in the limit) in the independent variable.

In a sense, applied mathematics may be compared to a hammer—the construction dynamics of the hammer are of little concern to a carpenter, but how to use it is all-important. Analogously, calculus formulas may be used mechanically and used well, provided that you have some vague notion of what you are doing.

Listed below are some basic formulas and examples of their use. *Note the relative positions of all parameters.*

The Formula Approach

1. $y = ax^b$

$$\frac{dy}{dx} = \frac{d(ax^b)}{dx} = abx^{b-1}$$

Many students in applied mathematics courses find the above formula difficult to understand although easy to apply. To improve intuitions, consider this proof.

Proof

$y = ax^b$

$$\frac{dy}{dx} = \lim_{\Delta x \to 0} \frac{\Delta y}{\Delta x} = \lim_{\Delta x \to 0} \frac{y_1 - y_0}{\Delta x} = \lim_{\Delta x \to 0} \frac{a(x + \Delta x)^b - ax^b}{\Delta x}$$

We expand this expression using the binomial theorem:

$$= \lim_{\Delta x \to 0} \frac{a[\binom{b}{0}x^0(\Delta x)^b + \binom{b}{1}x^1(\Delta x)^{b-1} + \cdots + \binom{b}{b}x^b(\Delta x)^0] - ax^b}{\Delta x}$$

$$= \lim_{\Delta x \to 0} \frac{a[(\Delta x)^b + bx(\Delta x)^{b-1} + \cdots + bx^{b-1}(\Delta x)^1 + x^b] - ax^b}{\Delta x}$$

$$= \lim_{\Delta x \to 0} \frac{a[(\Delta x)^b + bx(\Delta x)^{b-1} + \cdots + bx^{b-1}(\Delta x)] + ax^b - ax^b}{\Delta x}$$

$$= \lim_{\Delta x \to 0} \frac{a(\Delta x)[(\Delta x)^{b-1} + bx(\Delta x)^{b-2} + \cdots + bx^{b-1}]}{\Delta x}$$

$$= \lim_{\Delta x \to 0} a[(\Delta x)^{b-1} + bx(\Delta x)^{b-2} + \cdots + bx^{b-1}]$$

Now we take the limit; that is, we let $\Delta x = 0$:

$$\frac{dy}{dx} = a[0 + 0 + \cdots + bx^{b-1}] = abx^{b-1}$$

We see that the formula approach results from the limit approach. The formulas that follow could also be proved in a similar fashion; however, we will not concern ourselves with any further such proofs.

EXAMPLE

$y = x^2$
$y' = 2x$

Derivatives   57

NOTE $ax^b = 1x^2$; apply formula (1).

(Observe that this is the same curve considered under the limit approach.)

EXAMPLE
___

$$y = 2x^3 - 6x + 2$$
$$f'(x) = 2(3)x^{3-1} - 6(1)x^{1-1} + 2(0)x^{0-1}$$
$$= 6x^2 - 6$$

NOTE Formula (1) is applied term by term, $-6x$ may be written $-6x^1$; 2 may be written $2x^0$, since $x^0 = 1$.

EXAMPLE
___

$$y = 5x^{-4}$$
$$\frac{dy}{dx} = 5(-4)x^{-4-1} = -20x^{-5}$$

EXAMPLE
___

$$y = (6 - 2x^3)^4$$
$$\frac{dy}{dx} = 4(6 - 2x^3)^3(-6x^2)$$

COMMENT The trick here is to treat the expression in parentheses initially as if it were a variable itself in simplest form, take the derivative of the parentheses, and then take the derivative of the expression within the parentheses. This process is referred to as the chain rule for taking a derivative and may be stated formally as

$$\frac{dy}{dx} = \frac{dy}{du}\frac{du}{dx}$$

It will help intuitions to contemplate the following example.

$$y = (4x^5)^3 = u^3$$
$$\frac{dy}{dx} = \frac{dy}{du}\frac{du}{dx}$$
$$\frac{dy}{dx} = 3(4x^5)^2(20x^4) = 3(16x^{10})(20x^4) = 960x^{14}$$

Note that the same results could have been achieved by rewriting the original

58

equation in its equivalent form.

$$y = (4x^5)^3 = 64x^{15}$$

$$\frac{dy}{dx} = 960x^{14}$$

---

2. $y = e^{-ax^b}$ ◀

$$\frac{dy}{dx} = \frac{d(e^{-ax^b})}{dx} = e^{-ax^b}\left(\frac{d(-ax^b)}{dx}\right) = -abx^{b-1}e^{-ax^b}$$

EXAMPLE

$$y = e^{-6x^2}$$

$$y' = e^{-6x^2}\left(\frac{d(-6x^2)}{dx}\right) = e^{-6x^2}(-6(2)x^{2-1}) = -12xe^{-6x^2}$$

---

3. $y = f(x)g(x)$ ◀

$$\frac{dy}{dx} = f(x)g'(x) + g(x)f'(x)$$

This is read, "The derivative with respect to x equals the first function times   NOTE
the derivative of the second, plus the second function times the derivative of
the first." This is known as the "product rule."

EXAMPLE

$$y = (3x^2 - 6)(2x^{-4} + 8x)$$

$$\frac{dy}{dx} = (3x^2 - 6)(-8x^{-5} + 8) + (2x^{-4} + 8x)(6x)$$

---

4. $y = \dfrac{f(x)}{g(x)}$ ◀

$$\frac{dy}{dx} = \frac{g(x)f'(x) - f(x)g'(x)}{[g(x)]^2}$$

This is read, "The derivative with respect to x equals the bottom function   NOTE
times the derivative of the top, minus the top function times the derivative of

Derivatives

59

the bottom, all divided by the bottom function squared." This is known as the "quotient rule."

EXAMPLE

$$y = \frac{3x^2 - 6}{2x^{-4} + 8x}$$

$$\frac{dy}{dx} = \frac{(2x^{-4} + 8x)(6x) - (3x^2 - 6)(-8x^{-5} + 8)}{(2x^{-4} + 8x)^2}$$

Why is Differentiation Important?

Differentiation is important to determine optimal values of functions. If we were able to graph all functions quickly, we would have little need for taking derivatives. But graphing (1) takes time, (2) is cumbersome, and (3) is not always possible (graphing more than three variables is generally considered impossible).

Let us use a simple example to illustrate the importance of differentiation. Graphed in Figure 5 is the function $y = 10x^3 - 75x^2 + 120x + 90$, which is assumed valid for the domain $0 \le x \le 5$.

Figure 5

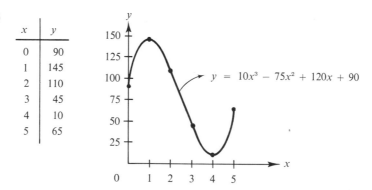

x	y
0	90
1	145
2	110
3	45
4	10
5	65

$y = 10x^3 - 75x^2 + 120x + 90$

Now it took some time to compute the y values and to draw the graph. Suppose we were interested simply in the positions of its peak and trough and we did not want to draw the graph. In other words, suppose we want to know the *maximum and minimum* of the curve without drawing it.

Figure 6 shows how some tangent lines to this curve would appear. Note that the tangents at both the peak and trough are flat; that is, the *slopes at these points are zero*. Now, since the first derivative gives us the slope curve, all we need do is set the slope curve equal to zero and solve the resulting equation. We will then have the points at which the slope is zero and, hence, the corresponding maximum and minimum points of the original curve. This is done on page 61.

60

Figure 6

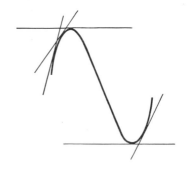

$$y = f(x) = 10x^3 - 75x^2 + 120x + 90$$
$$f'(x) = 30x^2 - 150x + 120 \qquad = 0 \longleftarrow \text{observe}$$

Dividing through by 30,

$$x^2 - 5x + 4 = 0$$

Factoring,

$$(x - 1)(x - 4) = 0$$

Setting each expression equal to 0, we get the desired points:

$$x = 1, 4$$

Observe that we still do not know which point is the maximum and which is the minimum. To decide this, we could, of course, substitute the points into the original expression [i.e., find $f(1)$ and $f(4)$] and see which point yields a high and which a low value. However, mathematicians have a much more sophisticated approach; they "test for second-order conditions." This test involves taking the second derivative [$f''(x)$], substituting the optimal values $(1, 4)$ in the second derivative expression [i.e., finding $f''(1)$ and $f''(4)$], and noting whether the resulting numerical values are positive or negative. If a value is positive, then the point is a local minimum, and vice versa. If the value is zero, then a turning point (slope changing signs) is involved. Note that before one can say that he has calculated the global (the whole curve—not just some midsection of it) maximum and minimum, the end points (in our example, the extreme values of the domain, 0 and 5) must be inserted in $f(x)$ to see if they produce a greater maximum or a lower minimum. There are mnemonic diagrams that help in recalling the sign-point relationships; the diagrams for the values obtained by inserting the optimal points in the second derivative are

Min

Max

Let us employ these rules to determine the maximum and minimum points in our example.

NOTE Pay close attention to the number of primes on $f(x)$, because they indicate whether we are discussing the original equation, $f(x)$, or the first derivative expression, $f'(x)$, etc.

$$f'(x) = 30x^2 - 150x + 120$$
$$f''(x) = 60x - 150$$
$$f''(1) = 60(1) - 150 = -90 \qquad \text{negative, therefore, a maximum point}$$
$$f''(4) = 60(4) - 150 = 90 \qquad \text{positive, therefore, a minimum point}$$

We check the end points:

$$f(0) = 90 \qquad \text{lower than } f(1) = 145$$
$$f(5) = 65 \qquad \text{greater than } f(4) = 10$$

Consequently, the global maximum occurs at $x = 1$, and the global minimum occurs at $x = 4$.

Partial Derivatives

Heretofore we have considered functions with one dependent and one independent variable. Now we turn our attention briefly to functions with more than one independent variable.

The notation for a multivariate function in general is $y = f(x_1, x_2, \cdots, x_n)$; however, since it is easier—in that subscripts are dispensed with—to deal with the variables x, y, and z, we shall discuss partial derivatives in terms of one dependent and two independent variables. The extension of the formula to more than two independent variables is straightforward and obvious.

The notation for a partial derivative is ∂. Thus, given the function $y = f(x, z)$, the partial of y with respect to, say, x would be indicated either as

$$\frac{\partial y}{\partial x} \quad \text{or} \quad \frac{\partial f(x, z)}{\partial x}$$

The process of taking a partial derivative is similar to the process of taking an ordinary derivative. The only mental chicanery involved is to treat the independent variable "not in use" as a constant. For instance, if we had the function $y = f(x, z)$ and we wanted to obtain $\partial y / \partial x$, x would be "in use," and we would treat z as if it were a number. Similarly, if we want $\partial y / \partial z$, x would now be treated as if it were a constant. The following example should clarify the procedure.

$$y = 6x^3 - 2xz + 5z^4$$
$$\frac{\partial y}{\partial x} = 18x^2 - 2z \qquad z \text{ is treated as a number}$$
$$\frac{\partial y}{\partial z} = -2x + 20z^3 \qquad x \text{ is treated as a number}$$

Now suppose there were a known side relation between the independent variables, for example, $x = 4z^2$. We could now calculate the total derivative of y (previously referred to as the ordinary derivative) in either of two ways:

1. We could substitute x or z and end up with a function with one dependent and one independent variable. y' could then be calculated in the ordinary fashion.

2. We could work through partial derivatives to obtain the total derivative. The formula to follow would be

$$\frac{dy}{dz} = \frac{\partial y}{\partial x}\frac{dx}{dz} + \frac{\partial y}{\partial z}\frac{dz}{dz} = \frac{\partial y}{\partial x}\frac{dx}{dz} + \frac{\partial y}{\partial z}$$

Let us illustrate these two approaches by continuing our example.

$$y = 6x^3 - 2xz + 5z^4 \qquad\qquad \textbf{\textit{a. Substitution}}$$

Substituting $x = 4z^2$

$$y = 6(4z^2)^3 - 2(4z^2)z + 5z^4$$

$$\frac{dy}{dz} = 18(4z^2)^2(8z) - 24z^2 + 20z^3 = 2{,}304z^5 + 20z^3 - 24z^2$$

$$y = 6x^3 - 2xz + 5z^4 \qquad\qquad \textbf{\textit{b. Partials}}$$

$\dfrac{\partial y}{\partial x}$ and $\dfrac{\partial y}{\partial z}$ are the same as before.

$$\frac{dx}{dz} = \frac{d(4z^2)}{dz} = 8z$$

Applying the formula

$$\frac{dy}{dz} : \frac{\partial y}{\partial x}\frac{dx}{dz} + \frac{\partial y}{\partial z}$$

we obtain

$$\frac{dy}{dz} = (18x^2 - 2z)8z - 2x + 20z^3$$

To see that our results are the same as under the prior approach, we substitute for x (recall $x = 4z^2$):

$$\frac{dy}{dz} = (18[4z^2]^2 - 2z)8z - 2(4z^2) + 20z^3 = 2{,}304z^5 + 20z^3 - 24z^2$$

One interesting application of partial derivatives occurs in the study of marginal productivity in economics. Since most of you are familiar with the marginal concepts of economics, it may improve understanding of partial derivatives to go into a brief discussion of marginal productivity.

In a nutshell and with no attempt to be rigorous, marginal productivity theory is concerned with the effect on total production if one unit of labor *or* one unit of capital is added or removed. The theory rests on a number of assumptions, the most crucial of which is the assumption of divisibility (i.e., that all other factors of production can be held constant while a change is made in one factor). Now it may or may not make sense to assume divisibility —to assume, for instance, that a worker may be added without giving him a machine. But we shall assume it does, since we are interested primarily in partial derivatives and in the fact that marginal productivity has the same approach of holding all other independent variables constant while allowing one to vary.

The best-known macroproduction function is the Cobb-Douglas function. Its notation and the derivation of both the marginal productivity of labor and the marginal productivity of capital are as shown below.

KEY
P = product
L = units of labor
a = share of product going to labor
K = units of capital

▶ *COBB-DOUGLAS FUNCTION*

$$P = L^a K^{1-a}$$

The marginal productivity of labor, $\partial P/\partial L$, is calculated as follows:

$$\frac{\partial P}{\partial L} = aL^{a-1}K^{1-a}$$

$$= \frac{aL^a}{L} K^{1-a} = \frac{a}{L} P$$

The marginal productivity of capital, $\partial P/\partial K$, is calculated as follows:

$$\frac{\partial P}{\partial K} = (1 - a)L^a K^{1-a-1}$$

$$= \frac{(1 - a)L^a K^{1-a}}{K} = \frac{(1 - a)P}{K}$$

Integration

If $F(x)$ is a function whose derivative is $F'(x) = f(x)$, then $F(x)$ is an integral of $f(x)$. This definition suggests that integration is a way to reverse the differentiation process. And so it is; when used in this fashion, integration is a means of finding "antiderivatives."

Figure 7

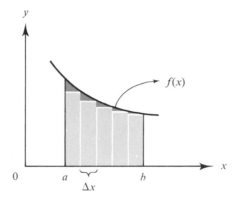

Figure 8

Another and perhaps more important use of integration, as far as applied mathematics is concerned, is that of finding the area under a given curve between two specified limits. Figure 7 shades the area under the curve $f(x)$ between the limits a and b. Actually, area is determined by a limit approach; rectangles of height $f(x_i)$ and width Δx are theoretically inscribed under a curve; then the width is decreased and the number of rectangles is increased until the darkened areas above each rectangle in Figure 8 disappear. Mathematically, we have

$$A = \lim_{\substack{n \to \infty \\ \Delta x \to 0}} \sum_{i=1}^{n} f(x_i) \Delta x \equiv \int_a^b f(x) \, dx = F(b) - F(a)$$

where A = area, and the distance between a and b is divided into n intervals of width Δx. The integral sign is $\int$, and dx indicates x as the variable of integration.

Let us return to our first example, where $f'(x) = 2x$, and find its area between $a = 2$ and $b = 5$. (We are using basic formula 5.)

$$\int_a^b f'(x) \, dx = \int_2^5 2x \, dx = x^2 \Big]_2^5 = 5^2 - 2^2 = 25 - 4 = 21$$

The a and b are referred to as limits of integration. Note that once $2x$ is integrated, we obtain our original function $y = f(x) = x^2$. This is the reason for considering integration a process for obtaining an antiderivative. Next we evaluate the resulting function x^2 by inserting our upper limit 5 for x and subtracting our lower limit 2.

It may aid intuitions to relate the process of integrating to obtain area to that of obtaining area by means of some formula that is familiar to most people. Let us consider finding the area of a triangle. The formula that most of us have memorized at one time or another is, "The area of a triangle equals one-half the base times the height," or, symbolically, $A = \frac{1}{2}bh$. We shall use integration to prove this formula.

The formula for the curve (recall that a straight line is merely a special form of a curve) requires explanation. We see that h is the y intercept and that the curve has a falling or negative slope. To determine the slope, we note that the fall (Δy) is $-h$ and that the run (Δx) is b; therefore, the slope is

$$\frac{\Delta y}{\Delta x} = \frac{-h}{b} \qquad \text{(It may help to consider rise} = -\text{fall.)}$$

Hence, the formula for the height y at any point x along the curve is

$$y = h - \frac{h}{b}x$$

(See Figure 9.) We can check the formula by inserting the end values of x:

$$y = f(x) = f(0)$$
$$= h - \frac{h}{b}(0) = h, \quad \text{the } y \text{ intercept}$$
$$y = f(x) = f(b)$$
$$= h - \frac{h}{b}(b) = 0, \quad \text{the } x \text{ intercept}$$

We proceed to calculate the area under the curve $y = h - (h/b)x$.

$$A = \int_0^b \left(h - \frac{h}{b}x \right) dx$$

To integrate, we again employ basic formula 5, which is to be presented shortly.

Figure 9

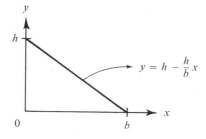

$$y = h - \frac{h}{b}x$$

Chapter 3: Calculus

$$A = hx - \frac{h}{b}\frac{x^2}{2}\Bigg]_0^b = h(b - 0) - \frac{h}{2b}(b^2 - 0^2)$$

$$= hb - \frac{hb}{2} = \frac{hb}{2}$$

This is the result of our familiar formula for area of a triangle, $A = \frac{1}{2}bh$.

5. $f'(x) = ax^b$

$$\int_c^d ax^b \, dx = \frac{ax^{b+1}}{b+1}\Bigg]_c^d = \frac{a}{b+1}(d^{b+1} - c^{b+1})$$

EXAMPLE

$$\int_2^5 2x \, dx = \int_2^5 2x^1 \, dx = \frac{2x^{1+1}}{1+1}\Bigg]_2^5 = x^2\Bigg]_2^5 = 21$$

Note that $2x = 2x^1$.

EXAMPLE

$$\int_1^4 (3x^2 - 2x^{-3} + 4) \, dx = \int_1^4 3x^2 \, dx - \int_1^4 2x^{-3} \, dx + \int_1^4 4 \, dx$$

$$= \frac{3x^{2+1}}{2+1} - \frac{2x^{-3+1}}{-3+1} + \frac{4x^1}{1}\Bigg]_1^4$$

$$= x^3 + x^{-2} + 4x\Bigg]_1^4$$

$$= [4^3 + 4^{-2} + 4(4)] - [1^3 + 1^{-2} + 4(1)]$$

$$= (64 + \tfrac{1}{16} + 16) - (1 + 1 + 4)$$

$$= 74\tfrac{1}{16}$$

---

6. $\int_a^b y \, dx$

One independent variable

Situation 1

Where y is a function of x (say, $y = 6x^3$), y should be replaced before the integration is performed.

EXAMPLE

$$\int_a^b y \, dx = \int_a^b 6x^3 \, dx = \frac{6x^4}{4}\Bigg]_a^b = \tfrac{3}{2}(b^4 - a^4)$$

Integration

Situation 2   *Two independent variables*

Where both x and y are independent variables [i.e., $z = f(x, y)$], "partial integration" should be performed. This is akin to taking a partial derivative; one variable is held constant while the other is integrated.

EXAMPLES

$$\int_2^5 x \, dy = xy\bigg]_2^5 = x(5 - 2) = 3x$$

$$\int_1^4 x^2 y \, dy = x^2 \frac{y^2}{2}\bigg]_1^4 = x^2\left(\frac{4^2}{2} - \frac{1^2}{2}\right) = \frac{15x^2}{2}$$

To arrive at a numerical answer in situation 2, it would be necessary to use double integration. For example,

$$\int_2^3 \int_1^4 x^2 y \, dy \, dx = \int_2^3 \left[\int_1^4 x^2 y \, dy\right] dx = \int_2^3 \frac{15x^2}{2} \, dx = \frac{5x^3}{2}\bigg]_2^3 = \frac{95}{2}$$

▶   **7.** $f'(x) = ae^{bx}$

$$\int_c^d ae^{bx} \, dx = \frac{a}{b} e^{bx}\bigg]_c^d = \frac{a}{b}(e^{bd} - e^{bc})$$

EXAMPLE

$$\int_0^1 4e^{2x} \, dx = \tfrac{4}{2}(e^{2(1)} - e^{2(0)}) = 2(7.3891 - 1)$$
$$= 12.7782$$

NOTE   Values for e appear in Table A.6.

▶   **8.** $f'(x) = xe^{-ax^2}$

$$\int_c^d xe^{-ax^2} \, dx = -\frac{1}{2a}[e^{-ad^2} - e^{-ac^2}]$$

EXAMPLE

$$\int_1^3 xe^{-x^2/2} \, dx = -\frac{1}{2(\tfrac{1}{2})}(e^{-3^2/2} - e^{-1^2/2})$$
$$= -(.0111 - .6065)$$
$$= .5954$$

9.　$\displaystyle \int_c^d e^{-ax^2}\,dx = \frac{\sqrt{2\pi}}{\sqrt{2a}} \int_{\sqrt{2a}\,c}^{\sqrt{2a}\,d} \frac{e^{-z^2/2}}{\sqrt{2\pi}}\,dz$　　◀

This does not seem to represent an improvement, yet it is. The expression under the right-hand integral is the formula for the normal curve, values for which appear in Table A.7. It will be instructive to prove the above formula, since it involves transformation of variables.

$$\int_c^d e^{-ax^2}\,dx = \int_c^d e^{-2ax^2/2}\,dx$$

Transformation of variables　　　　　　　　　　　　　　　　**NOTE**

　Let $z = \sqrt{2a}\,x$ (note that $z^2 = 2ax^2$). Then,

$$\frac{dz}{dx} = \sqrt{2a} \quad \text{and} \quad dx = \frac{dz}{\sqrt{2a}}$$

Now the limits of integration must be changed. Since $z = \sqrt{2a}\,x$,

$\left.\begin{array}{l} z \text{ upper} = \sqrt{2a}\,d \\[4pt] z \text{ lower} = \sqrt{2a}\,c \end{array}\right\}$ (substituting d and c for x in the formula for z)

We now substitute the values associated with the new variable z.

$$= \int_{\sqrt{2a}\,c}^{\sqrt{2a}\,d} e^{-z^2/2}\,\frac{dz}{\sqrt{2a}}$$

We now invoke a theorem of calculus, which states

$$\int ax\,dx = a \int x\,dx, \qquad \text{where } a \text{ is some constant}$$

$$= \frac{1}{\sqrt{2a}} \int_{\sqrt{2a}\,c}^{\sqrt{2a}\,d} e^{-z^2/2}\,dz$$

We multiply the above expression by 1 in the form $\sqrt{2\pi}/\sqrt{2\pi}$:

$$= \frac{\sqrt{2\pi}}{\sqrt{2a}} \int_{\sqrt{2a}\,c}^{\sqrt{2a}\,d} \frac{e^{-z^2/2}\,dz}{\sqrt{2\pi}}$$

This completes the proof; let us see how Table A.7 may be used by introducing an example.

$$\int_1^2 e^{-2x^2}\, dx = \frac{\sqrt{2\pi}}{\sqrt{4}} \int_{\sqrt{4}\,1}^{\sqrt{4}\,2} \frac{e^{-z^2/2}\, dz}{\sqrt{2\pi}}$$

Since $\pi = \frac{22}{7}$,

$$\cong \frac{2.5}{2} \int_2^4 \frac{e^{-z^2/2}\, dz}{\sqrt{2\pi}}$$

$$\cong 1.25(.5000 - .4772)$$

$$= .0285$$

Integration by Parts

Integration by parts is another widely used calculus theorem. The theorem states: $\int U\, dv = UV] - \int V\, du$. Here, U and V are functions of an independent variable. The illustration below demonstrates integration by parts.

$$NPV = \int_2^{12} \underbrace{(6{,}000 - 500t)}_{U}\underbrace{e^{-0.1t}\, dt}_{dv}$$

Let $U = 6{,}000 - 500t$

$\dfrac{du}{dt} = -500$ (i.e., $du = -500\, dt$)

$dv = e^{-0.1t}\, dt$

$V = \int dv = \int e^{-0.1t}\, dt = -10e^{-0.1t}$

$$\int U\, dv = [\quad U \quad\quad V \quad] - \int \quad V \quad\quad du$$

$$= [(6{,}000 - 500t)(-10e^{-0.1t})]_0^{12} - \int_0^{12} (-10e^{-0.1t})(-500\, dt)$$

$$= [(6{,}000 - 500t)(-10e^{-0.1t}) + 50{,}000e^{-0.1t}]_0^{12}$$

$$= [(5{,}000t - 10{,}000)e^{-0.1t}]_0^{12}$$

$$= 50{,}000e^{-1.2} + 10{,}000e^0$$

$$= 50{,}000(.30119) + 10{,}000$$

$$= 25{,}059.50$$

Derivative of an Integral

We often encounter the situation where a derivative of an integral has to be taken with respect to a variable in the upper limit of the integral. A calculus theorem that speeds up this calculation is

$$\frac{d}{dw} \int_a^w f(x)\, dx = f(w)$$

that is, evaluate the original function at w; w is a variable, a is a constant.

Another theorem states

$$f(x)g(x) = g(x)f(x) = h(x)$$

An example that combines these theorems is

$$\frac{d}{dn} \int_0^n (6{,}000 - 500t)e^{-0.1t}\, dt = (6{,}000 - 500n)e^{-0.1n}$$

In words, we merely substitute n for t in the expression to be integrated (known as the integrand).

Demonstration of validity of answer:

$$F = \int_0^n (6{,}000 - 500t)e^{-0.1t}\, dt$$

Let

$$U = 6{,}000 - 500t$$
$$dv = e^{-0.1t}$$

Then,

$$du = -500\, dt$$
$$V = -10e^{-0.1t}$$

$$F = [\quad U \qquad\qquad V \qquad] - \int V\, du$$

$$F = (6{,}000 - 500t)(-10e^{-0.1t})]_0^n - \int_0^n (-10e^{-0.1t})(-500\, dt)$$

$$F = (500t - 6{,}000)10e^{-0.1t}]_0^n + 50{,}000e^{-0.1t}]_0^n$$

$$F = (5{,}000t - 10{,}000)e^{-0.1t}]_0^n = (5{,}000n - 10{,}000)e^{-0.1n} + 10{,}000$$

$$\frac{dF}{dn} = (5{,}000n - 10{,}000)(-0.1e^{-0.1n}) + e^{-0.1n}(5{,}000) + 0$$

$$= (1{,}000 - 500n)e^{-0.1n} + 5{,}000e^{-0.1n} = (6{,}000 - 500n)e^{-0.1n}$$

Suppose now that there are two variables in the integrand and the problem requires taking the derivative of the integral. This is a complicated operation but one that will not only be useful in the work ahead but that also will illustrate much of the preceding calculus material.

GIVEN   Functions of $x = h(x), k(x), g(x)$
Function of x and $y = f(x, y)$

$f[x, h(x)]$ is evaluated by taking the original function $f(x, y)$ and substituting   NOTE
$h(x)$ for y.

$$\frac{dg(x)}{dx} = \int_{h(x)}^{k(x)} \frac{\partial f(x, y)}{\partial x}\, dy + f[x, k(x)]\frac{dk(x)}{dx} - f[x, h(x)]\frac{dh(x)}{dx}$$

$$z = \int_0^x 2(y^2 - x^3 y)\,dy + \int_x^3 \frac{(5y^2 - x^2 y)}{2}\,dy$$

$$\frac{dz}{dx} = \int_0^x -6x^2 y\,dy + 2[x^2 - x^3(x)]\frac{d(x)}{dx} - 2\left[0^2 - x^3(0)\frac{d(0)}{dx}\right]$$

$$+ \int_x^3 -xy\,dy + \frac{1}{2}[5(3)^2 - x^2(3)]\frac{d(3)}{dx} - \frac{1}{2}[5x^2 - x^2(x)]\frac{d(x)}{dx}$$

$$= -\int_0^x 6x^2 y\,dy + 2x^2 - 2x^4 - \int_x^3 xy\,dy - \frac{5x^2}{2} + \frac{x^3}{2}$$

$$= -\frac{6x^2 y^2}{2}\Bigg]_0^x + 2x^2 - 2x^4 - \frac{xy^2}{2}\Bigg]_x^3 - \frac{5x^2}{2} + \frac{x^3}{2}$$

$$= -3x^4 + 2x^2 - 2x^4 - \left(\frac{9x}{2} - \frac{x^3}{2}\right) - \frac{5x^2}{2} + \frac{x^3}{2}$$

$$= -5x^4 + x^3 - \frac{x^2}{2} - \frac{9x}{2}$$

It would be instructive to verify these results by resolving the example without the aid of the stated theorem.

$$z = \int_0^x 2(y^2 - x^3 y)\,dy + \int_x^3 \frac{(5y^2 - x^2 y)}{2}\,dy$$

$$= 2\left[\frac{y^3}{3} - \frac{x^3 y^2}{2}\right]_0^x + \frac{1}{2}\left[\frac{5y^3}{3} - \frac{x^2 y^2}{2}\right]_x^3$$

$$= 2\left[\frac{x^3}{3} - \frac{x^5}{2}\right] + \frac{1}{2}\left[45 - \frac{9x^2}{2} - \left(\frac{5x^3}{3} - \frac{x^4}{2}\right)\right]$$

$$= -x^5 + \frac{x^4}{4} - \frac{x^3}{6} - \frac{9x^2}{4} + \frac{45}{2}$$

$$\frac{dz}{dx} = -5x^4 + x^3 - \frac{x^2}{3} - \frac{9x}{2}$$

Problems

1. Match the following functions with their derivatives:

$f(x)$		$f'(x)$

(a) $y = 6x^4$ ( ) $y' = 24x^2e^{4x^3}$

(b) $y = 8x^{-3} + 3x^2 + 2x + 25$ ( ) $y' = 24x^3$

(c) $y = (6 - x^2)(4x^3 - 3x)$ ( ) $y' = -48xe^{-4x^2}$

(d) $y = -6x^{-5}$ ( ) $y' = \dfrac{(4x + 2)^3(10x + 24x^{-5}) - (5x^2 - 6x^{-4})3(4x + 2)^2 4}{(4x + 2)^6}$

(e) $y = \dfrac{x^4}{(7 - 3x^2)}$ ( ) $y' = -24x^{-4} + 6x + 2$

(f) $y = 6e^{-4x^2}$ ( ) $y' = (x - 6)3(3x^2 - 2)^2(6x) + (3x^2 - 2)^3(1)$

(g) $y = (7x^3 - 5x)^5$ ( ) $y' = (6 - x^2)(12x^2 - 3) + (4x^3 + 3x)(-2x)$

(h) $y = (x - 6)(3x^2 - 2)^3$ ( ) $y' = \dfrac{(7 - 3x^2)(4x^3) - x^4(-6x)}{(7 - 3x^2)^2}$

(i) $y = 2e^{4x^3}$ ( ) $y' = 30x^{-6}$

(j) $y = \dfrac{(5x^2 - 6x^{-4})}{(4x + 2)^3}$ ( ) $y' = 5(7x^3 - 5x)^4(21x^2 - 5)$

Answer: i, a, f, j, b, h, c, e, d, g

2. Find the maximum and minimum for the following functions:

    (a) $f(x) = x(12 - 2x)^2$, for $0 \leq x \leq 8$

    (b) $f(x) = \dfrac{x^3}{3} - x^2 - 15x$, for $-5 \leq x \leq 10$

Answer: (a) Max. $= 2$, min. $= 6$; (b) max. $= 10$, min. $= 5$

3. Find the optimal production quantity from the data below.

               Selling price per unit $(Q) = P = \$7{,}000 - \$0.002Q^2$

               Total cost of production $= \$2{,}000{,}000 + \$1{,}000Q$

What is the maximum profit?

Total sales revenue $= QP =$ units sold $\times$ price per unit   **Hint**
Optimal production occurs where marginal revenue $=$ marginal cost

Answer: Optimal quantity $= 1{,}000$ units; maximum profit $= \$2{,}000{,}000$

4. Find the total derivative from the data below (a) using partials and (b) using substitution immediately.

    $z = f(x, y) = 8x^4 - 6xy - 2y^3$

    Parametric (side) function: $x = y^{-4}$

5. Evaluate the following:

(a) $\displaystyle\int_{2}^{5} x^3\, dx$

(b) $\displaystyle\int_{1}^{4} 3x^{-4}\, dx$

(c) $\displaystyle\int_{2}^{3} (8x^3 - 6x^{-3} + 2)\, dx$

(d) $\displaystyle\int_{0}^{6} (-2x^{-3} + x^4 + 2x + 5)\, dx$

(e) $\displaystyle\int_{5}^{10} 6e^{0.3x}\, dx$

(f) $\displaystyle\int_{1}^{5} xe^{-0.2x^2}\, dx$

(g) $\displaystyle\int_{0}^{0.5} e^{-4.5x^2}\, dx$

Answers: (a) $\dfrac{609}{4}$ (b) $\dfrac{63}{64}$

$$\text{(c)}\quad \frac{8x^4}{4} - \frac{6x^{-2}}{-2}\ 2x\Big]_{2}^{3} = 2x^4 + \frac{3}{x^2} + 2x\Big]_{2}^{3}$$

$$= 2(3)^4 + \frac{3}{3^2} + 2(3) - \left[2(2)^4 + \frac{3}{2^2} + 2(2)\right]$$

$$= \frac{1{,}579}{12}$$

(d) $-\infty$ (e) 312.08

$$\text{(f)}\quad \frac{e^{-0.2x^2}}{-0.4}\Big]_{1}^{5} = -2.5(e^{-5} - e^{-0.2})$$ (g) 0.361

$$= -2.5(.0067 - .8187) = 2.03$$

Derivative of an integral **6.** Find the optimal value of x in two ways.

$$y = \int_{0}^{x} (2{,}000 - 50z)e^{-0.2z}\, dz$$

Hint Find dy/dx.

Answer: $x = 40$

Derivative of an integral **7.** Find dz/dx in two ways.

$$z = \int_{0}^{x} 3(y^3 - x^2)\frac{y^3}{4}\, dy + \int_{x}^{4} (2 + 4x^3)\frac{y^3}{4}\, dy$$

Hint Rewrite integrands in nonfactored form.

Answer: $\dfrac{dz}{dx} = -x^6 - \dfrac{9x^5}{8} - \dfrac{x^3}{2} + 192x^2$

8. Since past operating data has shown that a certain type of machine lasts physically for approximately eight years, A Company has adopted the policy of using an eight-year period for purposes of computing depreciation on these machines. One accountant on its staff, however, feels this estimate of economic life is unrealistic in this age of rapid technological advances. Accordingly, he amassed the information below (through discussion with production personnel and correspondence with equipment manufacturers) for a machine recently acquired by the company.

Investment (including purchase price, transportation, and installation)	$12,000
Salvage value anytime after first year's use	$ 5,000
Estimated annual earnings[5] of new machine net of both operating costs and probable earnings sacrificed by not securing a replacement piece of equipment when such becomes available on the market	$4,000 − 600t$
Rate of return required by the company in such investments	20%

Use continuous discounting.

(a) What is the economic life of this newly acquired machine?

(b) Should the company have made the investment?

The solution to this problem involves taking the derivative of an integral. When the resulting derivative is set equal to zero, an equation will result, the solution of which will require trial-and-error use of the table of exponentials (Table A.6).

---

[5] t = number of years the machine is held.

4

Probability Theory

Much of the analytic work an accountant does involves predictions of the future. In capital budgeting, for instance, estimates of future revenues are made. The figures chosen are actually expected values or arithmetic means, although no explicit recognition of this fact is usually given. Figures used in this way are considered deterministic, that is, known with certainty (intuitively, deterministic figures are thought of as being as definite as if they had been specified in a legal contract). Actually, uncertainties are embodied in all estimates, and the degree of uncertainty increases the farther into the future the estimator gets. It is foolish to ignore uncertainties, since extensive (or even slight) deviations from expectations may be intolerable.

Probability theory can be used to recognize uncertainties. It also helps to obtain the arithmetic mean or expected value. The merits of this property are sometimes overlooked. In obtaining this single value, conflicting values are blended. For instance, one view of an estimate may be that a loss of $50,000 will occur, whereas another view may be that $200,000 will be earned. The inconsistency in these views poses little difficulty, however, if we are able to estimate the probability of the loss and that of the gain. In this way, we weigh both views and recognize both of them, rather than limit ourselves to one or the other. If the probability of the loss is 3 chances in 10 and that of the gain is 7 in 10, then the expected earnings are $0.3(-\$50,000) + 0.7(\$200,000) =$

$125,000. Thus, probability theory constitutes a unique way of treating simultaneously alternatives otherwise inconsistent and incompatible with one another.

When using probability theory in making decisions, it is important to recognize that human limitations may be present. We may introduce probability (and later, utility theory) into our analytic models to quantify certain of the decision maker's qualitative feelings; that is, our goal is to make our model an analog of the man's intuitive processes. However, we run the risk of attempting to force the man's intuitions into the rigid confines of our model. Placing such restrictions on the decision maker is unwise. Therefore, when we ask him to assign probabilities to certain events, we must do so cautiously and suit all refinements to his level of probabilistic sophistication.[1] After all, the decision maker ultimately chooses all investments; he is free to ignore any analytic studies (all of which are made merely to help him make up his mind).

Probability Theory Fundamentals

Basic Concepts
If an event is sure to happen, it has a probability of 1; if the event cannot possibly take place, it has a probability of 0. An event either happens or does not happen; for this reason, there is no such thing as a negative probability. Either the probability is zero or it is positive, and if it is positive, the probability is either equal to 1 (the sure event) or less than 1. If we designate an event by x and the probability of the event by $P(x)$, we may restate the foregoing mathematically as follows: $0 \leq P(x) \leq 1$. It is usually not difficult to decide whether an event is either sure of happening [$P(x) = 1$] or impossible [$P(x) = 0$]. What poses difficulty is deciding the probability of any event between these extremes.

The summation of the probabilities of all possible events equals 1. This fact may be stated in the discrete case as follows:

$$1 = \sum_{i=1}^{n} P(x_i)$$

In the continuous case, the formula is

$$1 = \int_{a}^{b} p(x)\, dx$$

Here, $p(x)$ is a function that states the probability of an event x. Strictly

---

[1] Many probabilists advocate early education in probability theory in order that the level of sophistication be raised. The extremists would have children of age 6 or 7 playing bridge, poker, and dice games and going to horse races. The objective would be to help children (future decision makers) to avoid comprehending all things in a deterministic way. Things are rarely black or white; they are usually shades of grey. To discover this suddenly at the age of 30, or 40, or 50 can be very disturbing.

speaking, in the continuous case, probability cannot be defined at a point but rather must be determined in terms of an interval.

$p(x) = e^{-x}, \quad \text{for} \quad 0 \leq x < \infty$

It would be theoretically wrong to calculate

$p(4) = e^{-4} = 0.0183$

It would be proper to calculate

$$p(4) \approx \int_{3.4999}^{4.4999} e^{-x}\, dx \approx -(e^{-4.5} - e^{-3.5}) = 0.0191$$

The reason for the above limits of integration is that were we to insist on rounding to integer (discrete) values, any number from 3.5 up to but not including 4.5 would be rounded to the value 4. For this reason, it would have been wrong to calculate

$$\int_{3}^{4} p(x)\, dx$$

However, where the values of x are large, adding 0.5 to each limit may be safely disregarded.

Arithmetic Mean

The arithmetic mean $(\bar{x})$ or expected value $[E(x)]$ may be obtained by multiplying each possible value of x (x designates a particular event) by its probability and summing the products. In the discrete case, this may be expressed as follows:

$$E(x) = \bar{x} = \sum x_i P(x_i)$$

Values of x	Probability of x	xP(x)
20	0.2	4
10	0.1	1
30	0.4	12
50	0.3	15

$$E(x) = \bar{x} = \sum xP(x) = 32$$

In the continuous case, summation is accomplished by integration, and we have the formula

$$E(x) = \bar{x} = \int_a^b xp(x)\,dx$$

EXAMPLE

The probability of any value of x is

$$p(x) = \frac{375x^2}{(1,000)^3}, \quad \text{for } 0 \le x \le 200$$

Proof that this is a legitimate probability distribution function may be obtained by seeing that when the function is integrated over the specified limits, the answer is one. This proof is

$$\int_0^{200} \frac{375x^2}{(1,000)^3}\,dx = \frac{125x^3}{(1,000)^3}\bigg]_0^{200} = \frac{125(200)^3}{(1,000)^3} = \frac{125(8,000,000)}{1,000,000,000} = 1$$

We proceed to find the mean:

$$E(x) = \int_0^{200} x\left[\frac{375x^2}{1,000^3}\right]dx = \int_0^{200} \frac{375x^3}{1,000^3}\,dx = \frac{375x^4}{4(1,000)^3}\bigg]_0^{200}$$

$$= \frac{375(1,600,000,000)}{4,000,000,000} = 150$$

The Normal Probability Distribution

The normal distribution or normal curve is more important than all the others, not only because it seems to be ubiquitous itself (many things are normally distributed), but also because other probability distributions may be well approximated by it under certain circumstances. This latter attribute of the normal curve has been stated and proved as the Central Limit Theorem. According to this theorem, if samples drawn from a population are sufficiently large, the arithmetic means of the samples will tend strongly to be normally distributed. Hence, the normal curve is very widely employed. Its formula is[2]

▶ **NORMAL CURVE**

$$\int_a^b \frac{1}{\sigma\sqrt{2\pi}} \exp\left[-\frac{1}{2}\left(\frac{x-\mu}{\sigma}\right)^2\right]dx$$

The normal curve is bell-shaped, as shown in Figure 10. The arithmetic mean (which is a measure of central tendency) of the population of the normal curve is here represented by μ, and it may be calculated by $\mu \equiv \sum x_i/n$, provided the population is finite and all its values (x_i) are known. However,

---

[2] $\exp[\ldots] = e^{(\ldots)}$

Figure 10

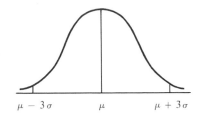

where these conditions are not present, the population mean may be estimated by

$\bar{x}$ = an estimate of the true population mean, μ KEY
$\bar{x}_j$ = the mean of the jth sample, which contained n items
N = the number of sample means, $\bar{x}_j$

$$\mu \simeq E(\bar{x}) \equiv \bar{\bar{x}} = \frac{\displaystyle\sum_{j=1}^{N}\sum_{i=1}^{n} x_{ij}}{Nn} = \frac{\displaystyle\sum_{j=1}^{N} \bar{x}_j}{N}$$

The symbol σ (sigma) is used to designate the standard deviation of the population. The standard deviation is a measure of dispersion of data about the population mean, that is, the distance the data are from μ. The standard deviation equals the square root of the variance of the population. If the population is finite and all its values are known, the variance (σ^2) is calculated as follows.

x_i = a single observation from a population   KEY
n = the size of a population
σ^2 = the variance of a population

$$\sigma^2 = \frac{\sum (x_i - \mu)^2}{n} = \frac{\sum (x^2 - 2x\mu + \mu^2)}{n}$$
$$= \frac{\sum x^2}{n} - 2\mu \frac{\sum x}{n} + \frac{\sum \mu^2}{n}$$

μ (which equals $\sum x/n$) is actually a parameter (a constant) of the population;   NOTE
hence, $\sum \mu^2 = \mu^2 + \mu^2 + \cdots + \mu^2 = n\mu^2$.

$$= \frac{\sum x^2}{n} - 2\mu^2 + \mu^2$$
$$= \frac{\sum x^2}{n} - \mu^2$$

or

$$= \frac{\sum x^2}{n} - \left(\frac{\sum x}{n}\right)^2$$

Since the standard deviation is the square root of the variance, we may write either

$$\sigma = \sqrt{\frac{\sum (x - \mu)^2}{n}}$$

which has the advantage of focusing attention on the deviation from the mean, or we may use

$$\sigma = \frac{1}{n}\sqrt{n\sum x^2 - \left(\sum x\right)^2}$$

which is simpler in that it is not necessary to compute the difference between each observation and the mean, that is, $(x - \mu)$.

If the population is infinite (or so large that it may be considered infinite) and not all its values (x_i) are known, the estimation of the standard deviation must be based on samples, and calculations become more complicated. We now recognize the standard deviation of the population and estimate it from either the standard deviation of a sample $[s(x)$ or simply $s]$ or the standard deviation of sample means $[s(\bar{x}_i)]$. The standard deviation of sample means is related to the standard deviation of the population by the formula $[s(\bar{x})]\sqrt{n} = \sigma$. An intuitive appreciation of the truth of this formula may be had by remembering that σ deals with the entire population of individual data, whereas $s(\bar{x})$ deals with data that have been averaged to start with; consequently, there is less dispersion where the data are averages than where they are individual events.

As a further complication, it is considered better practice by most statisticians—especially where the sample size is small—to modify the standard deviation formula to recognize something called "degrees of freedom." To be brief, "degrees of freedom" recognize the fact that

$$\sum_{i=1}^{n} (x_i - \bar{x}) = 0$$

Hence, if we know $(n - 1)$ of these deviations and their sum is, say, $+7$, the nth deviation must be -7. The standard deviation is based, therefore, on $(n - 1)$ independent differences and one dependent difference. The number of independent differences is referred to as the number of degrees of freedom. The modified formula for the standard deviation becomes

$$s = \sqrt{\frac{n\sum x^2 - \left(\sum x\right)^2}{n(n - 1)}}$$

Where estimation is based on sample means, the formula becomes

$s(\bar{x}_i)$ = the standard deviation of sample means

$$\sigma \simeq s(\bar{x}_i) = \sqrt{\frac{\sum\left(\bar{x} - \bar{\bar{x}}\right)^2}{N - 1}}$$

A company is applying statistical quality control procedures in an attempt to control the costs of its five branches. The branches are the same size and are situated in like communities, and the business is not characterized by seasonal fluctuations. To obtain estimates of the mean of a certain cost, the company has averaged quarterly reports of the cost for each branch. Thus, one branch had the following readings for this cost: \$20,000; \$18,200; \$18,000; and \$21,400. The arithmetic mean for this branch was, therefore,

$$\bar{x} = \frac{\sum x}{n} = \frac{\$77,600}{4} = \$19,400$$

Similarly computed averages for the other four branches were \$20,800; \$19,000; \$20,200; and \$18,600. Consequently, the population mean may be determined as follows:

$$\mu \simeq \bar{\bar{x}} = \frac{\sum \bar{x}}{N} = \frac{\$98,000}{5} = \$19,600$$

The standard deviation σ may be calculated by constructing a table similar to

$\bar{x}_i$	μ	$\bar{x}_i - \mu$	$(\bar{x}_i - \mu)^2$
\$19,400	\$19,600	\$ −200	\$ 40,000
20,800	19,600	1,200	1,440,000
19,000	19,600	− 600	360,000
20,200	19,600	600	360,000
18,600	19,600	− 1,000	1,000,000
$\sum \bar{x} = \$98,000$			$\sum (\bar{x} - \mu)^2 = \$3,200,000$

$$\sigma = \sqrt{\frac{\sum (\bar{x} - \mu)^2}{N - 1}} = \sqrt{\frac{3,200,000}{5 - 1}} = \$894.50$$

1. One of the important attributes of σ is that $\mu \pm 3\sigma$ can be shown to include 99.73% of the normally distributed population.

2. In practice, the values for μ and σ are rarely known because most populations are infinite; hence, the values of samples are used as proxies.

Setting Control Limits

With these values of μ and σ at hand, management now wishes to choose decision rules in order that acceptable ranges of performance may be determined. In other words, when a branch submits a quarterly report of this cost, management wants to have predetermined figures that designate whether performance is acceptable or whether it requires further investigation. Two things could happen at any time:

1. The performance could be in control, but it falls outside the acceptable range and is needlessly investigated (this is known as a type I or α error); or

2. The performance could actually be out of control—in the sense that the population mean has shifted—but because it falls in the acceptable range, we fail to detect the change (this is known as a type II or β error).

Management must decide what risks of these errors it is willing to take. Furthermore, the risks work inversely to one another; if the α risk decreases, the β risk increases, and vice versa. It is these decisions that determine how tight the standard or budget will be. Let us continue our example.

EXAMPLE (continued)

Management decides that it is willing to risk a type I error (investigating acceptable performance needlessly) 10% of the time (i.e., 5% when performance is on the low side and 5% when it is on the high side). Management also wants to know what percentage the population mean would have to change while retaining the same standard deviation in order that it could have 80% confidence that the change would be detected. (Observe that 80% is the probability of *not* making a β error.)

The upper and lower control limits corresponding to the α risk may be determined as follows. First turn a normal curve on its side in order to understand why the limits are called "upper" and "lower." Any performance falling within the limits is acceptable, and any performance outside the limits requires further investigation. See Figure 11. We consult the body of Table A.7 to find the number of standard deviations corresponding to a probability of 0.4500. We see, by interpolation, that 1.645 standard deviations is our answer. Therefore, our limits become

$$\mu \pm 1.645\sigma$$
$$19,600 \pm 1.645(894.50)$$
$$UCL = 21,071$$
$$LCL = 18,129$$

Chapter 4 : Probability Theory

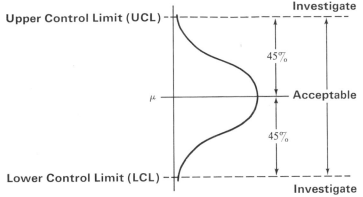

Figure 11

Upper Control Limit (UCL)

Investigate

45%

μ —————— Acceptable

45%

Lower Control Limit (LCL)

Investigate

Now, any quarterly cost x such that $(18,129 \leq x \leq 21,071)$ is true will be considered to be in control, but any x outside these limits would call for investigation.

To understand what the β error is all about, study Figure 12. As matters presently stand, (the "old" curve) $\mu = 19,600$, and the upper control limit is 21,071. If the quarterly cost x were greater than 21,071, we would say that further investigation was necessary. But suppose μ had actually changed so that the state of affairs found us in the "new" curve. Further suppose that x was less than 21,071. Now, because of our set limits based on the "old" curve, we would have no suspicions that μ had changed, and we would say that performance was acceptable and that no further investigation was necessary. But further investigation should be made since things have changed; therefore, since we do not do anything further, we commit a β error.

The probability of making a β error is calculated by assuming that the population has shifted to the "new" curve and then finding the probability to the left of the "old" upper control limit, 21,071. From the total probability of the left-hand side of the "new" curve [this is 0.5000, since the normal curve is symmetrical to the left and right of the mean and the total area (or cumulative probability) under the curve is 1] we subtract the probability of being between 21,071 and ?, the mean of the "new" curve. Management requires the β error to be a maximum of 20%.

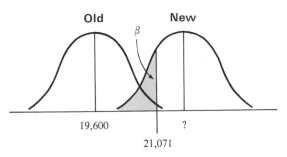

Old   New   **Figure 12**

β

19,600   ?

21,071

$$0.5000 - p(21{,}071 \leq x \leq ?) = 0.2000$$
$$p(21{,}071 \leq x \leq ?) = 0.3000$$

We wish to find the number (z) of standard deviations from the mean that will yield a probability of 0.3000. Actually, we apply the formula

$$z = \frac{x - \mu}{\sigma}$$

However, Table A.7 tabulates only the right side of the normal curve, and we are interested in the left. To adjust for this, we can change the formula to $z = (\mu - x)/\sigma$. We therefore have

$$p(z) = p\left(\frac{? - 21{,}071}{894.50}\right) = 0.3000$$

For the $p(z)$ to equal 0.3000, z must be 0.8418.

$$\frac{? - 21{,}071}{894.50} = 0.8418$$

$$? = 21{,}824$$

We can now convert this value to a percentage and tell management what change (either plus or minus — since symmetry is present and would produce the same % change) must take place in order to be 80% sure of detecting the shift in population means.

"New mean"	21,824
"Old" mean	− 19,600
Change	2,224

$$\frac{2{,}224}{19{,}600} \cong 11.3\%$$

If management were unsatisfied with the necessity of an 11.3% change before it could be detected, it would have to increase the α risk.

The implication for accounting in these procedures is that consideration should be given to changing conventional budgeting approaches. Conventionally, even a flexible budget results in a single figure for a particular expense. Then, when actual operations take place, the budget figure is subtracted from the actual figure to determine the accounting variance. If this variance is significant, it is investigated further. It would make more sense to conceive of the budget as a range or band, rather than as a single figure. Less hardship would probably result in the long run; moreover, production foremen already have an understanding of statistical quality control and might be more favorably inclined to accept budget controls.[3]

EXAMPLE

Table A.7 tabulates values for the standardized normal curve. The process of standardization involves transforming variables in such a way as to make $\mu = 0$ and $\sigma = 1$. It is important to understand this transformation process. Suppose $\mu = 2,000$, $\sigma = 800$, and we want to find the probability that a certain event will fall between the values $2,500 \leq x \leq 3,000$. In non-standardized terms, we wish to find the solution to

$$\int_{2,500}^{3,000} \frac{1}{800\sqrt{2\pi}} \exp\left[-\frac{1}{2}\left(\frac{x-2,000}{800}\right)^2\right] dx$$

To transform this problem so that we may use Table A.7, we proceed as follows (those who have not been exposed to calculus should consult the preceding chapter):

Let

$$z = \frac{x - 2,000}{800}$$

Then

$$dz = \frac{dx}{800}$$

and the upper limit of integration becomes

$$z = \frac{3,000 - 2,000}{800} = 1.25$$

and the lower limit becomes

$$z = \frac{2,500 - 2,000}{800} = 0.625$$

With these changes, the integral becomes

$$\frac{800}{800} \int_{0.625}^{1.25} \frac{e^{-1/2z^2}}{\sqrt{2\pi}} dz = (0.3944 - 0.2340) = 0.1604$$

---

[3] An interesting alternative approach to applying statistical techniques to budgeting may be found in H. Bierman, L. Fouraker, and R. Jaedicke, "A Use of Probability and Statistics in Performance Evaluation," *The Accounting Review*, July, 1961.

Essentially, these authors incorporate the notion that it is desirable to investigate those performance variations where the expected rewards $E(R)$ from correcting the situation exceed the expected cost $E(C)$ of investigating. Given $E(R)$ and $E(C)$, the authors proceed to calculate a critical probability P according to the formula $P = [E(R) - E(C)]/E(R)$. If P exceeds the probability that the particular magnitude of variation will occur, an investigation is undertaken.

Note that Table A.7 gives values for one side of the normal curve only, that is, from μ to z. Essentially, when using the table, values from 0 to z_1 are subtracted from values from 0 to z_2. [In the example, we have $(0.3944 - 0) - (0.2340 - 0)$.]

<hr />

Obtaining Subjective Estimates of Probabilities

Let us see how probabilities and the normal curve might be used. An engineer might assign probabilities to the number of barrels of oil a new well will deliver each day as follows:

Barrels (x)	Probability P(x)	xP(x)
100	0.05	5
200	0.10	20
300	0.20	60
400	0.30	120
500	0.20	100
600	0.10	60
700	0.05	35
		400

$$\bar{x} = \sum xP(x)$$

The above estimates have been symmetrically distributed around an average daily quantity $\bar{x}$ of 400 barrels. Apparently the well is sure to deliver at least 100 barrels but never more than 700 barrels. If you do not insist on mathematical rigor, the estimates and their probabilities can now be translated to normal curve terminology by observing that $\bar{x} \pm 3\sigma$ (here $\bar{x}$ is a proxy for μ) covers essentially the whole (99.73%) range of possibilities. Then, by substituting figures, you can determine σ:

$$\bar{x} + 3\sigma = 400 + 3\sigma = 700$$
$$\sigma = 100$$

(Alternately, we could have gotten the same value for σ by solving $400 - 3\sigma = 100$.) With the parameter values, $\mu (\approx \bar{x})$ and σ, at hand, the normal curve may be employed in all future estimates.

The estimates in the above example may be based on empirical data for other oil wells in similar locations. However, it is also very likely that the engineer might intuitively feel that this well is in some ways distinct from all the other wells. He might assume a normal distribution of the number of barrels delivered daily and be willing only to estimate the mean within a certain range. Thus, he might decide that the mean had a 50% probability of being in the range of 300 to 500 barrels. Because of the symmetry of the normal curve, the engineer's estimate may be restated as: The mean is 400 barrels with a 25% probability of being greater or lesser by 100 barrels. Since $\frac{2}{3}\sigma$ yields a probability of approximately 25%, we can determine σ as follows:

$$\frac{2}{3} = \frac{x - \bar{x}}{\sigma} = \frac{500 - 400}{\sigma}$$

$$\tfrac{2}{3}\sigma = 100$$

$$\sigma = 150$$

Note that this mode of estimating does not require the skill (and patience) that the first method did. Moreover, the present method is in keeping with a lower (and more realistic) level of probabilistic sophistication. Hence, it avoids confining a decision maker to the rigidity of a complicated model.

On the other hand, the decision maker may have a profound appreciation of probability theory. If this is so, he may be willing to devote the time necessary to determine his subjective probability weightings. The procedure most often used is referred to as the standard gamble technique and is not complicated, although it is time consuming. In its simplest form, the decision maker is asked to choose between two courses of action—one that has certainty of a particular reward and the other that has a probability of a very attractive reward and a complementary probability of an unattractive reward. In equation form, we have

The Standard Gamble Technique

$$\$a = \$bP + \$c(1 - P)$$

$\$a$ = the reward to be received with certainty if the first alternative (conceptually, this alternative might consist of some prize in a fictitious lottery) is adopted

$\$b$ = the very attractive reward of the second alternative $\$b > \$a$

$\$c$ = the unattractive reward of the second alternative $\$c < \$a$

P = the probability of receiving $\$b$; this probability is to be calculated

KEY

For example,

$$\$500 = \$700P + \$100(1 - P)$$
$$\$500 = \$600P + \$100$$
$$\tfrac{2}{3} = P$$

Consequently, if $P(\$b)$ is $\frac{2}{3}$, the decision maker would be indifferent between the two alternatives. If, in his opinion, $P(\$b)$ exceeds $\frac{2}{3}$, the decision maker would choose the second alternative. He now has a guide to the probabilities of $700 and $100, because the "break-even" probabilities have been established and he can more easily decide, subjectively, how much he thinks the true probabilities will differ from $\frac{2}{3}$.

Suppose, however, that we wish to assign subjective probabilities to several values. The values selected should be means of ranges (i.e., the mean of the range from 20,000 to 30,000 is 25,000). Then, two or more adjacent mean values should be placed in a hypothetical lottery and assigned probabilities. These assigned probabilities should next be varied until the decision maker becomes indifferent between the lottery and the company's chances of receiving the same mean values. The probabilities resulting in indifference are then the preliminary probabilities for the selected mean values. Next, two or more other mean values are selected in addition to one of the values previously used. The process is then repeated for this new set of values until all values have been assigned probabilities. All that remains now is to interrelate all the sets of values by dealing with the points common from one set to the next. This is best described by an example.

EXAMPLE _____

Assume that it is desired to assign probabilities to the range midpoint values of $5,000, $10,000, $15,000, $20,000, and $25,000; further assume that the decision maker becomes indifferent between the lottery tickets and the firm's chances when the probabilities in the lotteries are as follows:

	Value	Preliminary Lottery Probabilities	Column A	Converted Probability Estimates
Lottery 1	$25,000	0.2	0.14	$\frac{14}{85}$
	20,000	0.3	0.21	$\frac{21}{85}$
	15,000	0.5 ⎫		
Lottery 2	15,000	0.7 ⎭	0.35	$\frac{35}{85}$
	10,000	0.2	0.10	$\frac{10}{85}$
	5,000	0.1	0.05	$\frac{5}{85}$
			0.85	

Since the $15,000 is the common point to both lotteries, the two preliminary probabilities may be multiplied to get 0.35 (i.e., 0.5 × 0.7). The probabilities of the first lottery are then multiplied by 0.7 (the preliminary probability of $15,000 in the second lottery) and those of the second lottery by 0.5 (the preliminary probability of $15,000 in the first lottery), and the common point is shown only once; this process produces the values shown in column A. By summing the values in column A and by showing individual values in that column as proportions of that sum, the values in the last column are obtained. This second technique could, of course, be applied to all points at once, rather than to overlapping subsets of points, but, if this were done, one of the ad-

Chapter 4 : Probability Theory

vantages of the technique would be lost. By choosing subsets, some check on the consistency of the estimator is afforded.[4]

Applications

In capital budgeting, certain criteria of investment acceptability are widely recognized; now we turn out attention to other, less popular, criteria. We shall first study sensitivity analysis and then utility theory. These refinements add some mathematical sophistication to the capital budgeting area and are definitely appealing from an intellectual viewpoint; however, it should be observed that the question of the use of probabilities and utility theory in capital budgeting has not yet been settled.

Sensitivity Analysis

The decision maker may require all proposals to have parameter safety margins. The parameters of concern are the estimates of earnings and life, and the safety margin is determined as follows:

1. Decide on the normal curve mean and standard deviation values for each of the investment parameters.
2. Calculate the value of the parameter that would just render the proposal acceptable.
3. Decide the probability of being in error by the difference; if this probability is less than a predetermined value, the proposal's parameter has a sufficient safety margin.

EXAMPLE

KEY

I = immediate investment in a proposal = $50,000
E = expected value of annual cash earnings = $15,000
E' = critical earnings
n = expected life of proposal = 6 yr
r = required rate of return = 8%

(a) Let us first test the sensitivity of E. The minimal earnings that would just render the proposal acceptable would be

$$I = E'P_{\overline{6}|8\%}$$
$$\$50,000 = E'(4.6229)$$
$$\$10,816 = E'$$

---

[4] The reader who wishes to delve further into this technique should consult R. Schlaifer, *Introduction to Statistics for Business Decisions*. New York: McGraw-Hill Book Co., 1961, ch. 2.

We now ask the decision maker to estimate (1) the amount of deviation in earnings he expects and (2) the safety margin he requires. Suppose he responds that he thinks the earnings estimate has a 25% probability of being off by $2,000 in either direction and that if there is a 20% probability of losing money on the proposal, he will reject it. The situation is shown in Figure 13. The standard deviation may be calculated as follows (consult Table A.7 to see that $\frac{2}{3}\sigma \approx 25\%$):

$$2,000 = \tfrac{2}{3}\sigma$$
$$3,000 = \sigma$$

The probability of the earnings being $10,816 (the critical value) or worse is the shaded area in Figure 13 and may be determined as follows:

Probability of $15,000 or less	0.5000
Probability of between $10,816 and $15,000	−0.4184

$$z = \frac{x - \bar{x}}{\sigma} = \frac{\$10,816 - \$15,000}{\$3,000} = -1.395$$

From Table A.7, $P(-1.395) \approx 0.4184$

$$\overline{\underline{0.0816}}$$

Figure 13

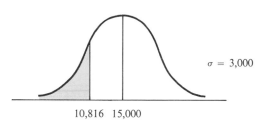

$\sigma = 3,000$

10,816 15,000

Hence, there is approximately only an 8% chance of loss and, consequently, a 12% safety margin (20% − 8%).

(b) Now let us test n. The minimum life that would just render the proposal acceptable is

$$I = EP\overline{?|}_{8\%}$$
$$\$50,000 = \$15,000P\overline{?|}_{8\%}$$
$$3.3333 = P\overline{?|}_{8\%}$$

By consulting the table for P, we see that $P\overline{4|}_{8\%} = 3.3121$; therefore, the critical life is approximately four years.

Suppose the decision maker decides that, owing to technological change and induced obsolescence, the estimate of life has a 30% probability of being on the high side by three years; furthermore, he feels as before that if there is a 20% probability of losing money on the proposal, it should be rejected. The normal curve presentation of the situation is shown in Figure 14.

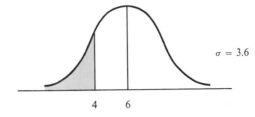

Figure 14

The standard deviation corresponding to 30% probability is 0.84σ. Therefore,

$3 = 0.84\sigma$

$3.6 \approx \sigma$

The probability of the life being four years (the critical value) or less is the shaded area in Figure 14.

Probability of six years or less	0.5000
Probability of between four and six years	-0.2105

$$z = \frac{x - \bar{x}}{\sigma} = \frac{4 - 6}{3.6} = -0.555$$

From Table A.7, $P(-0.555) \approx 0.2105$

$$\overline{0.2895}$$

Because there is approximately a 29% probability of loss, the proposal should be rejected on the basis of this test. However, it should be recognized (1) that the two tests are not independent of one another (i.e., the test for E assumes n, and the test for n assumes E) and (2) that the proposal comfortably passed the sensitivity test for E. The decision maker may, therefore, want to take a second look at his estimates.

Management seeks the maximization of long-run profits, and every action taken is a reflection of this goal. Money spent on the creation of a good corporate image, for instance, is expended among other reasons in hopes that

1. investors will be influenced to purchase stock;
2. loyal and talented employees will be attracted; and
3. customers will be convinced of competitive superiority.

The maximization of long-run profits, however, is not always best served by maximizing net present values of investments. Rather, it is theoretically preferable to maximize net expected present utility—provided it can be measured. As the name implies, expected present utility involves probability

Utility Theory and Loss Functions

theory, discounting, and utility theory. We have already discussed the first two; now let us see what is meant by utility theory.

If someone were to offer me the opportunity of purchasing a raffle ticket in the forthcoming Irish Sweepstakes (and let us say the prize is $5,000,000) for $25, I would reject the offer. Why? I would reject it because the loss of the $25 if I did not win means more to me at this stage in my financial life than the slim possibility of winning $5,000,000. How would you feel about it? Many things would govern your feelings, including

1. random thoughts, such as how many golf balls you could get for the $25;

2. your present financial status—if you are wealthy, $25 may not be more than an imperceptible pittance;

3. how much time you like to devote to dreaming about the consequences of winning $5,000,000; and

4. to what extent gambling actually appeals to you.

Most people differ in their evaluation of utilities, and this fact makes it unwise to consider imputing one's personal utility function to someone else. However, it is important to assess the decision maker's utility function if it is possible to do so without channeling his thought processes into the rigid confines of a mathematical formula.

A utility function may be determined in much the same manner we determined point estimates of probabilities. The approach is very similar to the standard gamble method previously discussed:

1. Start with two extreme rewards, x_0 and x_n, and assign them utility measures of, say, 0 and 1.

2. Take any reward x (where $x_0 < x < x_n$), assign it a probability of 1 (certainty), and set it equal to the expected value of alternative extreme rewards.

3. Assign a probability of P to one extreme reward and $(1 - P)$ to the other extreme. Vary P until the decision maker is indifferent.

4. Substitute utilities of 0 and 1 for the extreme rewards, and solve for the utility of reward x.

5. Repeat the process for a new x, but this time substitute the previous reward x for the reward x_0.

EXAMPLE

$x_0 = \$0$ [utility $(U) = 0$]
$x_n = \$50,000$ (utility $= 1$)

Find the respective utilities of $10,000, $30,000, and $60,000. Assume the decision maker becomes indifferent at the probabilities shown on page 95.

Chapter 4 : Probability Theory

$U(\$10,000) = \frac{1}{3}U(\$50,000) + \frac{2}{3}U(\$0) \qquad = \frac{1}{3}(1) + \frac{2}{3}(0) = \frac{1}{3}$

$U(\$20,000) = \frac{1}{4}U(\$50,000) + \frac{3}{4}U(\$10,000) = \frac{1}{4}(1) + \frac{3}{4}(\frac{1}{3}) = \frac{1}{2}$

$U(\$20,000) = \frac{4}{5}U(\$10,000) + \frac{1}{5}U(\$60,000)$

$\qquad \frac{1}{2} = \frac{4}{5}(\frac{1}{3}) \qquad\qquad + \frac{1}{5}U(\$60,000)$

$U(\$60,000) = \frac{7}{6}$

In this manner, utility measures for any set of points may be established. The consistency of the measures can be checked by varying the rewards and their probabilities. A curve may then be fitted to these points.

It is generally agreed that most people do not have a linear utility function, for this implies that the utility of losing \$1,000 is equal to the utility of gaining \$1,000. Were a linear utility function to be assumed, maximizing net present utility would reduce to maximizing net present monetary value. It is usually postulated that the law of diminishing returns is at work and that the utility function takes the form of a second degree polynomial, as shown in Figure 15.

Figure 15

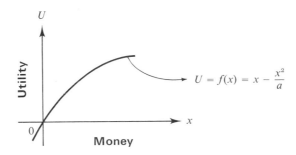

We see from this curve that the utility for negative sums of money, that is, losses, approaches negative infinity very rapidly. We also see that the utility for gains is great at first and then levels off (diminishing utility). The point of maximum utility occurs when the first derivative of U equals zero:

$$\frac{dU}{dx} = b - \frac{2x}{a} = 0$$

$$x = \frac{ab}{2}$$

Under conditions of uncertainty, the cash flows used in analyses are expected values (i.e., arithmetic means). Such expected values are figures reflecting central tendency, and where there is central tendency, there is usually dispersion. At a certain point, loss on the investment takes place. A sophisticated analyst may divide his analysis into loss and gain portions and apply utility theory formulas to the separate portions.

Loss Functions

A cost analyst predicts that annual cash earnings from a proposal will be normally distributed with a 50% probability of falling in the range $45,500 to $54,500. The life of the proposal is eight years, and the required rate of return is 10%. An investment of $240,000 is immediately required if the proposal is to be accepted. The utility function of the decision maker has been determined to be

$$U = \frac{x}{3} - \frac{x^2}{100,000}$$

Should the investment be undertaken?

Solution Since the normal distribution is involved, symmetry causes the mean earnings to be $50,000 with a 25% probability ($\frac{2}{3}\sigma$) of a $4,500 deviation either way. The standard deviation may be calculated as follows:

$$\$4,500 = \tfrac{2}{3}\sigma$$
$$\$6,750 = \sigma$$

The present values of the mean earnings and standard deviations are

$$\$50,000P_{\overline{8}|10\%} = \$50,000(5.335) = \$266,750$$
$$\$6,750P_{\overline{8}|10\%} = \$36,010$$

The loss function—otherwise known as the expected opportunity loss (*EOL*)—is the addition of all possible loss values (*L*) weighted by their probabilities [*P(L)*]. Essentially, we wish to calculate $EOL = \int LP(L)\,dl$. Every dollar earned that is less than the investment is a dollar lost; therefore, loss $L = \$240,000 - x$ for the interval $-\infty < x \le 240,000$. Similarly, there is a gain function that may be expressed $G = x - \$240,000$ for the interval $240,000 \le x < \infty$. These functions may be superimposed on the normal curve as shown in Figure 16. Note that L has been stated in such a way that its values will always be positive. Also note that, as stated, with the exception of the limits, $-L = G$.

The expected net present value $E(NPV)$ of the investment may be calculated as follows:

$$E(NPV) = \int_{240,000}^{\infty} \frac{(x - 240,000)\exp\left[-\frac{1}{2}\left(\dfrac{x - 266,750}{36,010}\right)^2\right]}{36,010\sqrt{2\pi}}\,dx$$
$$- \int_{-\infty}^{240,000} \frac{(240,000 - x)\exp\left[-\frac{1}{2}\left(\dfrac{x - 266,750}{36,010}\right)^2\right]}{36,010\sqrt{2\pi}}\,dx$$

The right-hand integral expresses losses as positive values. If we wish to recognize losses as negative values, we may merely change $(240,000 - x)$ to $(x - 240,000)$. With this change $E(NPV)$ becomes

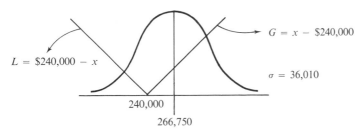

Figure 16

$G = x - \$240,000$

$L = \$240,000 - x$

$\sigma = 36,010$

240,000

266,750

$$E(NPV) = \int_{-\infty}^{\infty} \frac{(x - 240,000)\exp\left[-\frac{1}{2}\left(\frac{x - 266,750}{36,010}\right)^2\right]}{36,010\sqrt{2\pi}}\, dx$$

This may be split up as follows [$p(x)$ denotes the normal curve portion of the integral]:

$$E(NPV) = \int_{-\infty}^{\infty} xp(x)\, dx - \$240,000 \int_{-\infty}^{\infty} p(x)\, dx$$

Since

$$\int_{-\infty}^{\infty} xp(x)\, dx = \bar{x}$$

and since the normal curve is a probability density function

$$\int_{-\infty}^{\infty} p(x)\, dx = 1$$

therefore,

$$E(NPV) = \bar{x} - (\$240,000)(1) = \$266,750 - \$240,000 = \$26,750.$$

Now we need calculate only either the expected gain or the expected loss, since we know $\$26,750 = E(G) - E(L)$.

$$E(L) = -\left\{ \int_{-\infty}^{240,000} \frac{(x - 240,000)\exp\left[-\frac{1}{2}\left(\frac{x - 266,750}{36,010}\right)^2\right]}{36,010\sqrt{2\pi}}\, dx \right\}$$

$$= -\left\{ \int_{-\infty}^{240,000} \frac{(x - 266,750)\exp\left[-\frac{1}{2}\left(\frac{x - 266,750}{36,010}\right)^2\right]}{36,010\sqrt{2\pi}}\, dx \right.$$

$$\left. + \frac{26,750}{36,010} \int_{-\infty}^{240,000} \frac{\exp\left[-\frac{1}{2}\left(\frac{x - 266,750}{36,010}\right)^2\right]}{\sqrt{2\pi}}\, dx \right\}$$

Transformation of variables:

NOTE

$$z = \frac{x - 266,750}{36,010} \qquad z_{upper} = \frac{240,000 - 266,750}{36,010} = -0.7428$$

$$36{,}010 \, dz = dx \qquad\qquad z_{\text{lower}} = \frac{-\infty - 266{,}750}{36{,}010} = -\infty$$

$$= -\left[\frac{36{,}010}{\sqrt{2\pi}} \int_{-\infty}^{-0.7428} ze^{-z^2/2} \, dz + 26{,}750 \int_{-\infty}^{-0.7428} \frac{e^{-z^2/2}}{\sqrt{2\pi}} \, dz\right]$$

Table A.7 in the Appendix tabulates values only for the right-hand side of a normal curve. To obtain values for the left-hand side, one reverses the order of integration, that is,

$$\int_{-\infty}^{-0.7428} = \int_{0.7428}^{\infty}$$

This could be demonstrated with a table of cumulative normal values. In this case, for instance, a cumulative table shows

$$P(z = -0.7428) = \quad 0.2288$$
$$-P(z \cong -\infty) = -0.0000$$
$$\int_{-\infty}^{-0.7428} = \quad \overline{0.2288}$$

The right-hand integral may be evaluated with interpolation from Table A.7; the left-hand portion may be evaluated from Table A.6:

$$E(L) = -[-14{,}404(e^{-0.2759} - e^{-\infty}) + 26{,}750(0.5000 - 0.2712)]$$
$$E(L) = 14{,}404(0.75891 - 0) - 26{,}750(0.2288) = \$4{,}811$$

The expected gain may be calculated from the formula previously presented:

$$\$26{,}750 = E(G) - E(L)$$
$$E(G) = \$26{,}750 + E(L)$$
$$E(G) = \$26{,}750 + \$4{,}811 = \$31{,}561$$

We may now determine the utility and acceptability of this proposal. The decision maker's utility formula is

$$U = \frac{x}{3} - \frac{x^2}{100{,}000}$$

The utility of a loss $= U(L) = \dfrac{-\$4{,}811}{3} - \dfrac{(-\$4{,}811)^2}{100{,}000} = -1{,}835$

The utility of a gain $= U(G) = \dfrac{\$31{,}561}{3} - \dfrac{(\$31{,}561)^2}{100{,}000} = \quad 559$

$$\text{Net expected disutility} \quad \overline{-1{,}276}$$

Consequently, the proposal would be rejected on a utility basis, even though it would have been accepted on an expected net present value [$E(NPV) = \$26{,}750$] basis.

Problems

1. A company wishes to establish upper and lower control limits for its overhead budget. In this way, management hopes that the number of needless investigations into insignificant variations from budget will be curtailed. Accordingly, the following costs have been incurred in the past when the budget has been set at the pertinent production level:

$102,000
96,000
108,400
106,700
99,400
100,000
98,000
94,000
109,200
101,800

Management believes that a 90% acceptance region should be established. Consequently, on the average, 5% of the variances in either direction will be needlessly investigated.

(a) What control limits should be set if a normal distribution is assumed?

(b) What is the magnitude of the β error should the population mean shift to $106,000?

2. The investment in a project is $32,000, and the required rate of return is 15%. The decision maker feels that neither the life nor the earnings parameter should have more than a 20% chance of resulting in loss. He has given you the following estimates, and the normal distribution is pertinent:

x = earnings
n = life

$P(6,000 \leq x \leq 10,000) = 0.50$
$P(8 \leq n \leq 10) = 0.40$

What chance of loss exists for x? For n? Should the investment be undertaken?

3. A business has estimated that the annual cash earning (E) of a project will be $70,000 and that this amount will be forthcoming each year for 18 years (n).

(a) If the project requires an initial investment of $490,000, what is its internal rate of return?

(b) If the cost of capital is 10%, should the project be accepted?

(c) If management feels that no investment that has a 30% chance of loss should be undertaken and that (1) $P(60,000 \leq E \leq 80,000) = 0.50$ and (2) $P(15 \leq n \leq 21) = 0.80$, should the project be accepted?

(d) If management has the utility function

$$U = 0.1X - \left(\frac{X}{20,000}\right)^2$$

and (1) cost of capital is 10% and (2) $P(60,000 \leq E \leq 80,000) = 0.50$, should the project be accepted?

5

Cost Analysis and Calculus

Cost analysis is perhaps the most dynamic area in accounting, and calculus is a very important tool of cost analysis. Imagination is a prerequisite to determining relevant costs, and calculus is used not only to estimate costs, but also to minimize them. In this chapter, we investigate the application of calculus (1) to predict labor and labor-associated costs via learning curves and (2) to determine the quantity of inventory that will minimize inventory costs.

Learning Curves

"Practice makes perfect" is an old cliché, but one that is only partially true. Anyone active in athletics is aware of deficiencies in the statement. For instance, the golfer who has an incorrect stance and who pulls across the ball could diligently practice these movements for years without improving, to say nothing of attaining perfection. A revised, truer aphorism would be "Practice of the right things leads to improvement and, perhaps eventually, to perfection."

In manufacturing, as in athletics, practice of the right things results in improvement. Hence, any repetitive operation that requires skilled or unskilled labor may be expected to take less time to complete as the employees and management acquire further experience. Of course, limits exist. In a manufacturing operation, a plateau (or equilibrium, or steady state) may be reached where further improvements are imperceptible. Whenever accountants base costs on some single standard labor time, they automatically assume that learning effects have stabilized, that the steady state has been attained. Unless the standard for labor time is regularly reviewed and revised when necessary, reliance is falsely placed on the associated standard costs. Cost estimates, budgets, and inventory valuations may be significantly in error! Consequently, whenever an operation is repetitive, requires labor, and is subject to managerial manipulation and technological change, the accountant would do well

1. to suspect that a learning effect is present,
2. to discard any single measure of standard labor time, and
3. to apply learning curve theory to his cost analysis work.[1]

Although *many* different learning curves are in use, the best known is the 80% learning curve first made popular in the aircraft industry. According to the learning curve as it was originally conceived, whenever *cumulative* production doubled, *the cumulative average time* per unit became 80% of what it was at the previous doubling point. Table 4 gives a concrete example.

Table 4

Units Made	Cumulative Units	Labor Time (hours)		
		Average	Total	Marginal
1	1	50	50	(1 unit) 50
1	2	(0.8 × 50) 40	(2 × 40) 80	(1 unit) 30
2	4	(0.8 × 40) 32	(4 × 32) 128	(2 units) 48
4	8	(0.8 × 32) 25.6	(8 × 25.6) 204.8	(4 units) 76.8

More recently, the results of empirical study have led to a redefinition of the learning curve (or, preferably to some, progress curve). Under the new definition of the 80% curve, whenever cumulative production doubles, the time it takes to produce unit n will be equal to 80% of the time it takes to

---

[1] For further theoretical discussion of learning curve theory, the following articles would be informative: Frank J. Andress, "The Learning Curve as a Production Tool," *Harvard Business Review*, January–February, 1954; Rolfe Wyer, "Learning Curve Techniques for Direct Labor Management," *N.A.A. Bulletin*, July, 1958, and Winfred B. Hirschmann, "Profit From the Learning Curve," *Harvard Business Review*, January–February, 1964.

An excellent presentation of the subject may also be found in W. J. Fabrycky and P. E. Torgersen, *Operations Economy: Industrial Applications of Operations Research* (Englewood Cliffs, N.J.: Prentice-Hall, Inc., 1966), ch. 5.

produce unit $n/2$. Table 5 presents the previous example in terms of the new definition.

		Labor Time (hours)			Table 5
Units Made	Cumulative Units	Marginal[a]	Total	Average	
1	1	50	50	50	
1	2	(50 × 0.8) 40	90	(90 ÷ 2) 45	
2	4	(40 × 0.8) 32	157.1	(157.1 ÷ 4) 39.3	
4	8	(32 × 0.8) 25.6	267.3	(267.3 ÷ 8) 33.4	

[a] Marginal times for units 3, 5, 6, and 7 are, respectively 35.1, 29.8, 28.1, and 26.7. The formula for determining them will be presented shortly. It will help to note that the time for unit 6 is 80% of that for unit 3.

By comparing the first time column in each table, the difference between the two learning curve definitions becomes clear. The "old" definition concerns itself with an average time, whereas the "new" definition concerns itself with a marginal time. Which definition applies will depend largely on the given situation under study.

It might be wise to clarify the marginal-average-total relationships before proceeding with the mathematical development of learning curves. For review purposes, consider an arbitrary example of marginal (MC), average (AC), and total (TC) cost. Let x be production volume. Then,

$$TC = 3x^4 + x^3 + 25$$

$$AC = \frac{\text{total cost}}{\text{volume}} = \frac{TC}{x} = \frac{3x^4 + x^3 + 25}{x} = 3x^3 + x^2 + \frac{25}{x}$$

$$MC = \text{first derivative of total cost} = \frac{d(TC)}{dx} = 12x^3 + 3x^2$$

Note that this assumes that x is a continuous and not a discrete variable. To get a little closer to home, let us restate the above costs using a simple power function and letters for parameters.

$$TC = \frac{Mx^{b+1}}{b+1}$$

$$AC = \frac{TC}{x} = \frac{Mx^{b+1}}{x(b+1)} = \frac{Mx^b}{b+1}$$

Assuming x is a continuous variable, we have

$$MC = (TC)' = \frac{d}{dx}\left[\frac{Mx^{b+1}}{b+1}\right] = \frac{(b+1)Mx^b}{b+1} = Mx^b$$

Learning Curves

The Marginal Curve

We shall develop the learning curve formulas under the "new" or marginal definition. The marginal curve may be stated as follows:

$$MT(x) = Mx^b$$

KEY $MT(x)$ = marginal time of the xth unit
M = marginal time for the first unit (i.e., $x = 1$)
x = independent variable standing for the unit produced
b = exponent expressing the improvement; b has the range $-1 < b \leq 0$

We might intuitively approach the calculation of b as follows. By definition, doubling of production leads to a time to produce unit n that is 80% of the time to produce unit $\frac{1}{2}n$. However, this improvement takes place at the same rate for each and every unit, not just for units 1, 2, 4, 8, 16, etc.; consequently, the variable x stands for any unit. Once given a value for x, we could observe that the value was twice the value of some previous value of x. We need to determine what power (exponent) could be associated with our *given* value of x (which is double some *previous* value of x) such that the resulting time is 80% of the time calculated for the *previous* value of x. Mathematically, this reduces to raising the number 2 (doubling) to some power (say b) in order that the number .8 (80% improvement) results. We proceed as follows:[2]

$$2^b = .8$$
$$b \log 2 = \log .8$$
$$b = \frac{\log .8}{\log 2} = \frac{9.9031 - 10}{.3010} = \frac{.9031 - 1}{.3010}$$

Since any log with a negative characteristic may be rewritten as the net of the mantissa and characteristic, we may simplify the above expression to read

$$b = \frac{.9031 - 1}{.3010} = \frac{-.0969}{.3010} = -.322$$

For the 80% curve, we now have

$$MT(x) = Mx^{-.322}$$

With this exponent, we allow for learning effects not only at the discrete doubling points, but also at any and all points along the curve. With the formula available, we shall be able to predict time at any point between or at doubling points. Without the formula, we could predict only at the doubling point.

Shown below is the calculation of the marginal time necessary to produce, say, the fifth unit given that 50 hours were needed to produce the first unit and that an 80% curve was in effect.

---

[2] A description of how to use log tables was presented in the first chapter.

Chapter 5 : Cost Analysis and Calculus

$$MT(5) = 50(5)^{-.322}$$
$$= \text{antilog (log } 50 - .322 \text{ log } 5)$$
$$= \text{antilog } [1.6990 - .322(.6990)]$$
$$= \text{antilog } (1.6990 - .2251)$$
$$= \text{antilog } (1.4739)$$
$$= 29.8$$

We turn our attention now to calculating total time, $TT(x)$. Because marginal time has been set up in terms of discrete units, the appropriate formula is

$$TT(x) = \sum_{i=1}^{x} MT(i) = \sum_{i=1}^{x} M(i)^{-.322}$$

Some closed-form expression for calculating this sum rapidly would be convenient; unfortunately, no antidifference technique applies in this situation. Of course, if a computer is available, performing the summation recursively is a simple matter. However, if no computer is at hand, approximating the value of summation by integration is a practical solution.

A good approximation to computing $TT(8)$, the total time for 8 units, results from integrating not from 0 to 8 but rather from .5 to 8.5 as follows:

$$TT(8) \approx \int_{.5}^{8.5} 50x^{-.322} \, dx = \frac{50}{.678} [(8.5)^{.678} - (.5)^{.678}]$$
$$= 73.746[\text{antilog } (.678 \text{ log } 8.5) - \text{antilog } (.678 \text{ log } .5)]$$

NOTE

antilog (.678 log 8.5):
    antilog [.678(.9294)]   = antilog (.6301) = 4.267

antilog (.678 log .5):
    antilog [.678(.6990 − 1)] = antilog [.678(−.3010)]
                          = antilog (−.2041)
                          = antilog [(1.0000 − .2041) − 1]
                          = antilog (.7959 − 1) = .625

$$= 73.746(4.267 - .625)$$
$$TT(8) \approx 268.6 \text{ hours}$$

Note how close this approximate value is to the value obtained by summation, 267.3, as shown in Table 5.[3]

---

[3] For reference purposes, the formulas for this example that would satisfy the "old" definition of learning curves are as follows:

$$AT(x) = Mx^b = 50x^{-.322}$$
$$TT(x) = Mx^{b+1} = \int (b+1)Mx^b \, dx = 50x^{.678}$$
$$MT(x) = (b+1)Mx^b = (-.322 + 1)50x^{-.322} = 33.9x^{-.322}$$

To approximate the time necessary to produce m units given that n have already been produced (or, in other words, to produce the next m units), the integration below would be performed.

$$TT(m|n) \approx \int_{n+.5}^{m+n+.5} Mx^b \, dx$$

Continuing our example, the time to produce the next four units given that four have already been produced is

$$TT(4|4) \approx \int_{4.5}^{8.5} 50x^{-.322} \, dx = \frac{50}{.678} [(8.5)^{.678} - (4.5)^{.678}]$$

$$\approx 73.746 \, [\text{antilog } (.678 \log 8.5) - \text{antilog } (.678 \log 4.5)]$$

antilog $(.678 \log 8.5) = 4.267$, as before

antilog $(.678 \log 4.5)$:
  antilog $[.678(.6532)] = $ antilog $(.4429) = 2.772$

$$\approx 73.746(4.267 - 2.772)$$
$$TT(4|4) \approx 110.3 \text{ hours}$$

Figure 17

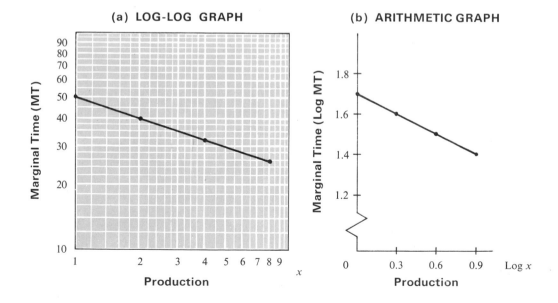

(a) LOG-LOG GRAPH   (b) ARITHMETIC GRAPH

Table 5, which employs summation, shows the total time for eight units to be 267.3 hours; for four units it is 157.1 hours. According to Table 5, then, $TT(4|4) = 110.2$ hours.

Many manufacturers who use learning curves prefer to eliminate the curvature by graphing on log-log paper. It can be seen that a straight line will result by taking the log of both sides of the basic learning curve function:

$$MT = Mx^b$$
$$\log MT = \log M + b \log x$$

This last equation is now in the general straight-line format, $y = a + bx$. Let us illustrate the "straightening" of our MT curve.

$$MT = 50x^{-.322}$$
$$\log MT = \log 50 - .322 \log x$$
$$= 1.6990 - .322 \log x$$

The log-log graph and arithmetic graph using logs are shown in Figure 17; they are based on the values given in Table 6.

Log-Log Graph		Arithmetic Graph Using Logs				Table 6
MT	x	$\log x$	$\log 50$	$-.322 \log x$	$\log MT$	
50	1	0	1.6990	0	1.6990	
40	2	.3010	1.6990	−.0969	1.6021	
32	4	.6021	1.6990	−.1939	1.5051	
25.6	8	.9031	1.6990	−.2908	1.4082	

In plotting the curve on log-log paper, the x and MT values are used. In plotting the curve on arithmetic paper, $\log x$ and $\log MT$ values are used.   **NOTE**

The marginal and average times for the example presented in Table 5 may be graphed as shown in Figure 18, which shows the rapid improvements in time at the beginning of the learning process, the gradual decrease in the marginal time, and the eventual stabilization of both times. The total curve is graphed in Figure 19.

Inventory Control

Inventory control refers to those procedures management employs to assure itself that appropriate quantities of inventory will be on hand to satisfy needs, and that the costs associated with this policy will be minimal. Accountants should be interested in inventory control for many reasons:

Figure 18

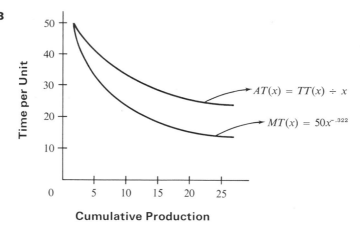

Cumulative Production

Figure 19

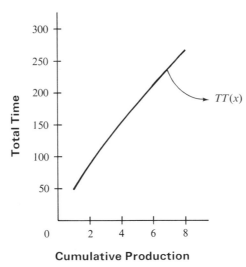

Cumulative Production

1. Control is one of the accountant's most important functions, and inventory control is but one phase of the broad field of control.

2. Balance sheet valuations and structural considerations are involved. For example, if inventory is overstocked, it is idle and may even be obsolete. If this is so, it may require either a decrease in inventory value or perhaps even segregation from the current assets to the "other assets" category as an idle asset.

3. New kinds of costs and cost concepts are involved in inventory control. Not only is there a cost of inventory shortage, but there are also different magnitudes of cost (as, for example, when a cost is assumed to be infinite) and a new cost dimension (as, for example, when costs are per unit, per time period).

4. Inventory control involves costs such as material, labor, and variable overhead collected for product costing purposes. Knowing how they are used for other purposes may influence how the costs are segregated in the first place.

5. Inventory control represents a popular avenue for familiarizing oneself with operations research OR techniques. If accountants are to perform management consulting services themselves (as opposed to hiring non-accountants as staff members and having them do the OR work), and if accountants wish to communicate with OR specialists, inventory control may well be the best bridge to understanding the researcher's mathematical model building.

6. The techniques of inventory control have potential for broader application. What do we mean by inventory? Is not cash an inventory? And accounts receivable?

Three broad types of inventory costs are subject to managerial control:

Inventory Costs

1. *Order or "setup" costs*   If the inventory item concerned is being purchased, the costs of placing and receiving an order are involved. If the inventory item is being manufactured, the costs of preparing the machinery are involved. In either case, the cost is fixed for each batch, and the control aspect lies in deciding how large each batch should be and, consequently, how often the fixed costs per batch should be incurred. Order costs include clerical expenses for placing and handling the order, transportation costs, and any other ordering incremental costs (i.e., costs that vary with the number of orders placed). Setup costs include payments to the employees for setting up the machines, costs associated with machine downtime (such as lost production), and costs of any spoilage attendant to checking machine settings.

2. *Holding costs*   Holding costs, or "carrying costs" as they are sometimes called, include costs associated with deterioration, obsolescence, storage, handling, interest, insurance, and taxes. Note that opportunity costs are intended here. What it costs to store inventory, for example, may well be what the space could be rented for to an outside party (i.e., the foregone rentals equal the cost of storing inventory). The interest charge, for another example, equals the earnings that could have been generated by investing an equal amount of funds, not necessarily in inventory, but in the next best investment, whatever that might be.

3. *Shortage costs*   Shortage, or "stockout," costs are those costs associated with failing to meet demand. Such failure may be from either (1) the consumer viewpoint, where a product cannot be delivered or can be delivered only after a delay; or (2) the producer standpoint, where machine or plant shutdown occurs because of lack of materials. Shortage

costs also include the costs of any preventative measures, such as the cost of carrying safety or buffer stocks.

Deterministic Demand

Where the demand for an inventory item is deterministic (i.e., known with certainty), management is confronted with deciding how many units should be run through in a given batch. The more units produced (or ordered) in a batch, the greater the carrying costs will be (since the average inventory on hand will be higher); however, the larger the batch size, the smaller will be the number of batches and the total setup (or ordering) costs. Assuming no shortages are permitted, we seek to balance setup costs against holding costs by producing (ordering) the most economic lot (batch) size.

Model A

The most straightforward example of a known demand situation occurs when a company has a contract stipulating that it will supply a customer a given number of units at a certain rate per time period for a specified duration of time. We shall deal with this problem in terms of graphs and general symbols.

KEY

R = total units required for specified time T (e.g., per year)
T = total duration of time (e.g., days per year)
Q = a variable indicating the number of units per batch
C_P = procurement or setup costs per batch
C_H = holding costs per unit per time period (e.g., per day)
L = inventory level; initial level = Q
t = a variable indicating time (e.g., number of days). t will also be used to designate the specific time interval between batches. Thus, t has the dual meaning of a variable and a specific value of that variable.

The quantity-time graph for this problem appears as shown in Figure 20. This problem may be solved either by calculus or by using the formula for the area of a triangle. First we observe that the total setup cost per year is equal to the setup cost per batch times the number of batches per year; that is, total

Figure 20

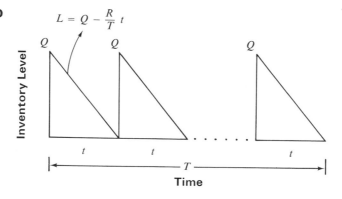

$$L = Q - \frac{R}{T} t$$

110

cost of setups per year $= C_P(R/Q)$. (Since we have R units required per year and we make Q units per batch, R/Q determines the number of batches per year.)

Next we need to determine total holding cost. Here we may determine holding cost per batch and multiply it by the number of batches. Since the area of a triangle is one-half the base times the height, the area of one of the above cycles (triangles in graph) is $\frac{1}{2}\,tQ$. Now t and Q are both unknown (variables), and it would help to have only one variable; therefore, we substitute for t. Three ways of obtaining the substitution formula are

1. We can observe that $T/t =$ the number of batches per year $= R/Q$.

$$\frac{T}{t} = \frac{R}{Q} \quad \text{and} \quad t = \frac{QT}{R}$$

2. We can use the formula for demand in each cycle, $L = Q - (R/T)t$. We note that when t days have passed, we have

$$L = 0, \ 0 = Q - (R/T)t$$

$$Q = \frac{R}{T}t \quad \text{and} \quad t = \frac{QT}{R}$$

the same results as before.

3. In a triangle, we can recall that slope $=$ rise/run, or, stated differently, slope(run) $=$ rise. Hence, we have

$$\left(\frac{R}{T}\right)t = Q$$

Some questions may arise as to how the inventory level formula was obtained. First note that T is measured in terms of the basic time unit. For instance, if T is a year, we speak of T as being, say, 300 working days per year. Then t is a certain number of days per batch and R/T yields the units required per day, the rate of demand.

We now have area, $tQ/2$, and note that it has a dimension of unit-days per batch (alternatively, if we consider Q as simply units, $\frac{1}{2}$ may be considered dimensionless)

$$\left(\frac{t \text{ days}}{\text{batch}} \times \frac{Q \text{ units}}{\text{batch}} \times \frac{1}{2} \text{ batch} = \frac{tQ}{2} \frac{\text{unit-days}}{\text{batch}}\right)$$

We can express this area entirely in terms of Q by substituting $t = QT/R$.

$$\text{Area} = \frac{QT}{R}\left(\frac{Q}{2}\right) = \frac{Q^2 T}{2R}$$

This result could also be obtained by integration:

$$\text{Area} = \int_0^t \left(Q - \frac{R}{T}t\right) dt = Qt - \frac{Rt^2}{2T}$$

By substituting $t = QT/R$,

$$Q\left(\frac{QT}{R}\right) - \frac{R}{2T}\left(\frac{QT}{R}\right)^2 = \frac{Q^2T}{R} - \frac{Q^2T}{2R} = \frac{Q^2T}{2R}$$

In brief, integration has proved the formula for the area of a triangle.

When the area of a cycle, which is measured in unit-days per batch, is multiplied by the holding cost, C_H, which is measured in dollars per unit-day, that is,

$$\$ \text{ per unit per day} = \frac{\$}{\text{unit}} \div \text{day} = \frac{\$}{\text{unit}} \times \frac{1}{\text{day}} = \frac{\$}{\text{unit-day}}$$

the result is the holding cost per batch. When this cost is multiplied by the number of batches per year

$$\frac{R \text{ units}}{\text{year}} \div \frac{Q \text{ units}}{\text{batch}} = \frac{R}{Q}\frac{\text{batches}}{\text{year}}$$

we obtain the total holding cost per year:

$$\text{Total holding cost per year} = \frac{C_HQ^2T}{2R}\left(\frac{R}{Q}\right) = \frac{C_HQT}{2}$$

The total inventory cost per year (TC) is then obtained by summing total setup costs per year and total holding costs per year:

$$TC = \overset{\textit{setup}}{\frac{C_PR}{Q}} + \overset{\textit{holding}}{\frac{C_HQT}{2}}$$

We have already performed a dimensional analysis to see that all terms in this equation are consistent, that is, that they are all measured in \$/yr. Checking the cost dimensions is important because inaccurate estimates of batch size Q may otherwise result. A serious error might result, for instance, if the accountant computed C_H in \$/unit/month rather than in \$/unit/day.

A cost-lot size graph for our inventory cost equation would appear as shown in Figure 21.

Figure 21

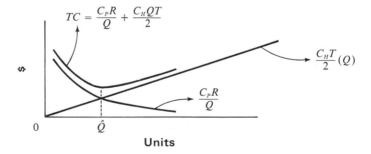

The minimum total cost occurs at the optimal value of Q, $\hat{Q}$. Note also that setup costs decrease as Q increases, whereas holding costs increase as average inventory $Q/2$ (Q goes from $\hat{Q}$ to 0 for an average of $Q/2$) increases. This value occurs when the total setup costs equal the total holding costs:[4]

$$\frac{C_P R}{Q} = \frac{C_H T Q}{2}$$

$$\hat{Q} = \sqrt{\frac{2C_P R}{C_H T}}$$

Suppose, however, that we did not wish to spend the time to graph the total cost equation and its components. We would then seek the minimum total cost by taking the first derivative of the total cost equation, setting it equal to zero, and solving the resulting equation to obtain the minimum point $\hat{Q}$. These procedures are performed below.

$$\frac{d(TC)}{dQ} = \frac{-C_P R}{Q^2} + \frac{C_H T}{2} = 0$$

$$\frac{C_P R}{Q^2} = \frac{C_H T}{2}$$

$$\hat{Q} = \sqrt{\frac{2C_P R}{C_H T}}$$

Since square root is involved, there are actually two values of Q: one is a maximum (the negative value) and the other is the desired minimum. We could take the second derivative of TC and insert our positive and negative

---

[4] An interesting modification of this one item lot size problem occurs when several inventory items benefit from the same setup or order cost (i.e., the setup cost is a common cost). Here it can be reasoned that the length of a cycle will be the same for all items and will be equal to the shortest cycle of the various items. (You place the order or setup for the shortest cycle item, and when you do so, the other items may be ordered or set up without adding to the setup or order cost.) Moreover, the items with the longer cycles automatically reduce their average inventories, hence their holding costs, when they shorten their cycles. Under these circumstances, several items all have the same cycle length t. The substitution formula for the ith item is

$$Q_i = \frac{R_i}{T} t$$

The total cost (TC) equation is

$$TC = \overset{\text{total setup}}{\frac{C_P R_i}{Q_i}} + \overset{\text{total holding}}{\frac{T \sum C_{Hi} Q_i}{2}}$$

By setting total setup cost equal to total holding cost (or by using calculus), we obtain

$$Q_i = \sqrt{\frac{2C_P R_i}{T \sum C_{Hi}}}$$

Q values, but it is unnecessary in this case because manufacturing negative quantities of Q is nonsensical.[5]

EXAMPLE

A manufacturer has a contract that specifies the delivery of 2,400 units per year at a uniform rate of 300 units per month. There are severe penalties for failing to meet this delivery schedule, and management has flatly refused to even consider back orders (temporary shortages). The cost accountant determined that the setup costs per batch amount to $490 and the holding costs per unit per month are $10. What batch size should be made?

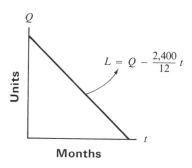

$$TC = \$490\left(\frac{2,400}{Q}\right) + \$10\left(\frac{2,400}{Q}\right)\int_0^t (Q - 200t)\, dt$$

$$TC = \frac{1,176,000}{Q} + 60Q$$

$$TC' = \frac{-1,176,000}{Q^2} + 60 = 0$$

$$\frac{1,176,000}{Q^2} = 60$$

$$\hat{Q} = \sqrt{\frac{1,176,000}{60}} = 140 \text{ units per batch}$$

COMMENT If desired, we could now use $\hat{Q}$ to determine values for t and TC.

---

[5] For the interested reader, the second derivative of TC is

$$TC'' = \frac{2C_P R}{Q^3}$$

When the negative value of Q is inserted, $TC'' < 0$, and we have a maximum:

$$TC''\left(-\sqrt{\frac{2C_P R}{C_H T}}\right) = \frac{2C_P R}{\left(-\sqrt{\frac{2C_P R}{C_H T}}\right)^3}$$

Chapter 5 : Cost Analysis and Calculus

Model A assumed instantaneous replenishment. We now assume that stock replenishment requires time but takes place at a uniform rate and that demand is met during production. These changes in assumptions complicate the economic lot size computations somewhat. To the list of symbols previously presented we add

r = units demanded per day
p = units produced per day
K = total cost per day

Model B may be diagramed as shown in Figure 22. It takes a bit of concentration to understand this diagram. One of the tricks in doing so is recognizing that when a slope is rising, production is taking place; when production ceases, a falling slope begins. The dashed lines indicate how either demand or production would look if orders were *not* filled during production. Thus, L_1 is the line showing the inventory level if production were uninterrupted by filling orders. Since orders are filled during production, the actual inventory level during production follows the L_2 equation. The advantage of interrupting production to fill orders is that the lengths of the cycle and, hence, the holding costs are reduced. This may be seen by rearranging lines, as shown in Figure 23.

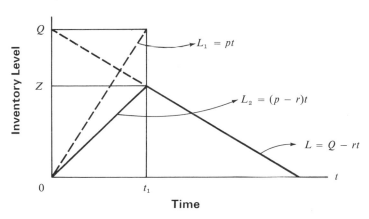

Figure 22

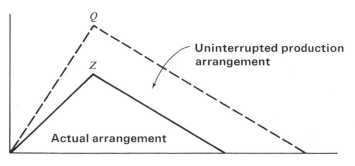

Figure 23

In Model B, we seek to minimize K, the total cost per day. The cost equation and its minimization are shown below.

$$K = \frac{C_P}{t} + \frac{C_H}{t}\left[\int_0^{t_1} (p - r)t \, dt + \int_{t_1}^{t} (Q - rt) \, dt\right]$$

It is wise to check dimensions for consistency:

$$\frac{\$}{\text{day}} = \frac{\$}{\text{batch}} \times \frac{\text{batch}}{\text{days}} + \frac{\$}{\text{unit(days)}} \times \frac{\text{batch}}{\text{days}} \times \frac{\text{unit(days)}}{\text{batch}}$$

We integrate and simplify:

$$K = \frac{C_P}{t} + \frac{C_H}{t}\left[\frac{(p - r)t_1^2}{2} + Q(t - t_1) - \frac{r}{2}(t^2 - t_1^2)\right]$$

$$= \frac{C_P}{t} + \frac{C_H}{t}\left[\frac{pt_1^2}{2} + Q(t - t_1) - \frac{rt^2}{2}\right]$$

We may substitute for t_1 by using the "pure" production line, $L_1 = pt$, and observing that $Q = pt_1$. Therefore, $t_1 = Q/p$.

$$K = \frac{C_P}{t} + \frac{C_H}{t}\left[\frac{Q^2}{2p} + Qt - \frac{Q^2}{p} - \frac{rt^2}{2}\right]$$

$$= \frac{C_P}{t} - \frac{C_H Q^2}{2pt} + C_H Q - \frac{C_H rt}{2}$$

We could at this point make the further substitution of $t = Q/r$ [determined by multiplying the slope (r) by the "run" (t) to obtain "rise" (Q)] and obtain an equation in terms of a single variable, Q. This would undoubtedly be the easiest (and, consequently, the wisest) thing to do, but we shall avail ourselves of the opportunity to work with partial derivatives.

$$\frac{dK}{dQ} = \frac{\partial K}{\partial Q}\frac{dQ}{dQ} + \frac{\partial K}{\partial t}\frac{dt}{dQ}$$

$$\frac{dK}{dQ} = \left[-\frac{C_H Q}{pt} + C_H\right](1) + \left[-\frac{C_P}{t^2} + \frac{C_H Q^2}{2pt^2} - \frac{C_H r}{2}\right]\left(\frac{1}{r}\right)$$

$$= C_H - \frac{C_H Q}{tp} - \frac{C_P}{t^2 r} + \frac{C_H Q^2}{2rpt^2} - \frac{C_H}{2}$$

We now substitute for t:

$$\frac{dK}{dQ} = \frac{C_H}{2} - \frac{C_H Q}{(Q/r)p} - \frac{C_P}{(Q/r)^2 r} + \frac{C_H Q^2}{2rp(Q/r)^2}$$

$$= \frac{C_H}{2} - \frac{C_H r}{p} - \frac{C_P r}{Q^2} + \frac{C_H r}{2p}$$

We simplify and set $dK/dQ = 0$ to obtain optimal Q:

$$\frac{dK}{dQ} = \frac{C_H}{2}\left(1 - \frac{r}{p}\right) - \frac{C_P r}{Q^2} = 0$$

$$\hat{Q} = \sqrt{\frac{2C_P r}{C_H(1 - r/p)}}$$

Consider how allowing shortages to occur would affect the economic lot size calculations. We need these new symbols:

Z = the maximum amount of inventory actually held

C_S = shortage costs per unit per time period (e.g., per day)

Assuming instantaneous replenishment, the problem may be diagramed as shown in Figure 24. Note that Q units are produced each time; however, since $Q - Z$ units are used to satisfy back orders (shortages), only Z units actually appear on the shelves.

Figure 24

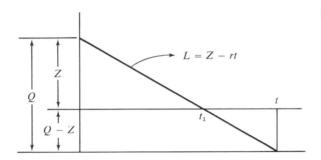

Since the area of a triangle is one-half the base times the height, we obtain the following equation for K:

$$K = \frac{C_P}{t} + \frac{C_H}{t}\frac{(Zt_1)}{2} + \frac{C_S}{t}\frac{(Q - Z)(t - t_1)}{2}$$

Substitution formulas:

$0 = Q - rt$	$0 = Z - rt_1$
$t = \dfrac{Q}{r}$	$t_1 = \dfrac{Z}{r}$

$$K = \frac{rC_P}{Q} + \frac{C_H Z^2}{2Q} + \frac{C_S}{2}\frac{(Q - Z)^2}{Q}$$

It will improve intuitions if we look at this problem from a different perspective. The same equation for K will result if we compute average inventory. During the holding phase of the cycle, the inventory goes from Z to 0 for an average of $Z/2$. Similarly, during the shortage phase of the cycle, the shortage goes from 0 to $(Q - Z)$ for an average of $(Q - Z)/2$. We need to know the proportion of the cycle time each of these averages is in effect so that we can weight each average in expressing the over-all average. To accomplish this, we may employ the geometric relationships of similar triangles in lieu of the above substitution formulas.

We have

$$\frac{Z}{Q} = \frac{t_1}{t} \quad \text{(This is read, "Z is to Q as } t_1 \text{ is to } t.\text{")}$$

$$t_1 = \frac{tZ}{Q}$$

Also,

$$\frac{Q - Z}{Q} = \frac{t - t_1}{r}$$

$$t - t_1 = \frac{t(Q - Z)}{Q}$$

We can calculate the average inventory held and weight it as follows:

Average Inventory Held	*Weighting*		*Substitution for t_1*
$\dfrac{Z}{2}$	$\left(\dfrac{t_1}{t}\right)$	$=$	$\dfrac{Z\left(t\dfrac{Z}{Q}\right)}{2t} = \dfrac{Z^2}{2Q}$

In a similar way, we can determine average shortage to be $(Q - Z)^2/2Q$. If we then insert our holding, setup, and shortage costs, we arrive at our previous formula for K:

$$K = \frac{rC_P}{Q} + \frac{C_H Z^2}{2Q} + \frac{C_S(Q - Z)^2}{2Q}$$

$$\frac{\partial K}{\partial Q} = -\frac{rC_P}{Q^2} - \frac{C_H Z^2}{2Q^2} + \frac{C_S}{2}\left[\frac{2Q(Q - Z) - (Q - Z)^2}{Q^2}\right]$$

$$= -\frac{rC_P}{Q^2} - \frac{C_H Z^2}{2Q^2} + \frac{C_S}{2}\frac{(Q^2 - Z^2)}{Q^2}$$

Simplifying and setting equal to zero to obtain optimal Q, we obtain

$$= \frac{1}{2Q^2}\left(-2rC_P - C_H Z^2 + C_S Q^2 - C_S Z^2\right) = 0$$

$$C_S Q^2 = 2rC_P + Z(C_H + C_S) \qquad \qquad *$$

$$\frac{\partial K}{\partial Z} = \frac{C_H Z}{Q} - \frac{C_S}{Q}(Q - Z) = 0$$

$$C_H Z = C_S Q - C_S Z$$

$$Z = \frac{C_S Q}{C_H + C_S}$$

Substitute the above value of Z in the starred equation to solve for $\hat{Q}$ simultaneously:

$$C_S Q^2 = 2rC_P + \left(\frac{C_S Q}{C_H + C_S}\right)(C_H + C_S)$$

$$C_S Q^2 - \frac{(C_S Q)^2}{C_H + C_S} = 2rC_P$$

$$C_S Q^2 \left[1 - \frac{C_S}{C_H + C_S}\right] = 2rC_P$$

$$\hat{Q} = \left[\frac{2rC_P(C_H + C_S)}{C_S C_H}\right]^{1/2}$$

An interesting mathematical observation here is that the absence of a non-circular side relationship between Z and Q makes it impossible to reduce this problem from three variables (K, Z, and Q) to two variables (K and Q). dk/dQ, therefore, cannot be calculated. Model B, on the other hand, started with three variables (K, t, and Q) but, because of the relationship between Q and t, ended with two variables (K and Q).

The cost accountant easily becomes intrigued with calculating shortage cost. In this model, C_S was taken as a cost per unit per day. No attention seems to have been paid to the fact that customers differ in their reactions to shortages. Some accept delays, others seek new suppliers; of course, if all suppliers are short, the search for a new supplier will be in vain. However, if a new supplier can be found, what is the extent of the cost of shortage? Is the single order all that is lost, or does the cost of shortage amount to the present value of the profit lost on all sales that would *probably* have taken place in the future? If all customers accept delays (shortages), is there any cost of shortage? Clearly, probability theory must be invoked in any attempt to calculate shortage cost. Probability theory repesents a very convenient way of treating simultaneously alternatives that would otherwise be incompatible and inconsistent.

Model D

Assume that the rate of demand is rapid at the start of the inventory cycle but gradually slows down, that inventory replenishment is immediate, and that no inventory shortages will be permitted (this is tantamount to saying that the cost of the inventory shortage is infinite). Under these circumstances, the model shown in Figure 25 is obtained.

Setup cost = $1,000 per batch
Holding cost = $2 per unit per day

We wish to determine the order quantity Q that will minimize $f(Q, t)$, the cost per day.

The relationship between variables Q and t is determined in the usual way.

Figure 25

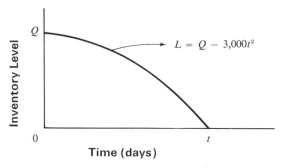

We note that when the inventory level L is zero, all the units ordered, Q, have been used, and that this has taken t days of usage (demand) at the rate of $3,000t^2$ units per day. In algebraic terms, at $L = 0$,

$$0 = Q - 3,000t^2$$
$$Q = 3,000t^2$$
$$t^2 = Q/3,000$$
$$t = (Q/3,000)^{1/2}$$

Now let us formulate our model of inventory costs per day, $f(Q, t)$. The inventory cost per day may be expressed as follows:

$$f(Q, t) = \frac{\$1,000}{t} + \frac{\$2}{t} \int_0^t (Q - 3,000t^3)\, dt$$

Integrating with respect to t gives the area under the curve (measured in unit days).

$$f(Q, t) = \frac{1,000}{t} + \frac{2}{t}\left(Qt - \frac{3,000t^3}{3}\right)$$

Simplifying, we obtain

$$= \frac{1,000}{t} + 2Q - 2,000t^2$$

Let us substitute for t its equivalent expression, $(Q/3,000)^{1/2}$.

$$f(q) = \frac{1,000}{(Q/3,000)^{1/2}} + 2Q - \frac{2,000}{3,000}Q$$

$$f(q) = 1,000\sqrt{3,000}Q^{-1/2} + \frac{4}{3}Q$$

It is convenient to do a dimensional analysis at this point (although other points would serve as well). For simplicity, let us reconvert the first term on the right of the equals sign to t terms; we then have

$$f(Q, t) = \frac{\$}{day} = \frac{\$1,000}{batch}\bigg/\frac{t \text{ days}}{batch} + \frac{\$2}{unit(days)}\left(\frac{2}{3}batch\right)\left(\frac{Q \text{ units}}{batch}\right)$$

$$= \frac{1,000}{T}\frac{\$}{\text{day}} + \frac{4Q}{3}\frac{\$}{\text{day}}$$

We see that our expressions conform one to another in that both sides of the equation are measured in \$/day.

$$f'(Q) = -\tfrac{1}{2}(1,000\sqrt{3,000})Q^{-3/2} + \tfrac{4}{3} = 0$$

$$\frac{500\sqrt{3,000}}{Q^{3/2}} = \frac{4}{3}$$

$$Q^{3/2} = \frac{3(500)\sqrt{3,000}}{4}$$

$$\hat{Q} = 750 \text{ units per batch}$$

NOTE

A general way of expressing the holding area for all the deterministic models, regardless of whether triangles or curves are involved or whether shortages are permitted, requires the restatement of rate of demand r in terms of economic lot size Q and cycle length t. The general expression is

$$L = L_{max} - Q\left(\frac{T}{t}\right)^{1/n}$$

KEY

L_{max} = the maximum level of inventory on the shelves (i.e., Z in the shortage model presented or Q where shortages are not permitted)

T = the time variable designation (introduced to distinguish the variable from its optimum value t, the cycle length)

n = the value used to express the pattern of demand; for example, uniform demand (graphed ⟍), $n = 1$; curved or power demand (graphed ⟍_), $n = 2$, or (graphed ⟍), $n = \tfrac{1}{2}$.

EXAMPLE

Model D is of the form $L = Q - rT^2$, and the area under this curve is $Qt - (rt^3)/3$ or $2Qt/3$. Because no shortages are permitted in Model D, $L_{max} = Q$ and $r = Q/t^2$ (since we had $Q = rt^2$). Substituting these values in $L = Q - rT^2$, we obtain

$$L = Q - \left(\frac{Q}{t^2}\right)T^2 = Q - Q\left(\frac{T}{t}\right)^2 = Q - Q\left(\frac{T}{t}\right)^{1/(1/2)} = L_{max} - Q\left(\frac{T}{t}\right)^{1/n}$$

The area is then

$$\int_0^t \left[Q - Q\left(\frac{T}{t}\right)^2\right] dT = \frac{2Qt}{3}$$

as before.

In our preceding discussion of inventory control, the rate of demand was assumed known. Consider now a situation in which demand is subject to a known, continuous probability distribution and we wish to know the number of units to order. The situation is such that the inventory must be sold within a short period of time or the investment in the inventory will be lost. The sales of perishable food items, newspapers, or magazines are some inventory examples following this pattern.

Suppose the number of units sold follows the probability distribution

$$p(x) = 0.000002x, \text{ for } 0 \leqslant x \leqslant 1,000$$

We wish to know the number of units to stock, given that the cost per unit is $150, the unit selling price is $300, and only $50 per unit may be recovered on unsold units. Then $150 is the profit made on each unit sold, and $100 is lost on each unsold unit. We need to determine the level of stock that will maximize expected profit. Our model is presented below.

KEY $E(P)$ = expected profit
x_s = units sold
x_o = units ordered

NOTE Expected profits involve both unknowns, x_s and x_o. Incidentally, if the use of x_s and x_o is confusing, substitute x for x_o and y for x_s in the manipulations that follow.

Three things may occur: either (1) inventory is greater than sales, or (2) inventory equals sales, or (3) inventory is less than sales. If inventory equals or exceeds sales (i.e., $x_o \geq x_s$), profits may be expressed as

$$\$150x_s - \$100(x_o - x_s) = \$250x_s - \$100x_o$$

But suppose sales equal or exceed inventory (i.e., $x_o \leq x_s$); the profits then are

$$\$150x_o$$

Figure 26 helps to visualize the range over which each expression is pertinent.

Figure 26

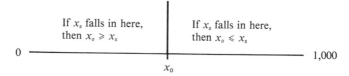

The equation for expected profit is

$$E(P) = \int_0^{x_o} (250x_s - 100x_o)(0.000002x_s) \, dx_s + \int_{x_o}^{1,000} 150x_o(0.000002x_s) \, dx_s$$

Chapter 5 : Cost Analysis and Calculus

$$= \int_0^{x_o} (0.0005x_s^2 - 0.0002x_s x_o) \, dx_s + \int_{x_o}^{1,000} 0.0003x_o x_s \, dx_s$$

We wish to maximize expected profit by selecting the best quantity of inventory to order. In other words, we seek $dE(P)/dx_o$.
We shall use the formula[6]

$$\frac{dg(x)}{dx} = \int_{h(x)}^{k(x)} \frac{\partial f(x, y)}{\partial x} \, dy + f[x, k(x)] \frac{dk(x)}{dx} - f[x, h(x)] \frac{dh(x)}{dx}$$

$$\frac{dE(P)}{dx_o} = \int_0^{x_o} (-0.0002x_s) \, dx_s + (0.0005x_o^2 - 0.0002x_o^2)(1) - 0$$

$$+ \int_{x_o}^{1,000} 0.0003x_s \, dx_s + 0 - 0.0003x_o^2(1)$$

$$= - \int_0^{x_o} 0.0002x_s \, dx_s + 0.0003x_o^2 + \int_{x_o}^{1,000} 0.0003x_s \, dx_s - 0.0003x_o^2$$

Simplifying and setting equal to zero to obtain the maximum,

$$0.0001x_o^2 = \frac{0.0003}{2} [1,000^2 - x_o^2]$$

$$0.00025x_o^2 = 150$$
$$x_o^2 = 600,000$$
$$\hat{x}_o \approx 775$$

An interesting fact could have been obtained had we substituted the letters P for the profit of $150 and L for the loss of $100. Then our equation would have been

$$E(P) = \int_0^{x_o} [(P + L)x_s - Lx_o]0.000002x_s \, dx_s + \int_{x_o}^{1,000} Px_o(0.000002x_s) \, dx_s$$

When $dE(P)/dx_o$ is calculated and set equal to zero, we obtain

$$0.000001x_o^2 = \frac{P}{L + P}$$

This states that inventory should be ordered in such a way that the cumulative probability of needing that amount or less lies in the ratio of profit per unit to the sum of profit per unit plus loss per unit. This is perfectly general;[7]

---

[6] See pages 71–72 for a fuller discussion of this formula.

[7] To see that the same results are generated by using the ratio of profit to profit plus loss, do the suggested integration:

$$\int_0^{x_o} 0.000002x_s \, dx_s = \frac{P}{P + L} = \frac{150}{150 + 100} = 0.6$$

We obtain
$$0.000001x_o^2 = 0.6$$
$$x_o^2 = 600,000$$
$$x_o = 775$$

it does not rely on the particular probability distribution, and it puts the determination of the inventory ordered squarely on the shoulders of the accountant who determines P and L. The person who calculates P and L hastily may be responsible for significant inventory losses or sales losses and for invalid inventory valuations on the balance sheet!

Probabilistic Demand: Further Observations

When one introduces probabilistic demand into inventory analysis, the subject of safety (buffer) stocks and reorder points must be given attention. Management generally formulates a policy regarding shortages; to put this policy into effect, safety stocks must be carried to be reasonably certain that fluctuating demand will not cause an excessive number of stockouts. Then, in general, given a specified safety stock, a reorder point is determined.

Figure 27

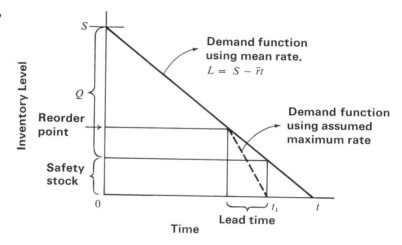

The relationship between the safety stock and the reorder point may be understood better after studying Figure 27, where a mean rate of usage has been employed to stipulate expected or normal usage. If allowed to go t days, the inventory level would be zero; however, the intention is to carry a safety stock and not let the level drop below zero. To be sure of not having a stockout, it seems logical to change the rate of demand to some assumed maximum rate (e.g., the mean rate plus two or three standard deviations) that would exactly exhaust inventory if the usual lead time transpired. [Lead time is the length of time it takes between the time an order (to supplier or to production superintendent) is placed and the time it is received.] Now, if the rate of demand remains normal, the replenishment order will be received at t_1 and the safety stock will never be needed. Safety stock, therefore, equals the assumed maximum rate of usage multiplied by the lead time. Reordering takes place when mean usage multiplied by the lead time brings us to the point of dipping into the safety stock.

Determining reorder point R is a simple matter when dealing with deterministic inventory models, since the question of buffer (safety) stocks does not arise. Where shortages are not permitted, $R = rL$, where L is the lead time. When shortages are economically advisable, demand during lead time equals the sum of R and the units short (S); that is, $R + S = rL$. However, where buffer stocks are carried, probability theory enters the computation, and the determination of R becomes more complicated. Simply stated, $R = B + \bar{r}\bar{L}$, where B stands for buffer stock and $\bar{r}$ and $\bar{L}$ stand for the respective mean values of demand and lead time. Then, if it were assumed that maximum demand would be equal, say, to $\bar{r}$ plus two standard deviations (s), the formulas would become $R = (\bar{r} + 2s)\bar{L} + \bar{r}\bar{L} = 2\bar{L}(\bar{r} + s)$. Unfortunately, space restrictions do not permit further probing into the complexities of determining R under probabilistic conditions; however, it can be pointed out that determining shortage frequently involves calculations very similar to the computation of expected loss presented under the heading "Loss Functions" in Chapter 4.

Let us end our brief study of inventory control by investigating how management decides upon the level of safety stock, given that stockouts will be permitted. From past history (or estimate), a graph (e.g., Figure 28) is drawn expressing service level (i.e., the percentage of time stockouts are *not* allowed) in terms of the cost of stocking that level. The inventory carrying costs are the usual clerical, transportation, obsolescence, deterioration, rent, insurance, and interest charges. The graph is used by observing that a given service level costs a certain amount, and by deciding whether improving the service level is worth the additional cost. For example, since it costs about $50,000 to have a 90% service level and about $60,000 to have a 95% service level, management would have to decide whether the 5% improvement was worth the $10,000 expense.

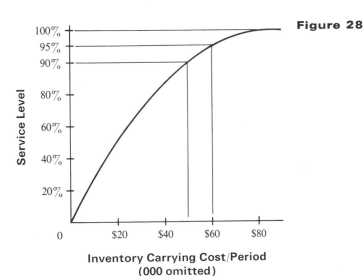

Figure 28

Inventory Carrying Cost/Period
(000 omitted)

Suggestions
for Further
Study There is a considerable literature built around inventory control. A few of the many interesting books you might consult are

Churchman, Ackoff, and Arnoff, *Introduction to Operations Research* (New York: John Wiley & Sons, Inc., 1957), Chapters 8–10.

J. F. Magee, *Production Planning and Inventory Control* (New York: McGraw-Hill Book Co., Inc., 1958).

Buchan and Koenigsberg, *Scientific Inventory Management* (Englewood Cliffs, N.J.: Prentice-Hall, Inc., 1963).

E. Naddor, *Inventory Systems* (New York: John Wiley & Sons, Inc., 1966).

Starr and Miller, *Inventory Control: Theory and Practice* (Englewood Cliffs, N.J.: Prentice-Hall, Inc., 1962).

Problems

Learning curve   1. A firm has constructed a learning curve for the marginal number of hours it expects it should take to produce a product. The curve is $M = 31x^{-0.38}$, where M = marginal hours and x = unit produced. Three hundred units of this product have already been produced, and an order for another 100 units has just been received. How many hours would the production of these 100 units be expected to take?

Answer: 335.5 hours

Learning curve   2. A firm produces machines subject to the learning curve

$$MT(x) = 60x^{-0.28}$$

(a) How much time is expected to be required to produce the next 200 units if the firm has already produced a total of 700 units?

(b) Of what use is a knowledge of learning curves to accountants?

Contrast between learning curve and set standard time   3. A manufacturer has just taken 300 hours to produce the first 10 units of a new product. Investigation showed that operations went smoothly, and, based on this fact, the chief accountant has authorized the use of a standard time of 30 hours per unit of product in all future cost estimates. Another accountant, who is convinced that an 80% learning curve affects this

Chapter 5 : Cost Analysis and Calculus

operation, tactfully implies that 30 hours per unit is excessive. The product is to be made regularly, and 1,000 units are to be produced by the end of the year. Of this 1,000, some 300 units are expected to be sold by the year's end.

The chief accountant states his feelings that there would probably be no significant difference in cost estimates and balance sheet valuations. To persuade his superior, the second accountant prepares figures showing (1) an estimate of the direct conversion costs necessary to produce the next 1,000 units under both the learning curve and 30 hours per unit assumptions, and (2) the difference in end-of-year balance sheet valuations and in profit figures (assuming that all variances from standard are treated as adjustments to the cost of sales figure). Direct labor cost per hour is $4, and variable overhead is $3 per direct labor hour.

(a) What estimates did the second accountant present to his superior?

(b) Can you suggest a diplomatic approach for the second accountant to follow in arguing for the adoption of the learning curve and the abandonment of the 30 hour standard approved by the chief accountant?

To determine the time for the first unit, solve for M in the following equation: **Hint**

$$300 = M \int_{0.5}^{10.5} x^{-0.322}\, dx$$

4.   A manufacturer is trying to decide whether to make or buy a particular item. It has been estimated that it will take 80 hours to make the first unit and that the time to produce unit n will be 70% of the time necessary for unit $\frac{1}{2}n$.   *Learning curves and the "make or buy" decision*

The pertinent factory costs are

Materials	$320 per unit
Labor	$5 per hour
"Out-of-pocket" overhead	$2 per hour
Profits foregone by diverting factory resources from production of next most profitable item	$1 per hour

If the item may be purchased for $440 per unit, approximately how many units would have to be manufactured before the company becomes indifferent between making and buying?

The solution depends on what is meant by indifference—does the decision   **Solution**
maker have a unit or cumulative notion in mind?

Unit basis

$$\$440 = \$320 + \$8[80 \times x^b]$$

$$2^b = .7$$

$$b = \frac{\log .7}{\log 2} = -\frac{.1549}{.3010} = -.5146$$

$$\frac{120}{640} = x^{-.5146}$$

$$(.1875)^{-1/.5146} = x$$

$$\text{antilog}\left[-\frac{1}{.5146}(-.7270)\right] = \text{antilog } 1.4127 = 25.87$$

Therefore, $x = 26$.

Cumulative basis (assuming continuity to avoid need for a computer)

$$440n = 320n + 8\int_0^n 80x^{-.5146}\,dx$$

$$\frac{120n}{640} = \frac{n^{.4854}}{.4854}$$

$$.4854\left(\frac{3}{16}\right) = \frac{n^{.4854}}{n} = n^{-.5146}$$

$$n \approx (.0910)^{-1/.5146} = (.0910)^{-1.943}$$
$$\log n = 1.943 \log (.0910) = -1.943(.9590 - 2) = -1.943(-1.0410)$$
$$= 2.0227$$
$$n = \text{antilog } (2.0227) = 105.4$$

On a cumulative basis, therefore, n approximately equals 105 units.

Thought question interrelating learning curves and lot sizes

5. Carrying costs could be expressed not only as $ per unit per time period as described in the chapter, but also as $ per $ of inventory value per time period. Since this is so, the interesting issue of valuing inventory is raised. One part of inventory valuation consists of direct labor cost, which, as we have seen, may be governed by some learning curve. Construct an inventory model (assume instantaneous replenishment, straight-line demand, and no shortages) that includes a learning curve.

Hint

The learning curve portion of the model may appear generally as

$$\int_p^{Q+p} Mx^{-b}\,dx$$

where p is the present point of cumulative production, and all other symbols are as defined in the chapter.

Observation

The derivative with respect to Q of the learning curve portion is $M(Q + p)^{-b}$. This introduces the present level of cumulative production into the lot size computation; consequently, the lot size will vary from one batch to the next. If this effect cannot be assumed away as insignificant, then the lot size models will require audit regularly.

Note

It is highly probable that a computer will be needed to solve your inventory model. Since this is so, avoid attempting to solve for Q manually unless you have many hours at your disposal.

Setup, holding, and shortage cost model

6. Solve the model diagramed on page 129 to determine

(a) the optimal lot size,

(b) the maximum quantity z to be held in inventory at any given time, and

(c) the maximum shortage w to be permitted.

Note

There is no noncircular parametric equation that permits the calculation of dK/dQ.

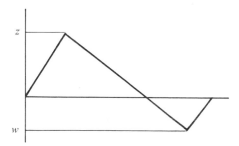

Problem 6

Answer: $\quad Q = \left[\dfrac{2C_P rp(C_H + C_S)}{C_S C_H(p - r)}\right]^{1/2}$

7. Determine the optimal lot size Q, where instantaneous replenishment occurs, shortages are permitted, and the power demand function $L = Z - 400T^2$ applies. Setup cost is $600 per batch, holding cost is $1 per unit per day, and shortage cost is $5 per unit per day.

   Power demand and shortage

   Answer: $\quad Q = 518$

8. A toy manufacturer has a contract calling for the delivery of 24,000 units of a particular item at the rate of 2,000 units per month. The manufacturer can produce these units at the rate of 5,000 units per month. If shortages are unthinkable, if setup costs are $2,700 per batch, and if holding costs are $0.50 per unit per month, how many units should be manufactured in a batch?

   Interrupted production

   Answer: $\quad$ 6,000 units

9. Solve for optimal lot size, safety stock, and average inventory, given

   Optimal lot size, average inventory, and safety stock

   $\quad 30,000 =$ units required for year (year $= 300$ working days)
   $\quad\quad$ $200 =$ ordering costs per batch
   $\quad\quad\quad$ $1 =$ holding costs per unit per day
   $\quad\quad\quad$ $\infty =$ shortage cost per unit per day

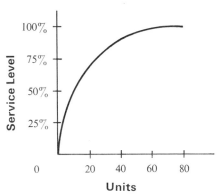

Problem 9

Management wishes to have a 90% service level.

Answer: $Q = 200$; safety stock $= 40$; average inventory $= 140$

*Probabilistic
demand and
inventory
opportunity
costs*

10. If the quantity stocked exceeds the quantity demanded for an inventory characterized by a limited "primary" life [i.e., the merchandise can only be sold as grade A for a certain time, after which it becomes grade B (stale, seconds—defective in some way)], the opportunity cost of holding is the loss sustained on selling the merchandise as "seconds." If the quantity demanded exceeds the quantity stocked, the opportunity cost of shortage may be assumed to be the foregone profits on the units not sold. Since these costs are subject to probabilistic demand, the costs are really expected opportunity costs. With these thoughts in mind, compute that value of inventory which minimizes total expected cost in the following circumstances. Sales price per unit is $100, and variable cost of production is $60 per unit. Any units remaining unsold after, say, one month may be sold as seconds for $50 per unit. Sales are normally distributed with a mean of 12,000 units and a 50% probability of being high or low by 2,000 units.

Comment   It would not have been necessary to estimate the standard deviation if the range of sales were specified. The mean plus and minus three standard deviations takes in 99.73% of the normal curve area. Consequently, a consistent restatement of the distribution of sales would be that sales were normally distributed over the domain $3,000 \le x \le 21,000$.

Hint   Use the approach described under Probabilistic Demand, p. 122. It will be easier to use $f(x)$ to represent the normal distribution and then substitute the actual distribution toward the end of the computations. It may facilitate matters to add and subtract a missing portion of an integral so that a cumulative distribution will cover its entire domain resulting in the value of 1. Then after a little algebraic factoring, the computation will appear in the form of footnote 7, p. 123.

Answer: $\hat{Q} = 14,520$

*Expected
shortage*

11. Compute expected shortage for the inventory model below. Demand (x) during lead time is normally distributed with $P(6,460 \le x \le 9,540) = 30\%$. Expected shortage can, therefore, be diagramed as follows:

Problem 11

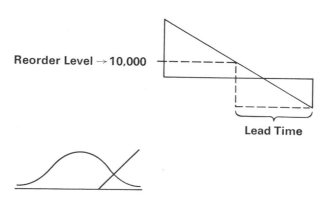

Reorder Level → 10,000

Lead Time

Chapter 5: Cost Analysis and Calculus

The solution to this problem is procedurally similar to the "loss function–utility theory" illustration at the end of Chapter 4.   **Hint**

Answer: $E(S) = 795$

12. In addition to many other products, a pastry shop bakes a particular kind of   ***Probabilistic demand***
     cake for which it is famous. Each cake sells for $0.70 and costs $0.30. Any
     cake not sold the same day it is baked is sold as stale merchandise (with
     labels removed) for $0.20. Regular sales follow the probability distribution
     below.

     $f(x) = 0.003 - 0.000004x, \quad \text{for } 0 \leq x \leq 1,000$

     (a) What quantity of this cake should be baked each day?

     (b) What quantity should be baked if stale cakes could be sold for $0.25
          each?

     Answer: (a) 347 cakes; (b) 407 cakes

6

Matrix Algebra

Matrix algebra has achieved great importance since the advent of computers and the development of linear programing. But even if computers and linear programing did not exist, matrix algebra would have a significant potential for the field of accounting. In this chapter, we present the matrix concepts.

Vectors and Vector Spaces

Vector space is a mathematical concept developed within the theory of matrix algebra. Intuitively, a vector space is a collection of points, such as, say, all the points that comprise the first quadrant of the graph of two variables, x and y. Because only two variables are concerned, their graph is a 2-dimensional vector space. By way of a more formal definition, a vector space consists of any set of n-dimensional vectors (i.e., points in n-space) over a field (such as the field of real numbers) that is closed under the operations of vector addition and scalar multiplication. "Closed" means that if these operations are performed, the resulting vector will still be in the given vector space.

What is a vector? A vector is a point (or directed magnitude) in a rectangular coordinate system and may be represented by the coordinates of the point. The number of coordinates determines the dimension of the vector.

Thus, in 2-dimensional space (or, more customarily, in 2-space), the vector (2, 3) indicates a point two units from the origin in a horizontal direction and three units from the origin in a vertical direction. The vector would be pictured as an arrow drawn from the origin to the point (2, 3). The graph of the vector would appear as shown in Figure 29, where the axes x and y have been relabeled x_1 and x_2. When we discuss n-space, it will be convenient to talk in terms of variables x_i rather than x, y, z, w, etc. A vector in 3-space, say (2, 3, 2), is represented in Figure 30.

Figure 29

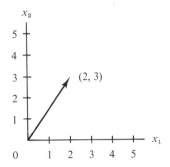

Figure 30

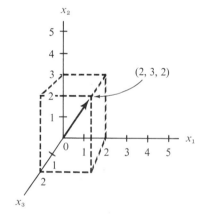

A vector in 5-space would have five coordinates, for example, $a = (a_1, a_2, a_3, a_4, a_5)$, where a is the notation for designating vector a, and its coordinates (which are usually referred to as elements) are $x_1 = a_1$, $x_2 = a_2$, $x_3 = a_3$, $x_4 = a_4$, $x_5 = a_5$.[1] A vector may be represented by either a vertical or a horizontal column of elements, whichever is convenient; consequently, a could be shown as

---

[1] No graph of this vector will be presented because it is considered impossible to graph any space with a dimension greater than 3.

$$a = \begin{bmatrix} a_1 \\ a_2 \\ a_3 \\ a_4 \\ a_5 \end{bmatrix} \quad \text{or} \quad a = [a_1, a_2, a_3, a_4, a_5]$$

When a is represented vertically, it is called a column vector or a five-by-one [indicated (5×1)] vector, that is, five elements in one column. Similarly, when a is represented horizontally, it is called a row vector or a one-by-five vector [indicated (1×5)], that is, one row with five elements.

What is meant by "closed under the operations of vector addition and scalar multiplication"? Closure under addition means that if any two vectors from a vector space are added, the resulting vector is also a vector from that space. Consider Figure 31. It can be seen that $a = (1, 2)$ and $b = (3, 1)$ would be two vectors that, when corresponding elements are added, yield $c = (4, 3)$. That is, in terms of column vectors,

$$\begin{bmatrix} 1 \\ 2 \end{bmatrix} + \begin{bmatrix} 3 \\ 1 \end{bmatrix} = \begin{bmatrix} 4 \\ 3 \end{bmatrix}$$

In terms of row vectors, $(1, 2) + (3, 1) = (4, 3)$. Of course, c could also result from adding other vectors, for example, $a = (4, 0)$ and $b = (0, 3)$. The graph demonstrates that vector a plus vector b forms vector c and that all three vectors are in 2-dimensional space. The location of a point c [or, in vector notation, (c_1, c_2), where elements $c_1 = x_1$ and $c_2 = x_2$] is determined graphically by completing a parallelogram and drawing c as the diagonal joining the origin and the opposite point of intersection.

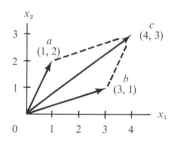

Figure 31

Closure under scalar multiplication means that the multiplication of some vector in the space by a scalar (i.e., a number, a constant) results in a vector, which is also included in that space. If we use the scalar 2, this may be depicted graphically, as shown in Figure 32, which demonstrates that both a and $2a$ are in 2-space; hence, the space is closed under scalar multiplication.

Note that a vector space is an analytical space for solving problems and

Figure 32

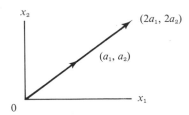

need not necessarily have a counterpart in physical space. The vertices of a pyramid may be represented in terms of vectors, and there would be a physical space counterpart (the actual pyramid). On the other hand, profits may be represented in some manner by a vector, but there is no corresponding solid. Profits might exist and even have a time dimension, but to speak of them as having length, width, and height in the physical sense of these words would be inappropriate.

Bases

In vector spaces it is important to formulate a basis for each such space. A basis is a set of vectors that may be used to express any point within the space as a linear combination of the basis vectors. Forming linear combinations is a process involving both scalar multiplication and vector addition. For example, assume that the basis vectors are $b_1 = (6, 0, 0)$, $b_2 = (0, 4, 0)$, and $b_3 = (0, 0, 14)$. To express $c = (3, 4, 2)$ in terms of the b_i, it is necessary to determine the appropriate set of scalars, λ_i, that satisfy the equation

$$c = \sum_{i=1}^{3} \lambda_i b_i$$

The scalars are $\frac{1}{2}$, 1, $\frac{1}{7}$, respectively, since $\frac{1}{2}(6, 0, 0) + 1(0, 4, 0) + \frac{1}{7}(0, 0, 14) = (3, 4, 2)$. Frequently, basis vectors themselves all have the form of vector c; that is, all elements are nonzero.

Let us investigate bases further by considering the following transitive relationship:

KEY a is any vector in n-space
B is a set of basis vectors for n-space
E is a set of n unit vectors[2]
R is the relation, "linear combination of"

aRB & $BRE \rightarrow aRE$

---

[2] A unit vector e_i is a vector in n-space which lies on an axis one unit away from the origin and which, therefore, has $(n - 1)$ elements equal to zero and one element whose value is one. For example,

Chapter 6: Matrix Algebra

a is a linear combination of *B* and *B* is a linear combination of *E* implies *a* is a linear combination of *E*.

Since any set of basis vectors is ultimately expressible in terms of unit vectors, the easiest way to formulate a basis for a space is to use a set of unit vectors directly. We now halt our discussion of bases and consider matrices and the various operations that can be performed on them.

Matrices

A common, though not very illuminating, definition describes a matrix as a rectangular array of numbers; however, understanding improves if a matrix is thought of as a set of one or more row (or column) vectors arranged like a grid. Whether you realize it or not, you are familiar with grids and, therefore, with matrices. A common employment of grids is in maps. For example, in consulting a map to locate city *X*, you may find that the index places the city in row 6, column j. The city, then, may be considered an element in a vector, and the map containing all the elements (cities) and vectors may be thought of as a matrix. An example of a matrix is

$$\begin{bmatrix} 3 & 2 & 1 & 4 \\ 0 & 2 & -1 & 5 \\ 6 & 1 & 2 & 2 \end{bmatrix}$$
$$(3 \times 4)$$

The above matrix has three rows and four columns; hence, it would be called a 3-by-4 matrix. Frequently, a matrix will be represented by a capital letter, rather than by the entire rectangular array of numbers. It is also common to talk about a matrix in general terms by using lower-case letters to represent elements. For example,

$$A$$
$$\begin{bmatrix} a_{11} & a_{12} & a_{13} \\ a_{21} & a_{22} & a_{23} \end{bmatrix}$$
$$(2 \times 3)$$

---

[2] *Continued*

$$e_1 = \begin{bmatrix} 1 \\ 0 \\ 0 \\ \vdots \\ 0 \end{bmatrix} \quad e_2 = \begin{bmatrix} 0 \\ 1 \\ 0 \\ \vdots \\ 0 \end{bmatrix} \quad e_3 = \begin{bmatrix} 0 \\ 0 \\ 1 \\ \vdots \\ 0 \end{bmatrix} \quad e_n = \begin{bmatrix} 0 \\ 0 \\ 0 \\ \vdots \\ 1 \end{bmatrix}$$

Thus, 3-space could be generated by e_1, e_2, and e_3. The vector $a = (2, 3, 1)$ is a linear combination of the basis vectors e_i and could, therefore, be written as $a = 2e_1 + 3e_2 + 1e_3 = 2(1, 0, 0) + 3(0, 1, 0) + 1(0, 0, 1)$.

The subscripts on each element indicate its position in the matrix; for example, element a_{23} appears in the second row and the third column. Any element in the matrix may be referred to as a_{ij}, where i is the row number and j is the column number.

A matrix may be partitioned into submatrices by drawing lines to indicate the desired division. This permits separate discussion and treatment of each submatrix. Examples of partitioned matrices and their submatrices would be

$$
\begin{array}{cc}
M & A \\[4pt]
\begin{bmatrix} M_1 \\ \hline M_2 \end{bmatrix}, & \begin{bmatrix} A_1 & \vdots & A_2 & \vdots & A_3 \end{bmatrix}
\end{array}
$$

Certain types of matrices will be especially useful in our discussions of the logical structure of accounting processes. An *identity matrix* (indicated by I) is a square matrix [i.e., a matrix with the same number of rows as there are columns, an $(n \times n)$ matrix], all elements of which are zero except those appearing on the main diagonal, which are ones. The main diagonal of a square matrix runs from the upper left-hand element, a_{11}, to the lower right-hand element, a_{nn}. (Note that the diagonal elements, a_{ii}, may be referred to by showing the subscript i equal to the subscript j; this is so because such elements occupy the same position in their respective rows as they do in their respective columns.) In a 3-dimensional problem, the identity matrix would appear as follows:

$$
\begin{array}{c}
I \\[4pt]
\begin{bmatrix} 1 & 0 & 0 \\ 0 & 1 & 0 \\ 0 & 0 & 1 \end{bmatrix}
\end{array}
$$

It can be seen that an identity matrix is but a collection of unit vectors, e_i.

The *diagonalized matrix* is similar to the identity matrix in that only the a_{ii} elements are nonzero, but it differs from the identity matrix in that the a_{ii} elements need not be ones nor, for that matter, equal to each other. An example of a diagonalized matrix is

$$
\begin{array}{c}
A \\[4pt]
\begin{bmatrix} 2 & 0 & 0 \\ 0 & 4 & 0 \\ 0 & 0 & -1 \end{bmatrix}
\end{array}
$$

It is important to know how to obtain the transpose of a matrix. The *transpose matrix* is one in which the rows in some original matrix are turned on end into columns of the transpose matrix; that is, a_{ij} in the transpose matrix is a_{ji} in the original matrix. The transpose matrix is frequently designated by a superscript T. An example of a matrix B and its transpose B^T is

$$\begin{array}{cc} B & B^T \\ \begin{bmatrix} 2 & 0 & -1 \\ 3 & 1 & 4 \end{bmatrix} & \begin{bmatrix} 2 & 3 \\ 0 & 1 \\ -1 & 4 \end{bmatrix} \end{array}$$

Single Transformation

In vector spaces it is frequently necessary to go from one space to another. Thus, an analytical problem may be stated in terms of vectors of, say, 3-space, and the solution is expected to be a vector (or vectors) in, say, 4-space. The mapping or transforming of vectors from one space to another is brought about by means of matrix multiplication. Exhibit 1 has been prepared to help you visualize what is done in the spacial transformation process. In this diagram, the original space of the problem is referred to as input space, and the solution space is called output space. A is a matrix that has converted (or transformed) a vector in n-space into a vector in r-space.

EXHIBIT 1

Input and Output Space

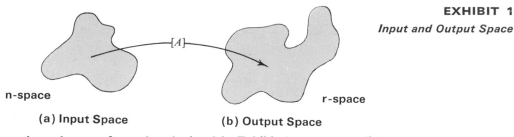

n-space   r-space

(a) Input Space   (b) Output Space

To see how the transformation depicted in Exhibit 1 was accomplished, let n-space be 2-space and r-space be 3-space. If b is the vector in 2-space, A the transformation matrix, and c the vector in 3-space, then $bA = c$. This transformation is accomplished by the following multiplication process.

$$\begin{array}{ccc} b & A & c \end{array}$$
$$(b_1, b_2) \begin{bmatrix} a_{11} & a_{12} & a_{13} \\ a_{21} & a_{22} & a_{23} \end{bmatrix} = [b_1 a_{11} + b_2 a_{21}, \, b_1 a_{12} + b_2 a_{22}, \, b_1 a_{13} + b_2 a_{23}]$$
$$(1 \times 2) \quad\quad (2 \times 3) \quad\quad\quad\quad\quad\quad\quad (1 \times 3)$$

Note that the number of columns in b equals the number of rows in A; this is known as the dimension rule of matrix multiplication. To multiply two matrices (recall that a vector is a matrix), the number of columns in the left-hand matrix *must* equal the number of rows in the right-hand matrix. Also note that the dimensions of c are equal to the row dimension of b and the column dimension of A. Knowing this is important because it enables you to arrange the product of two matrices in proper order.

Listing the elements of c as shown above proves cumbersome. To facilitate the listing, sigma notation is usually employed. The actual multiplication is accomplished according to the equation

$$c_k = \sum_{j=1}^{2} b_j a_{jk}$$

where $j = 1, 2$ and $k = 1, 2, 3$. For example,

$$c_2 = \sum_{j=1}^{2} b_j a_{j2} = b_1 a_{12} + b_2 a_{22}$$

In terms of sigma notation, the entire vector

$$c = \left[\sum_{j=1}^{2} b_j a_{j1}, \sum_{j=1}^{2} b_j a_{j2}, \sum_{j=1}^{2} b_j a_{j3} \right]$$

To abbreviate further, only the first and last terms need be shown, and the limits of summation may be omitted. Thus,

$$c = \left[\sum b_j a_{j1}, \ldots, \sum b_j a_{j3} \right]$$

These shortcuts may not seem to be much of an improvement, but their value becomes more apparent as dimensions of the matrices increase. A numerical example of the above multiplication is

$$\overset{b}{(2, 3)} \overset{A}{\begin{bmatrix} 0 & 2 & 3 \\ 1 & -1 & 2 \end{bmatrix}} = \overset{c}{[2(0) + 3(1), 2(2) + 3(-1), 2(3) + 3(2)]} = \overset{c}{[3, 1, 12]}$$

Note that a (1×2) vector multiplying a (2×3) matrix yields a (1×3) vector.

To develop matrix multiplication further, assume that input space contains a series of points (i.e., several vectors) that require transformation to output space. In terms of general notation, the process would appear as follows:

$$\overset{B}{\underset{(s \times n)}{\begin{bmatrix} b_{11} & \cdots & b_{1n} \\ \vdots & & \vdots \\ b_{s1} & \cdots & b_{sn} \end{bmatrix}}} \overset{A}{\underset{(n \times r)}{\begin{bmatrix} a_{11} & \cdots & a_{1r} \\ \vdots & & \vdots \\ a_{n1} & \cdots & a_{nr} \end{bmatrix}}} = \overset{C}{\underset{(s \times r)}{\begin{bmatrix} \sum b_{1j} a_{j1} & \cdots & \sum b_{1j} a_{jr} \\ \vdots & & \vdots \\ \sum b_{sj} a_{j1} & \cdots & \sum b_{sj} a_{jr} \end{bmatrix}}}$$

For example,

$$\sum b_{1j} a_{j1} = b_{11} a_{11} + b_{12} a_{21} + \cdots + b_{1n} a_{n1}$$

Once again the dimension rules may be observed at work. Furthermore, the notation has been complicated by the introduction of double subscripts on the elements in matrix B. In the preceding example, only a single subscript was necessary to indicate in which column of vector b an element was to be found. Because matrix B contains s row vectors, it now becomes necessary to indicate in which row and in which column an element appears. The situation may be clarified somewhat by noting that in the general element b_{ij}, the $i = 1, 2, \ldots, s$ (there are s rows) and the $j = 1, 2, \ldots, n$ (each vector is in n-space so there are n columns). Then, because the dimension rule of multiplication requires the columns of the left-hand matrix to be equal to the rows of the right-hand matrix, the general element of matrix A is a_{jk}, where $j = 1, 2, \ldots, n$ as before, and $k = 1, 2, \ldots, r$ (each vector in output space has r elements). Therefore, in expressing the elements of matrix C, the summation is over the common subscript j, and each element c_{ik} (the i indicates the row from B and the k indicates the column from A) has the original row subscript appended to the b_{ij} appearing in $\sum b_{ij} a_{jk}$ and the original column subscript appended to the a_{jk}.

A numerical example that illustrates the techniques of matrix multiplication is

$$
\begin{matrix} B & A \\ \end{matrix} \qquad\qquad\qquad\qquad C \qquad\qquad\qquad\qquad\qquad C
$$

$$
\begin{bmatrix} 0 & 1 \\ 2 & 3 \end{bmatrix} \begin{bmatrix} 4 & 5 & 6 \\ 7 & 8 & 9 \end{bmatrix} = \begin{bmatrix} 0(4) + 1(7), & 0(5) + 1(8), & 0(6) + 1(9) \\ 2(4) + 3(7), & 2(5) + 3(8), & 2(6) + 3(9) \end{bmatrix} = \begin{bmatrix} 7 & 8 & 9 \\ 29 & 34 & 39 \end{bmatrix}
$$

$$
(2 \times 2) \quad (2 \times 3) \qquad\qquad\qquad\qquad (2 \times 3) \qquad\qquad\qquad\qquad (2 \times 3)
$$

This example brings to light an important property of matrix multiplication: matrix multiplication is not commutative;[3] that is, the product BA is defined in the above example, but because of the dimension rule, AB is not defined. A 2-by-3 matrix cannot multiply a 2-by-2 matrix. Even if the dimension rule did not interfere, the elements in the matrix obtained by BA would not be the same as those obtained by AB unless one of the matrices was a scalar matrix (a diagonalized matrix where all a_{ii} are equal to some scalar) or unless both matrices were symmetric (a symmetric matrix is a matrix that is equal to its transpose $[A = A^T]$).

Now let us consider the multiplication of partitioned matrices. First of all, the partitions must be drawn so that the submatrices to be multiplied still obey the dimensional rule. Wherever the partitions are drawn, the usual procedure of multiplication of column and row elements and the summing of individual products must be halted, and the results to that point must be

---

[3] Some other properties of matrices are

1. *Addition and subtraction* Provided their dimensions are identical:
   (a) Matrix addition (or subtraction) is associative; that is, $(A + B) + C = A + (B + C)$ and $(A - B) - C = A - (B + C)$.
   (b) Matrix addition is commutative; that is, $A + B = B + A$.

2. *Multiplication* Provided the dimension rules are satisfied:
   (a) Matrix multiplication is associative; that is, $(AB)C = A(BC)$.

entered in separate matrices. In the following example, matrix A has been partitioned after columns 2 and 4, and matrix B has been correspondingly partitioned after rows 2 and 4. Three matrices result from the multiplication of the separate submatrices. Their elements are obtained from the multiplications

$$\sum_{j=1}^{2} a_{ij}b_{jk}, \quad \sum_{j=3}^{4} a_{ij}b_{jk}, \quad \text{and} \quad a_{i5}b_{5k}$$

and when the resulting product matrices are added, the original matrix C, which would have resulted if the partitioning had been ignored, is obtained.

$$A$$
$$\begin{bmatrix} 2 & 3 & \vdots & 1 & -2 & \vdots & 3 \\ 1 & 2 & \vdots & 5 & 4 & \vdots & 5 \end{bmatrix}$$

$$B \qquad\qquad\qquad\qquad\qquad\qquad\qquad C$$

$$\times \begin{bmatrix} 3 & 1 & -1 \\ 2 & 4 & 6 \\ \hdashline -3 & 0 & 2 \\ 4 & 1 & 5 \\ \hdashline -2 & 2 & 3 \end{bmatrix} = \left[\begin{bmatrix} 12 & 14 & 16 \\ 7 & 9 & 11 \end{bmatrix} + \begin{bmatrix} -11 & -2 & -8 \\ 1 & 4 & 30 \end{bmatrix} + \begin{bmatrix} -6 & 6 & 9 \\ -10 & 10 & 15 \end{bmatrix} \right]$$

$$= \begin{bmatrix} -5 & 18 & 17 \\ -2 & 23 & 56 \end{bmatrix}$$

Summary In mathematics, the framework for allocation problems is found in vector spaces, and the allocation process itself is carried out by transformation matrices. A matrix may be defined as something that consists of rows and columns of numbers. These rows and columns of numbers are referred to as vectors, and a matrix consists of one or more vectors. This is a row vector:

$$(1, 3, -1, 4)$$

This is a column vector:

$$\begin{bmatrix} 8 \\ 2 \\ 0 \end{bmatrix}$$

An example of a matrix containing more than a single vector is

$$\begin{bmatrix} 2 & 1 & 0 \\ 1 & -2 & 5 \end{bmatrix}$$

Vectors and matrices may be added and subtracted element by element, provided they have the same dimensions. For example,

$$\begin{bmatrix} 2 & 1 & 0 \\ 1 & -2 & 5 \end{bmatrix} + \begin{bmatrix} 3 & 5 & 2 \\ 6 & -1 & 0 \end{bmatrix} = \begin{bmatrix} 5 & 6 & 2 \\ 7 & -3 & 5 \end{bmatrix}$$

Vectors and matrices may be multiplied, provided the number of columns in the left-hand matrix equals the number of rows in the right-hand matrix. The exact procedure for multiplication is expressed in the formula

$$c_{ik} = \sum_{j=1}^{n} a_{ij}b_{jk} = a_{i1}b_{1k} + \cdots + a_{in}b_{nk}$$

where $i = 1, 2, \ldots, m$
$\quad\quad j = 1, 2, \ldots, n$
$\quad\quad k = 1, 2, \ldots, r$

Consider this problem.

$$
\begin{array}{ccc}
A & B & \\
\begin{bmatrix} a_{11} & a_{12} & a_{13} \\ a_{21} & a_{22} & a_{23} \end{bmatrix}
\begin{bmatrix} b_{11} & b_{12} & b_{13} & b_{14} \\ b_{21} & b_{22} & b_{23} & b_{24} \\ b_{31} & b_{32} & b_{33} & b_{34} \end{bmatrix}
& = & [C] \\
(2 \times 3) & (3 \times 4) & (2 \times 4)
\end{array}
$$

a_{ij} represents any element from matrix A; the subscript i indicates the row number, and the subscript j indicates the column number.

b_{jk} represents any element from matrix B; the subscript j indicates the row number, while the subscript k indicates the column number.

Let us substitute arbitrary numerical values and see what matrix C looks like.

$$
\begin{array}{ccc}
A & B & C \\
\begin{bmatrix} 2 & 1 & 0 \\ 1 & -2 & 5 \end{bmatrix}
\begin{bmatrix} -2 & 3 & -1 & 4 \\ 1 & 8 & 1 & 0 \\ 4 & 0 & 2 & 4 \end{bmatrix}
& = & \begin{bmatrix} -3 & 14 & -1 & 8 \\ 16 & -13 & 7 & 24 \end{bmatrix}
\end{array}
$$

To see how an element of matrix C is determined, let us apply the formula to determine c_{23}.

$$c_{23} = \sum_{j=1}^{3} a_{2j}b_{j3} = 1(-1) - 2(1) + 5(2) = 7$$

Consider the following set of simultaneous equations.

$$2x_1 - 3x_2 - 1x_3 = 36{,}000$$
$$1x_1 + 2x_2 + 1x_3 = 90{,}000 \qquad (1)$$
$$0x_1 + 1x_2 + 3x_3 = 72{,}000$$

Solving Simultaneous Equations

The above system of equations may be restated in matrices as follows:

$$\overset{A}{\begin{bmatrix} 2 & -3 & -1 \\ 1 & 2 & 1 \\ 0 & 1 & 3 \end{bmatrix}} \overset{x}{\begin{bmatrix} x_1 \\ x_2 \\ x_3 \end{bmatrix}} = \overset{b}{\begin{bmatrix} 36{,}000 \\ 90{,}000 \\ 72{,}000 \end{bmatrix}} \qquad (2)$$

By performing the indicated matrix multiplication in (2), it can be seen that the original system of equations (1) results. To solve for x, the inverse of matrix A (i.e., A^{-1}) must be calculated (provided that it exists). The inverse of a matrix is such that the identity matrix results when the matrix and its inverse are multiplied (i.e., $AA^{-1} = A^{-1}A = I$). In concept, A^{-1} is much like the reciprocal of a number; instead of dividing another expression by the number, multiplication of the expression by the number's reciprocal may be performed. Because division by a matrix is not allowed in matrix algebra, resort is had to multiplying by the inverse matrix. Accordingly, the solution to the problem in (2) proceeds as follows:

1. $Ax = b$
2. $A^{-1}Ax = A^{-1}b$
3. $Ix = A^{-1}b$
4. $x = A^{-1}b$ (Inversion techniques will be presented shortly.)

In the second step, both sides of the equation are multiplied on the left by A^{-1}. Then, since $A^{-1}A$ equals the identity matrix, as shown in step 3, and since the identity matrix multiplying some matrix leaves the matrix unchanged (this is like multiplying another number by 1), the solution x appears in step 4. For this problem, the solution is

$$\overset{x}{\begin{bmatrix} x_1 \\ x_2 \\ x_3 \end{bmatrix}} = \overset{A^{-1}}{\begin{bmatrix} \frac{5}{18} & \frac{4}{9} & -\frac{1}{18} \\ -\frac{1}{6} & \frac{1}{3} & -\frac{1}{6} \\ \frac{1}{18} & -\frac{1}{9} & \frac{7}{18} \end{bmatrix}} \overset{b}{\begin{bmatrix} 36{,}000 \\ 90{,}000 \\ 72{,}000 \end{bmatrix}} = \overset{x}{\begin{bmatrix} 46{,}000 \\ 12{,}000 \\ 20{,}000 \end{bmatrix}}$$

Compound Transformation

We must explore yet another aspect of the transformation process. Very often additional transformations beyond the first are required. In other words, there are both intermediate and terminal output spaces. It may be that the intermediate stages of transformation are of little interest to the person requiring the solution to the problem. If this is the case, a compound transformation matrix may be formulated by multiplying together the separate transformation matrices.

One compound transformation matrix of special importance arises when the system of simultaneous equations is such that the coefficients of the

          Chapter 6: Matrix Algebra

variables are stated as percentages less than or equal to 100% and the ultimate solution to the problem is such that the total[4] of the original vector of constants must not be changed. In other words, the individual elements of the vector of constants must be redistributed in such a way that the total of the vector remains unchanged. An effective matrix E may be employed to obtain ultimate solutions directly.

To illustrate the calculation and effects of an effective matrix, consider the problem presented in Exhibit 2, where a system of relationships among variables is expressed in terms of percentages. The question is raised, "What is the ultimate value of each variable x_i?" The first transformation employs an inverse matrix to determine the intermediate increased values of the variables. At this stage, x is in intermediate output space; it now becomes necessary to transform x from intermediate output space to terminal output space. The second transformation is accomplished by a diagonalized matrix containing the residual percentages for the variables. The calculation of one of these residual percentages may be of some interest. If x_2 owns 20% of x_1 and x_3 owns 5% of x_1, x_1 nominally retains only 75% of its own value.

Exhibit 3 presents the calculation of the effective matrix E for the problem presented in Exhibit 2. E circumvents intermediate output space. Essentially, an effective matrix first determines the residual percentages and then places them in a diagonalized matrix diag(SA) (which is the same as matrix R in Exhibit 2). A^{-1} is then multiplied by diag(SA) to obtain the effective matrix E. E has the property that the sum of the elements in each column vector is one; consequently, when E multiplies a vector, the elements of the vector are changed and redistributed but the total of the vector remains the same. As shown in Exhibit 3, $Ex = x'$, which is the same solution arrived at in Exhibit 2.

EXHIBIT 2

Compound Transformation Example

Diagram of relationships among variables x_i (arrows indicate +):

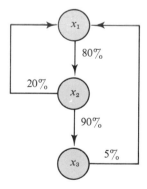

---

[4] The total of a vector may be obtained by multiplying it by what is known as a sum vector. A sum vector is a vector all elements of which are ones. An example of the

Observe that the residual percentages for x_1, x_2, and x_3 are 75%, 20%, and 10%, respectively.

Original system:

$$x_1 = 20{,}000 + 80\% x_2$$
$$x_2 = 60{,}000 + 20\% x_1 + 90\% x_3$$
$$x_3 = 10{,}000 + 5\% x_1$$

Restated in matrices:

$$
\begin{matrix} A \end{matrix} \qquad \begin{matrix} x \end{matrix} \qquad \begin{matrix} b \end{matrix}
$$

$$
\begin{bmatrix} 1.00 & -0.80 & 0.00 \\ -0.20 & 1.00 & -0.90 \\ -0.05 & 0.00 & 1.00 \end{bmatrix}
\begin{bmatrix} x_1 \\ x_2 \\ x_3 \end{bmatrix}
=
\begin{bmatrix} 20{,}000 \\ 60{,}000 \\ 10{,}000 \end{bmatrix}
$$

Solution   *First transformation:*

$$
\begin{matrix} A^{-1} \end{matrix} \qquad\qquad \begin{matrix} b \end{matrix} \qquad \begin{matrix} x \end{matrix}
$$

$$
\begin{bmatrix} 1.24378 & 0.99502 & 0.89553 \\ 0.30473 & 1.24378 & 1.11941 \\ 0.06219 & 0.04975 & 1.04478 \end{bmatrix}
\begin{bmatrix} 20{,}000 \\ 60{,}000 \\ 10{,}000 \end{bmatrix}
=
\begin{bmatrix} 93{,}532 \\ 91{,}916 \\ 14{,}676 \end{bmatrix}
$$

Second transformation:

$$
\begin{matrix} R \end{matrix} \qquad\qquad \begin{matrix} x \end{matrix} \qquad \begin{matrix} x' \end{matrix}
$$

$$
\begin{bmatrix} 0.75 & 0 & 0 \\ 0 & 0.20 & 0 \\ 0 & 0 & 0.10 \end{bmatrix}
\begin{bmatrix} 93{,}532 \\ 91{,}916 \\ 14{,}676 \end{bmatrix}
=
\begin{bmatrix} 70{,}149 \\ 18{,}383 \\ 1{,}468 \end{bmatrix}
= \text{ the ultimate value for each variable } x_i
$$

EXHIBIT 3
The Calculation of the Effective Matrix

$$E = \text{diag}(SA)A^{-1}$$

where E = an effective matrix, that is, a matrix in which the individual column elements e_{ij} total one:

$$1 = \sum_{i=1}^{n} e_{ij}$$

---

[4] *Continued*
procedure is

Sum Vector	Vector of Constants		Total of Vector of Constants
[1, 1, 1]	$\begin{bmatrix} 2 \\ 4 \\ 6 \end{bmatrix}$	=	[12]

S = the sum vector

diag = "express the product as a diagonalized matrix"

$$
\begin{array}{ccc}
S & A & SA
\end{array}
$$

$$
[1, 1, 1]
\begin{bmatrix}
1 & -0.80 & 0 \\
-0.20 & 1 & -0.90 \\
-0.05 & 0 & 1
\end{bmatrix}
= [0.75, 0.20, 0.10]
$$

Effective matrix:

$$
\begin{array}{ccc}
\text{diag}(SA) & A^{-1} & E
\end{array}
$$

$$
\begin{bmatrix}
0.75 & 0 & 0 \\
0 & 0.20 & 0 \\
0 & 0 & 0.10
\end{bmatrix}
\begin{bmatrix}
1.24378 & 0.99502 & 0.89553 \\
0.30473 & 1.24378 & 1.11941 \\
0.06219 & 0.04975 & 1.04478
\end{bmatrix}
=
\begin{bmatrix}
0.93284 & 0.74626 & 0.67164 \\
0.06095 & 0.24876 & 0.22388 \\
0.00621 & 0.00498 & 0.10448
\end{bmatrix}
$$

$SE = S$ **CHECK**

$$
\begin{array}{ccc}
S & E & S
\end{array}
$$

$$
[1, 1, 1]
\begin{bmatrix}
0.93284 & 0.74626 & 0.67164 \\
0.06095 & 0.24876 & 0.22388 \\
0.00621 & 0.00498 & 0.10448
\end{bmatrix}
= [1, 1, 1]
$$

Solution to the problem in Exhibit 2:

$$
\begin{array}{ccc}
E & x & x'
\end{array}
$$

$$
\begin{bmatrix}
0.93284 & 0.74626 & 0.67164 \\
0.06095 & 0.24876 & 0.22388 \\
0.00621 & 0.00498 & 0.10448
\end{bmatrix}
\begin{bmatrix}
20,000 \\
60,000 \\
10,000
\end{bmatrix}
=
\begin{bmatrix}
70,149 \\
18,383 \\
1,468
\end{bmatrix}
$$

Compound transformations may involve multiplying more than two separate transformation matrices. In the process, it may be necessary to transpose some transformation matrix and to adjust other matrices accordingly. In such instances, it may be necessary to call upon a theorem that states that the transpose of the product of two matrices is equal to the product of their transposes in reverse order; that is,

$$C^T = (AB)^T = B^T A^T$$

Matrix Inversion

There are a number of ways of obtaining an inverse to a given matrix. The traditional methods, one of which will presently be described, rely on the need for all the vectors in the matrix to be linearly independent; that is, no one vector in the matrix may be expressible as a linear combination of the remaining vectors. In terms of sigma notation, this amounts to saying that there is *no* set of scalars (not all zero) λ_i such that the following expression holds true:[5]

$$b_k = \sum_{\substack{i=1 \\ i \neq k}}^{n} \lambda_i b_i$$

Intuitively, the notion is that, given a set of n unknowns, there must be n equations if a unique solution to the system is to be obtained. If one of the equations is a multiple of another equation, for example, the system reduces to n unknowns and $n - 1$ equations and no unique solution can be computed. Testing for linear independence usually involves ascertaining whether the determinant of the matrix is zero or not. If the determinant is not zero, the system is linearly independent and an inverse may be calculated.

In accounting, it is unlikely that one equation in a system will be a multiple of another; therefore, it is reasonably safe to dispense with the test for linear independence and to proceed directly to the computations of the inverse. If the computations fail, you would be justified in suspecting that linear dependence was a likely cause. The technique for inversion that we will now consider is the Gauss-Jordan Method, which has the virtues of being both fairly efficient and relatively easy to follow.

The Gauss-Jordan Method of Matrix Inversion

The Gauss-Jordan Method augments the matrix to be inverted by appending the identity matrix alongside. Then, whatever is done to the original matrix is also done to the identity matrix. After a series of elementary row operations, the identity matrix reappears on the side opposite its original position, and in its former position the inverse matrix is found. Symbolically,

$$\begin{bmatrix} A & \vdots & I \end{bmatrix} \quad \text{becomes} \quad \begin{bmatrix} I & \vdots & A^{-1} \end{bmatrix}$$

The elementary row operations involve two types of rows: the pivot row (which will be indicated by the subscript r) and all other rows (which will be indicated by the subscript i). Once the row operations have been performed with r as the pivot row, another row is selected from the former i rows (usually, though not necessarily, the i row selected is the former $r + 1$ row) and designated as the new pivot row. The calculations are repeated until all rows have been used as pivots. The elementary row operations are as follows:

---

[5] Alternatively, b_k can be included with the remaining vectors, and the set can be termed linearly independent provided there is *no* set of scalars other than $\lambda_i = 0$ such that

$$\sum_{i=1}^{n} \lambda_i b_i = \bar{0} \quad \text{(the null or zero vector)}$$

λ_{ij} = an element in row i ($i = 1, 2, \ldots, s$) and column j ($j = 1, 2, \ldots, t$)

λ_{rk} = the pivot element; k is the column that in the next iteration (pass) will be a unit vector, e_r, that is, a column vector with a one in row r and zeros everywhere else

$\dfrac{\lambda_{ik}}{\lambda_{rk}}$ = the rate of exchange of row i with row r

$(\ )$ = a superscript that indicates the iteration of the figure in question; (p) represents the present iteration and (n) represents the next iteration

The formula for elements in row r is

$$\lambda_{rj}^{(n)} = \frac{\lambda_{rj}^{(p)}}{\lambda_{rk}^{(p)}}$$

The formula for elements in row i is

$$\lambda_{ij}^{(n)} = \lambda_{ij}^{(p)} - \frac{\lambda_{ik}^{(p)}}{\lambda_{rk}^{(p)}} (\lambda_{rj}^{(p)})$$

Figure 33 contains a flow chart to clarify procedures.

The notation $d \rightarrow d + 1$ means to replace the present reading of subscript d with the reading $d + 1$.

$$\begin{bmatrix} \boxed{2} & -3 & -1 & \vdots & 1 & 0 & 0 \\ 1 & 2 & 1 & \vdots & 0 & 1 & 0 \\ 0 & 1 & 3 & \vdots & 0 & 0 & 1 \end{bmatrix}$$

$$\rightarrow \lambda_{rk} = a_{11} = 2$$
$$\frac{\lambda_{ik}}{\lambda_{rk}} = \frac{a_{21}}{a_{11}} = \frac{1}{2}$$
$$\frac{\lambda_{ik}}{\lambda_{rk}} = \frac{a_{31}}{a_{11}} = \frac{0}{2} = 0$$

The first iteration will be

PIVOT ROW $(2 \quad -3 \quad -1 \quad 1 \quad 0 \quad 0) \div 2 = (1 \quad -\frac{3}{2} \quad -\frac{1}{2} \quad \frac{1}{2} \quad 0 \quad 0)$

OTHER ROWS $(1 \quad 2 \quad 1 \quad 0 \quad 1 \quad 0)$

$-\frac{1}{2}(2 \quad -3 \quad -1 \quad 1 \quad 0 \quad 0)$

ROW 2 $(0 \quad \frac{7}{2} \quad \frac{3}{2} \quad -\frac{1}{2} \quad 1 \quad 0)$

$(0 \quad 1 \quad 3 \quad 0 \quad 0 \quad 1)$

$-0(2 \quad -3 \quad -1 \quad 1 \quad 0 \quad 0)$

ROW 3 $(0 \quad 1 \quad 3 \quad 0 \quad 0 \quad 1)$

Figure 33

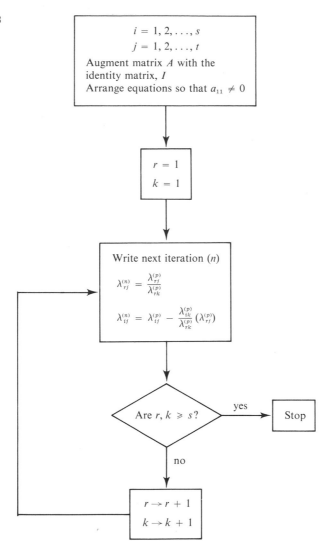

$$i = 1, 2, \ldots, s$$
$$j = 1, 2, \ldots, t$$
Augment matrix A with the
identity matrix, I
Arrange equations so that $a_{11} \neq 0$

$r = 1$
$k = 1$

Write next iteration (n)

$$\lambda_{rj}^{(n)} = \frac{\lambda_{rj}^{(p)}}{\lambda_{rk}^{(p)}}$$

$$\lambda_{ij}^{(n)} = \lambda_{ij}^{(p)} - \frac{\lambda_{ik}^{(p)}}{\lambda_{rk}^{(p)}}(\lambda_{rj}^{(p)})$$

Are $r, k \geqslant s$?   yes   Stop

no

$r \to r + 1$
$k \to k + 1$

Results

$$\begin{bmatrix} 1 & -\frac{3}{2} & -\frac{1}{2} & \vdots & \frac{1}{2} & 0 & 0 \\ 0 & \left(\frac{7}{2}\right) & \frac{3}{2} & \vdots & -\frac{1}{2} & 1 & 0 \\ 0 & 1 & 3 & \vdots & 0 & 0 & 1 \end{bmatrix}$$

$\uparrow$

$$\frac{\lambda_{ik}}{\lambda_{rk}} = \frac{\lambda_{12}}{\lambda_{22}} = -\frac{3}{2} \div \frac{7}{2} = \frac{-3}{7}$$

$$\to \lambda_{rk} = \lambda_{22} = \frac{7}{2}$$

$$\frac{\lambda_{ik}}{\lambda_{rk}} = \frac{\lambda_{32}}{\lambda_{22}} = 1 \div \frac{7}{2} = \frac{2}{7}$$

The second iteration will be

PIVOT ROW $\quad (0 \quad \tfrac{7}{2} \quad \tfrac{3}{2} \quad -\tfrac{1}{2} \quad 1 \quad 0) \div \tfrac{7}{2} = (0 \quad 1 \quad \tfrac{3}{7} \quad -\tfrac{1}{7} \quad \tfrac{2}{7} \quad 0)$

OTHER ROWS $\quad (1 \quad -\tfrac{3}{2} \quad -\tfrac{1}{2} \quad \tfrac{1}{2} \quad 0 \quad 0)$

$\qquad\qquad\qquad -(-\tfrac{3}{7})(0 \quad \tfrac{7}{2} \quad \tfrac{3}{2} \quad -\tfrac{1}{2} \quad 1 \quad 0)$

ROW 1 $\qquad\quad (1 \quad 0 \quad \tfrac{1}{7} \quad \tfrac{2}{7} \quad \tfrac{3}{7} \quad 0)$

$\qquad\qquad\qquad\qquad (0 \quad 1 \quad 3 \quad 0 \quad 0 \quad 1)$

$\qquad\qquad\qquad -\tfrac{2}{7}(0 \quad \tfrac{7}{2} \quad \tfrac{3}{2} \quad -\tfrac{1}{2} \quad 1 \quad 0)$

ROW 3 $\qquad\quad (0 \quad 0 \quad \tfrac{18}{7} \quad \tfrac{1}{7} \quad -\tfrac{2}{7} \quad 1)$

Results

$$
\begin{bmatrix}
1 & 0 & \tfrac{1}{7} & \vdots & \tfrac{2}{7} & \tfrac{3}{7} & 0 \\
0 & 1 & \tfrac{3}{7} & \vdots & -\tfrac{1}{7} & \tfrac{2}{7} & 0 \\
0 & 0 & \boxed{\tfrac{18}{7}} & \vdots & \tfrac{1}{7} & -\tfrac{2}{7} & 1
\end{bmatrix}
$$

$$\frac{\lambda_{ik}}{\lambda_{rk}} = \frac{\lambda_{13}}{\lambda_{33}} = \frac{1}{7} \div \frac{18}{7} = \frac{1}{18}$$

$$\frac{\lambda_{ik}}{\lambda_{rk}} = \frac{\lambda_{23}}{\lambda_{33}} = \frac{3}{7} \div \frac{18}{7} = \frac{1}{6}$$

$$\rightarrow \lambda_{rk} = \lambda_{33} = \frac{18}{7}$$

The last iteration will be

PIVOT ROW $\quad (0 \quad 0 \quad \tfrac{18}{7} \quad \tfrac{1}{7} \quad -\tfrac{2}{7} \quad 1) \div \tfrac{18}{7} = (0 \quad 0 \quad 1 \quad \tfrac{1}{18} \quad -\tfrac{1}{9} \quad \tfrac{7}{18})$

OTHER ROWS $\quad (1 \quad 0 \quad \tfrac{1}{7} \quad \tfrac{2}{7} \quad \tfrac{3}{7} \quad 0)$

$\qquad\qquad\qquad -\tfrac{1}{18}(0 \quad 0 \quad \tfrac{18}{7} \quad \tfrac{1}{7} \quad -\tfrac{2}{7} \quad 1)$

ROW 1 $\qquad\quad (1 \quad 0 \quad 0 \quad \tfrac{5}{18} \quad \tfrac{4}{9} \quad -\tfrac{1}{18})$

$\qquad\qquad\qquad\qquad (0 \quad 1 \quad \tfrac{3}{7} \quad -\tfrac{1}{7} \quad \tfrac{2}{7} \quad 0)$

$\qquad\qquad\qquad -\tfrac{1}{6}(0 \quad 0 \quad \tfrac{18}{7} \quad \tfrac{1}{7} \quad -\tfrac{2}{7} \quad 1)$

ROW 2 $\qquad\quad (0 \quad 1 \quad 0 \quad -\tfrac{1}{6} \quad \tfrac{1}{3} \quad -\tfrac{1}{6})$

Results

$$
\begin{array}{ccc}
\quad I & & A^{-1}
\end{array}
$$

$$
\begin{bmatrix}
1 & 0 & 0 & \vdots & \tfrac{5}{18} & \tfrac{4}{9} & -\tfrac{1}{18} \\
0 & 1 & 0 & \vdots & -\tfrac{1}{6} & \tfrac{1}{3} & -\tfrac{1}{6} \\
0 & 0 & 1 & \vdots & \tfrac{1}{18} & -\tfrac{1}{9} & \tfrac{7}{18}
\end{bmatrix}
$$

Proof

$$
\begin{array}{ccc}
A & A^{-1} & I
\end{array}
$$

$$
\begin{bmatrix} 2 & -3 & -1 \\ 1 & 2 & 1 \\ 0 & 1 & 3 \end{bmatrix}
\begin{bmatrix} \frac{5}{18} & \frac{4}{9} & -\frac{1}{18} \\ -\frac{1}{6} & \frac{1}{3} & -\frac{1}{6} \\ \frac{1}{18} & -\frac{1}{9} & \frac{7}{18} \end{bmatrix}
=
\begin{bmatrix} 1 & 0 & 0 \\ 0 & 1 & 0 \\ 0 & 0 & 1 \end{bmatrix}
$$

A Simplified Method for Inverting a 2×2 Matrix

A simplified method is available in the special case where a 2×2 matrix is to be inverted. It is set forth in the solution of the following example.

EXAMPLE

Original system of equations:

$$4x_1 + x_2 = 17$$
$$3x_1 + 2x_2 = 19$$

Restating the system of equations in matrices yields

$$
\begin{array}{ccc}
A & x & b
\end{array}
$$

$$
\begin{bmatrix} 4 & 1 \\ 3 & 2 \end{bmatrix}
\begin{bmatrix} x_1 \\ x_2 \end{bmatrix}
=
\begin{bmatrix} 17 \\ 19 \end{bmatrix}
$$

NOTE It is wise to check the restated setup by mentally performing the matrix multiplication $Ax = b$ to see that the original system is obtained.

The basic procedure for solving the equation remains the same as described previously:

$$
\begin{aligned}
A\,x &= b \\
A^{-1}A\,x &= A^{-1}b \\
I\quad x &= A^{-1}b \\
x &= A^{-1}b
\end{aligned}
$$

Because A is a 2×2 matrix, we may form A^{-1} by interchanging the main diagonal elements of A, changing the signs of the cross-diagonal elements, and dividing the resulting elements by the determinant of the matrix, that is, the product of the main diagonal elements minus the product of the cross-diagonal elements (in our example, $4(2) - 3(1) = 5$). The solution to this example is

$$
\begin{array}{cccc}
x & A^{-1} & b & x
\end{array}
$$

$$
\begin{bmatrix} x_1 \\ x_2 \end{bmatrix}
=
\begin{bmatrix} \frac{2}{5} & -\frac{1}{5} \\ -\frac{3}{5} & \frac{4}{5} \end{bmatrix}
\qquad
\begin{bmatrix} 17 \\ 19 \end{bmatrix}
=
\begin{bmatrix} 3 \\ 5 \end{bmatrix}
$$

Therefore, $x_1 = 3$ and $x_2 = 5$.

We now return to the subject of bases and ask two questions:

1. When is a set of vectors not a basis?
2. Is there only one basis for each vector space, or, in other words, is a basis unique?

Let us illustrate our answers to the above questions with the following vectors:

$$
\begin{array}{ccccc}
x_1 & x_2 & x_3 & x_4 & x_5 \\
\begin{bmatrix} 6 \\ 0 \\ 0 \end{bmatrix} & \begin{bmatrix} 0 \\ 4 \\ 0 \end{bmatrix} & \begin{bmatrix} 0 \\ 0 \\ 14 \end{bmatrix} & \begin{bmatrix} 0 \\ 0 \\ 2 \end{bmatrix} & \begin{bmatrix} 1 \\ 1 \\ 1 \end{bmatrix}
\end{array}
$$

One has a basis for a space (3-space in this example) when a set of n ($n = 3$ in our example) vectors from n-space is linearly independent. Another way of saying this is that a matrix composed of the n linearly independent vectors is nonsingular; that is, the matrix has a nonzero determinant. For computational purposes, this all reduces to saying that a basis matrix has an inverse, or conversely, if a matrix does not have an inverse, its vectors do not constitute a basis.

To illustrate a set of vectors that is not a basis, you could choose vectors x_1, x_3, and x_4:

$$
\begin{bmatrix}
6 & 0 & 0 \\
0 & 0 & 0 \\
0 & 14 & 2
\end{bmatrix}
$$

This matrix does not have an inverse; hence, the vectors are linearly dependent ($x_3 = 7x_4$) and do not form a basis for 3-space.

To illustrate the fact that a basis is not unique, note that different bases result from the combinations $B_1 = (x_1, x_2, x_3)$ and $B_2 = (x_1, x_2, x_5)$:

$$
\begin{array}{cc}
B_1 & B_1^{-1} \\
\begin{bmatrix}
6 & 0 & 0 \\
0 & 4 & 0 \\
0 & 0 & 14
\end{bmatrix}
\rightarrow
\begin{bmatrix}
\frac{1}{6} & 0 & 0 \\
0 & \frac{1}{4} & 0 \\
0 & 0 & \frac{1}{14}
\end{bmatrix}
\end{array}
$$

$$
\begin{array}{cc}
B_2 & B_2^{-1}
\end{array}
$$

$$
\begin{bmatrix} 6 & 0 & 1 \\ 0 & 4 & 1 \\ 0 & 0 & 1 \end{bmatrix} \rightarrow
\begin{bmatrix} \frac{1}{6} & 0 & -\frac{1}{6} \\ 0 & \frac{1}{4} & -\frac{1}{4} \\ 0 & 0 & 1 \end{bmatrix}
$$

Because both matrices B_1 and B_2 have inverses, we have shown that a given vector space has more than one basis. This fact is important in the theory of linear programing.

Problems

Matrix multiplication

1. Find AB given

$$
\begin{array}{cc}
A & B
\end{array}
$$

$$
\begin{bmatrix} 0 & 3 \\ -1 & 2 \\ 2 & 1 \end{bmatrix} \quad \begin{bmatrix} 1 & 2 & 3 & -2 \\ 0 & 1 & 2 & 3 \end{bmatrix}
$$

Matrix inversion and multiplication

2. Solve for x and y using matrices:

$$
\begin{aligned}
3x - y &= 6 \\
-2x + 3y &= 10
\end{aligned}
$$

Transposing

3. Show that $(AB)^T = B^T A^T$, given

$$
\begin{array}{cc}
A & B
\end{array}
$$

$$
\begin{bmatrix} 3 & -1 \\ 2 & 4 \end{bmatrix} \quad \begin{bmatrix} 6 & 1 & 2 & 2 \\ 3 & 0 & -1 & 5 \end{bmatrix}
$$

Vector addition

4. $\begin{bmatrix} 3 \\ 0 \\ -1 \end{bmatrix} + \begin{bmatrix} 2 \\ 5 \\ 1 \end{bmatrix} = ?$

Linear combinations and matrix inversion

5. In the section on bases, an example listed the basis vectors as $(6, 0, 0)$, $(0, 4, 0)$, and $(0, 0, 14)$ and then gave the set of scalars that could be used to express the vector $(3, 4, 2)$ as a linear combination of these basis vectors. Use matrix inversion to determine the appropriate set of scalars.

Chapter 6: Matrix Algebra

Let the unknown scalars be designated x_i, and solve the equation below:

Hint

$$
\begin{array}{ccc}
A & x & b
\end{array}
$$

$$
\begin{bmatrix} 6 & 0 & 0 \\ 0 & 4 & 0 \\ 0 & 0 & 14 \end{bmatrix}
\begin{bmatrix} x_1 \\ x_2 \\ x_3 \end{bmatrix} =
\begin{bmatrix} 3 \\ 4 \\ 2 \end{bmatrix}
$$

6. Given that the basis vectors are

Linear combinations and matrix inversion

$$
\begin{bmatrix} 6 \\ 4 \end{bmatrix} \quad \text{and} \quad \begin{bmatrix} 2 \\ 1 \end{bmatrix}
$$

express the vector

$$
\begin{bmatrix} 5 \\ 2 \end{bmatrix}
$$

as a linear combination of the basis vectors.

Answer: The appropriate scalars are $-\tfrac{1}{2}$ and 4.

7. Use the following matrix formula and the given data to compute a multiple regression line.

Matrix multiplication, transposing, and inversion

$$
B = (X^T X)^{-1} X^T Y
$$

x_1	x_2	y
1	2	57
3	5	69
0	3	56
2	2	60

A requirement of the formulation of matrix X is the insertion of a column of ones to provide for the calculation of a constant term in the regression equation—should such a term exist.

Note

Answer:

$$
\begin{array}{ccc}
X^T & X & X^T X
\end{array}
$$

$$
\begin{bmatrix} 1 & 1 & 1 & 1 \\ 1 & 3 & 0 & 2 \\ 2 & 5 & 3 & 2 \end{bmatrix}
\begin{bmatrix} 1 & 1 & 2 \\ 1 & 3 & 5 \\ 1 & 0 & 3 \\ 1 & 2 & 2 \end{bmatrix} =
\begin{bmatrix} 4 & 6 & 12 \\ 6 & 14 & 21 \\ 12 & 21 & 42 \end{bmatrix}
$$

$$
\begin{array}{ccccc}
B & = & (X^T X)^{-1} & X^T & Y
\end{array}
$$

$$
\begin{bmatrix} 50 \\ 3 \\ 2 \end{bmatrix} =
\begin{bmatrix} \tfrac{7}{4} & 0 & -\tfrac{1}{2} \\ 0 & \tfrac{2}{7} & -\tfrac{1}{7} \\ -\tfrac{1}{2} & -\tfrac{1}{7} & -\tfrac{5}{21} \end{bmatrix}
\begin{bmatrix} 1 & 1 & 1 & 1 \\ 1 & 3 & 0 & 2 \\ 2 & 5 & 3 & 2 \end{bmatrix}
\begin{bmatrix} 57 \\ 69 \\ 56 \\ 60 \end{bmatrix}
$$

The equation is, therefore,

$y = 50 + 3x_1 + 2x_2$

The matrix formulation of multiple regression analysis provides a valid approach for any number of variables; hence, the one matrix formula replaces many other sets of formulas. The set of formulas that would ordinarily be employed for the above is

$$\sum y = aN + b \sum x_1 + c \sum x_2$$

$$\sum x_1 y = a \sum x_1 + b \sum x_1^2 + c \sum x_1 x_2$$

$$\sum x_2 y = a \sum x_2 + b \sum x_1 x_2 + c \sum x_2^2$$

Multiple regression and overhead cost prediction

8. A company wishes to determine the behavior of certain of its overhead costs. These costs are thought to be dependent on volume of production and extent of supervision. From the historical data below, you are to use matrices to fit a multiple regression equation. You must then determine what costs should be when volume is expected to be 5,000 direct labor hours with four supervisors in attendance.

$x_1 = $ *thousands* of direct labor hours for the month

$x_2 = $ number of supervisors employed

$y = $ total monthly costs

x_1	x_2	y
2	2	42,526
1	1	23,026
3	2	57,526
4	3	77,026

7

Matrix Algebra and Accounting

Data processing in such areas of accounting as allocation of primary and secondary overhead costs, job order and process costing, preparing consolidated financial statements, distributing partnership profits, preparing dissolution statements, budgeting, and analyzing the flow of funds is approached as if each area were substantially unrelated to the next except for the involvement of value in one form or another. Because all these areas process financial data (henceforth referred to as inputs), this chapter is devoted to examining the fundamental logical structure of these accounting data-processing procedures.

The logical structure of accounting data-processing procedures evolves from treating problems attendant to the acquiring, valuing, and allocating of input data. Initially, the acquisition phase involves both identifying data on service inputs and deciding which should be considered separately and which should be considered together (i.e., aggregated). Next, these data on inputs must be assigned values according to the rules of the particular accounting area. Finally, the valued inputs must be allocated to the output classifications of each area. But what are these outputs? And what criteria govern the allocating processes? Is the allocation direct to outputs, or should intermediate stages be recognized? Are measurement problems encountered in the flow of data? Must each phase of the acquisition, valuation, and allocation processes be considered distinct from the others, or can all parts be integrated into some over-all system? These are some of the logical issues this chapter addresses. In the course of discussion, other logical problems will be introduced; most of these problems will be resolved within the theoretical framework of vector spaces.

This chapter is divided into two sections. In the first section, matrix algebra is applied to several accounting areas; in the second section, analogies are drawn between matrix algebra and the logical structure of accounting processes.

Selected Accounting Applications of Matrix Algebra

Let us examine how matrix algebra may be applied to several familiar accounting problems. We shall begin with a very straightforward problem.

Depreciation Schedules Exhibit 1 contains an accounting problem that requires an ordinary transformation matrix. Here it is necessary to prepare a depreciation lapse schedule, and the elements in the transformation vector measure rates of usage (depreciation) for each time period. Input space has been represented by unit vectors, but the residual values of each asset have been subtracted from each unit vector to leave the depreciation base values. This type of logical problem arises frequently in accounting. It may be referred to as a branching problem, because it involves the segregation of input data into two or more groups, each of which requires different transformation (or no transformation, as in the residual book values in the depreciation illustration). Here the branching is treated by taking from 100% (represented by the unit vectors in the identity matrix) the residual 20% (represented by a scalar multiplication of the identity matrix). Alternatively, the branching problem can be treated without involving matrices by separating residual values and depreciable bases.

EXHIBIT 1

Accounting Problem Employing an Ordinary Transformation Matrix

Accounting area:	Depreciation lapse schedule preparation.
Input data:	Three machines acquired at costs of $75,000, $37,500, $112,500, respectively.
Transformation data:	Usage (depreciation) is to be measured by the sum-of-the-years'-digits method using economic life of 3 years and 20% residual value.

Output data: Usage is to be allocated to yearly time periods.

Input Space Transformation Matrix **Output Space**
(lapse schedule)

$(I - 20\%_o I)$ $\quad\quad \lambda \quad\quad\quad r \quad = \quad\quad\quad\quad 0$

$$\begin{bmatrix} 0.8 & 0 & 0 \\ 0 & 0.8 & 0 \\ 0 & 0 & 0.8 \end{bmatrix} \begin{bmatrix} 75,000 \\ 37,500 \\ 112,500 \end{bmatrix} [\tfrac{1}{2} \ \tfrac{1}{3} \ \tfrac{1}{6}] =$$

	Year 1	Year 2	Year 3
	30,000	20,000	10,000
	15,000	10,000	5,000
	45,000	30,000	15,000
Total Depreciation	90,000	60,000	30,000

I = identity matrix (an ordered collection of unit vectors) **KEY**
λ = vector containing cost of asset i, where $i = 1, 2, 3$
r = rate vector containing elements r_j, which show the rate of depreciation for period j, where $j = 1, 2, 3$. Usage rates were determined according to the sum-of-the-years'-digits depreciation method.
O = output matrix containing elements o_{ij}, which show the depreciation charge for asset i in period j

Then, the depreciable bases [i.e., $(I - 20\%_o I)\lambda$] are entered directly into a vector, thereby reducing the transformation to

$$\begin{bmatrix} 60,000 \\ 30,000 \\ 90,000 \end{bmatrix} [\tfrac{1}{2} \ \tfrac{1}{3} \ \tfrac{1}{6}] = \begin{bmatrix} 30,000 & 20,000 & 10,000 \\ 15,000 & 10,000 & 5,000 \\ 45,000 & 30,000 & 15,000 \end{bmatrix}$$

This is the same result as shown in Exhibit 1.

Exhibit 2 shows a transformation requiring the use of an inverse matrix. Here **Computing**
the elements a_{ij} in matrix A show the interest of expense i in expense j, where **Bonuses**
$i, j = B$ (loans), F (franchise tax), and T (federal income tax). The interests are determined in accord with given statutory-contractual rates.

EXHIBIT 2

Accounting Problem Requiring
an Inverse Transformation Matrix

KEY

B = executives' bonus
F = franchise tax
T = federal tax on income
$100,000 = profits before B, F, and T

Original system of equations:

$$B = 0.1(\$100,000 - F - T)$$
$$F = 0.05(\$100,000 - B)$$
$$T = 0.50(\$100,000 - B - F)$$

Rearranged system:

$$10,000 = B + 0.1F + 0.1T$$
$$5,000 = 0.05B + F + 0T$$
$$50,000 = 0.5B + 0.5F + T$$

Restated system:

$$
\begin{matrix} g \end{matrix} \qquad \begin{matrix} A \end{matrix} \qquad \begin{matrix} x \end{matrix}
$$

$$
\begin{bmatrix} 10,000 \\ 5,000 \\ 50,000 \end{bmatrix} = \begin{bmatrix} 1 & 0.1 & 0.1 \\ 0.05 & 1 & 0 \\ 0.5 & 0.5 & 1 \end{bmatrix} \begin{bmatrix} B \\ F \\ T \end{bmatrix}
$$

KEY g = vector of constants in the rearranged system
A = matrix of coefficients of the rearranged system
x = solution vector

Solution **Input Space**   **Transformation Matrix**   **Output Space**

$$
\begin{matrix} x \end{matrix} \qquad\qquad \begin{matrix} A^{-1} \end{matrix} \qquad\qquad\qquad \begin{matrix} g \end{matrix}
$$

$$
\begin{bmatrix} B \\ F \\ T \end{bmatrix} = \begin{bmatrix} 1.05541 & -0.05277 & -0.10554 \\ -0.05277 & 1.00263 & 0.00528 \\ -0.50132 & -0.47493 & 1.05013 \end{bmatrix} \begin{bmatrix} 10,000 \\ 5,000 \\ 50,000 \end{bmatrix} = \begin{bmatrix} 5,013 \\ 4,749 \\ 45,119 \end{bmatrix}
$$

Preparing the Statement of Affairs

When a business terminates, it is customary to prepare a special financial report called the statement of affairs. The following basic questions underlie the preparation of the statement of affairs:

1. What assets are owned by the business?
2. What will these assets bring on the market either collectively or individually?
3. Who are the claimants to these assets?
4. How much is each claimant entitled to?
5. Which claimant should be satisfied first?

The ledgers of the business do not generally show all the assets and their realizable values. Some assets are immediately charged to the expenses of the period, rather than being capitalized; such assets are frequently referred to as "secret reserves." Goodwill is an intangible asset similar to secret reserves. If the goodwill or secret reserves have realizable value, then they must be reinstated on the ledgers. Likewise, if any assets on the ledgers have realizable values different from their ledger values, the ledger values must be changed.

Certain claimants of the business have priority over others; that is, their claims must be settled first. Employees' back wages (to a certain limit) and unpaid government taxes are examples of liabilities with priority status. Other liabilities are fully secured; for example, a mortgage payable may be secured by the pledging of specific property with a greater value than the amount of the indebtedness. Some liabilities, such as notes payable, are partially secured. In this case, the assets pledged have less value than the amount of the indebtedness. Then there are the unsecured creditors (represented by the accounts payable of the business) who have not had any specific assets (other than the good name of the business) pledged to them. Finally, the owners receive the residue of the assets not used to satisfy liabilities.

Exhibit 3 presents data for an illustrative problem. Existing ledger values, realizable values, and contractual arrangements are included among these data. The matrix formulation of the problem is shown in Exhibit 4. The statement of affairs (matrix S) is generated by $AP = S$, where A is a diagonalized matrix containing the realizable values of the various assets (regrouped according to their status as free assets, assets pledged in full security, and assets pledged in partial security), and P is a matrix showing the proportionate interests of each type of claimant in each asset category.

EXHIBIT 3

Data for Statement of Affairs

Cash	$ 300	Accounts payable	$23,000	*Balance*
Accounts receivable	9,000	Accrued wages	600	*Sheet*
Inventory	18,700	Notes payable	5,000	
Bonds of X Company	3,000	Mortgage payable	15,000	
Land and buildings (net)	25,000	Capital stock	12,000	
		Retained earnings	400	
	$56,000		$56,000	

Additional data:

1. $1,000 of the accounts receivable is considered doubtful of being collected beyond a $600 figure.

2. It is thought that the inventory can be sold at a $500 profit.

3. The bonds of X Company have a market value of $3,200. The bonds have been pledged as security for the notes payable.

4. A buyer has offered $26,500 for the land and buildings. The land and buildings are collateral for the mortgage payable.

EXHIBIT 4

Matrix Approach to the Statement of Affairs

$$
\underset{A}{\begin{bmatrix} \text{Pledged—} & \text{Pledged—} & \\ \text{Full} & \text{Partial} & \text{Free} \\ \text{Security} & \text{Security} & \text{Assets} \\ 15{,}000 & & \\ & 3{,}200 & \\ & & 39{,}600 \end{bmatrix}}
\underset{P}{\begin{bmatrix} \text{Priority} & \text{Fully} & \text{Partially} & \text{Unsecured} & \text{Owners} \\ & \text{Secured} & \text{Secured} & & \\ 0 & 1 & 0 & 0 & 0 \\ 0 & 0 & 1 & 0 & 0 \\ \frac{6}{396} & 0 & \frac{18}{396} & \frac{230}{396} & \frac{142}{396} \end{bmatrix}}
= \underset{S}{\begin{matrix} \text{Statement} \\ \text{of affairs} \end{matrix}}
$$

S

Assets:	Liabilities Having Priority	Fully Secured Liabilities	Partially Secured Liabilities	Unsecured Liabilities	Owners	Totals
Pledged in full security (Land)	$ 0	$15,000	$ 0	$ 0	$ 0	$15,000
Pledged in partial security (Bonds owned)	0	0	3,200	0	0	3,200
Free (see note)	600	0	1,800	23,000	14,200	39,600
	$600	$15,000	$5,000	$23,000	$14,200	$57,800

NOTE

Free assets include

Cash	$ 300
Accounts receivable	8,600
Merchandise	19,200
Land and buildings ($26,500 − $15,000)	11,500
	$39,600

To determine the proportionate interests of each claimant in each asset, it is first necessary to calculate the residual interest of the owners. This is customarily formalized into a supplemental report known as the Deficiency Account. A deficiency account takes the owners' equity figures before the ledger is corrected to reflect realizable values, adds anticipated gains on realization, and subtracts anticipated losses to arrive at the amount that the owners are expected to receive in liquidation. In other words, the deficiency account reconciles the before- and after-dissolution owners' equity figures. In our example, the reconciliation appears as follows:

Owners' equity per books	$12,400	***Deficiency Account***
Gains on realization:		
Land and buildings	1,500	
Bonds of *X* Company	200	
Merchandise	500	
	$14,600	
Loss on realization:		
Accounts receivable	400	
Amount payable to owners in liquidation	$14,200	

In general, the next step in calculating proportionate interests is to decide whether there are sufficient assets beyond those that are pledged as collateral to permit the payment in full of the liabilities with priority. If the assets are sufficient, as in our example, the value of the pledged assets is deducted from the total assets to obtain the denominator of the proportions for free assets. The numerator for each claimant is the net amount due the claimant after the pledged assets are distributed. To illustrate these calculations, refer to Exhibit 4 and observe the following:

1. All of the bonds owned are distributed to partially secured creditors by inserting a 1 in matrix P in row 2 column 3 and zeros in all the other columns of row 2.

2. The fully secured creditors receive their entire claim ($15,000) by inserting a 1 in row 1 column 2 of matrix P.

3. The denominator of the proportionate interests in row 3 of matrix P equals total realizable value ($57,800) minus assets pledged ($3,200 + $15,000), or $39,600; the numerators are the amounts of the claims not satisfied by distributing pledged assets (i.e., Priority = $600; Fully Secured = $15,000 − $15,000 = 0; Partially Secured = $5,000 − $3,200 = $1,800; Unsecured = $23,000; Owners = $14,200).

In our formulation of the dissolution statement, we have not distributed certain accounts receivable or certain items of inventory to each claimant. Although such distribution would be possible, it is nevertheless customary to liquidate the assets first and then to distribute cash.

Matrix *S* points up the allocation of inputs (assets) to outputs (claimants). By totaling columns, the amounts due each claimant are clearly shown; by totaling rows, the expected realizable values for the assets are clearly shown. The traditional format of the statement of affairs, which is presented in Exhibit 5, does not emphasize the input-output allocation, nor does it show clearly how much each claimant receives; that is, the information is there in the statement but you have to be careful to find it. This is because of the offsetting, which takes place with pledged assets.

EXHIBIT 5

Conventional Statement of Affairs

Book Value				Expected to Realize
	ASSETS PLEDGED WITH FULLY SECURED CREDITORS			
$25,000	*Land and buildings:*			
	Estimated value		$26,500	
	Less mortgage payments—contra		15,000	$11,500
	ASSETS PLEDGED WITH PARTIALLY SECURED CREDITORS			
3,000	*Bonds of X Company—deducted contra*			
	Estimated value		$ 3,200	
	FREE ASSETS			
300	*Cash*			300
9,000	*Accounts receivable:*			
	$8,000	Good		8,000
	$1,000	Doubtful		600
	$9,000			
18,700	*Merchandise*			19,200
	TOTAL FREE ASSETS			$39,600
	DEDUCT LIABILITIES HAVING PRIORITY— PER CONTRA			600
$56,000				$39,000

Book Value				Expected to Rank
	LIABILITIES HAVING PRIORITY			
$ 600	*Accrued wages—deducted contra*			
	FULLY SECURED LIABILITIES			
15,000	*Mortgage payable—deducted contra*			
	PARTIALLY SECURED LIABILITIES			
5,000	*Notes payable*		$5,000	
	Less bonds of X Company		3,200	$1,800

	UNSECURED LIABILITIES		
$23,000	*Accounts payable*		$23,000
	NET WORTH PER BOOKS		
12,000	*Capital stock*		
400	*Retained earnings*		
	TOTAL UNSECURED LIABILITIES		$24,800
	EXCESS OF NET FREE ASSETS OVER UNSECURED		
	LIABILITIES		14,200
$56,000			$39,000

Process cost accounting consists of many complicated procedures, which can become most confusing. The concept of what must be done is straightforward enough: A variety of cost inputs needs to be assigned to the products manufactured, and a report summarizing the flows must be prepared. Fortunately, matrices provide a means of making the procedures as straightforward as the concept. Because this chapter is centered on matrix algebra and not on cost accounting, our discussions will be restricted to process costing for a single product under the average costing assumption.

Preparing the Cost Report

In a process costing problem, products pass from one functional department to the next. For instance, a metal product of some sort may be begun in a cutting department and may go from there to a grinding department and from there to an assembling department. The inputs involved are goods-received-from-the-preceding-department, departmental direct materials, departmental direct labor, and departmental applied overhead. Actually, only three inputs are necessary, materials, labor, and overhead, but it facilitates tracing the flow of costs to include a fourth input (goods-from-preceding-department), which is an aggregation of the first three.

The flow of production is traced in terms of a quantity measure known as equivalent production. Equivalent production is what it says—an equivalent of production. Thus, if 6,000 units were in process and were two-thirds complete, we would speak of them as 4,000 equivalent units. The assumption in mind is that if we had worked on only 4,000 units instead of the 6,000, we would have completed all 4,000 units. It is important to note that there are several designations for equivalent production. We may have equivalent production of preceding-departmental-goods (or materials), equivalent production of (departmental) materials, and equivalent production of (departmental) conversion.[1] This is because a given unit of product may be in different stages of completion as far as each of its component input costs is

---

[1] Departmental conversion costs consist of direct labor and applied overhead. Since overhead costs are frequently applied on the basis of direct labor hours, direct labor costs and applied overhead costs are frequently functions of the same variable (direct labor hours) and may be considered together for product costing purposes.

concerned. We may, for instance, add all the materials at the start of processing and at midprocess say that the products are complete as to material costs but only half complete as to conversion costs.

This brings the discussion to the output designations of process costing. Three things can happen to each unit in process:

1. The unit may be completed (transferred).

2. The unit may still be in process.

3. The unit may be lost or spoiled at various stages of processing.

Exhibit 6 presents both the matrices used to compute equivalent production for a single product under the average costing method and the matrices used to allocate costs to the transferred, ending inventory, and lost destinations. The equivalent production matrix A and vector b have been partitioned into submatrices in such a way that the indicated multiplications of the submatrices provide vectors showing the respective equivalent units found in each of the three destinations for each of the three types of input equivalent productions. The three separate vectors containing equivalent unit data then reappear in matrix D. The totals for each type of equivalent production, that is, E_P, E_M, and E_C, are used in the calculation of the unit costs U_i, which appear in matrix U. Finally, the multiplication UD produces the required cost report R. An example will be presented shortly to illustrate these calculations, but first let us investigate matrix A more closely.

EXHIBIT 6

Process Cost Matrices: Average Method, Single Product

Equivalent production computation:

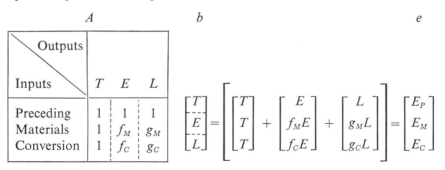

Unit cost formula:

$$U_i = \sum_{j=1}^{2} I_j \div E_i$$

Cost allocation:

$$
\begin{array}{c}
U \\
\begin{bmatrix}
U_P & 0 & 0 \\
0 & U_M & 0 \\
0 & 0 & U_C
\end{bmatrix}
\end{array}
\begin{array}{c}
D \\
\begin{bmatrix}
T & E & L \\
T & f_M E & g_M L \\
T & f_C E & g_C L
\end{bmatrix}
\end{array}
=
\begin{array}{c}
R\ (\text{cost report}) \\
\begin{bmatrix}
U_P T & U_P E & U_P L \\
U_M T & U_M f_M E & U_M g_M L \\
U_C T & U_C f_C E & U_C g_C L
\end{bmatrix}
\end{array}
$$

KEY

A = matrix containing proportions of each output quantity appearing in each input category. Note that the rows (labeled) show the input categories, while the columns show the output designations.

b = a vector showing the total quantities in each of the three output designations (T, E, L)

e = a vector that shows the equivalent production (E_i) for each type of input

T = units transferred

E = units in ending inventory

L = units lost

f_i = fraction of ending inventory completed in terms of input i

g_i = fraction of lost units completed in terms of input i

U_i = unit cost of input i; $i = P$ (preceding department's transferred production costs), M (direct materials), C (conversion costs)

I_j = total cost of input I ($I = P, M, C$, as defined above under index i) appearing in opening inventory ($j = 1$) or in the costs incurred during the present period ($j = 2$)

E_i = equivalent production of i

D = matrix composed of the equivalent production vectors

A technical note on the multiplication Ab will improve understanding. The partitioning of matrices must be done in such a way that multiplication of the submatrices is still defined. Wherever the partitions (dotted lines) are drawn, the multiplication of column and row elements and the summing of individual products must be halted and the results entered in separate matrices (as mentioned in Chapter 6) (vectors in Exhibit 6). These separate matrices may then be added to obtain the product matrix (vector) that would have been obtained had the partitioning been ignored. In the matrix approach to process costing, both the individual vectors and the total vector e are needed. The elements of the total vector e are used in calculating unit costs for each type of input, whereas the individual vectors, which show the equivalent production of each type of input in each output designation, are entered "as is" in matrix D.

If there were more than a single type of direct material or direct labor involved, matrix A would be enlarged to include a separate row for each type. Note also that the matrix formulation circumvents another of the annoying little problems that usually arise in process costing. Where units added by a department increase (decrease) the total number of units being worked on (reference here is to the familiar "units gained" discussed at length in most accounting texts), it is customary to convert the units received from the previous department into the unit of measure of the present department (assuming the units of measure of the two departments differ) and to re-compute the unit costs of the goods received by adjusting for the new total units being processed. By concentrating solely on the units in the output designations (vector b), the conversion is automatically provided for.[2]

Let us turn our attention now to the subject of lost units. Lost units raise many perplexing issues, some of which are susceptible to several interpreta-tions, depending on one's viewpoint. The discussions ahead will imply that lost units are those damaged or spoiled in some way; however, the word "lost" may be used in a more generic sense to include any production, be it joint products, byproducts, or scrap, no longer considered part of the main product of interest. Some of the arguments to be presented could easily be adapted to this generic conception of "lost."

Logical issues involved in lost units merit careful consideration in planning for control. What extent of loss is normal for the type of processing? How should the accountant recognize the lost units? How will whatever the ac-countant does abet control? In some processes, a certain amount of loss or spoilage or shrinkage is unavoidable and normal; what is of concern is preventing loss from becoming excessive or abnormal. When excessive loss does occur, the accountant's role is to call attention to it. By doing so, upper management becomes informed and can take steps to see that the problem is corrected.

The accountant may provide for normal spoilage by including an estimate of the cost involved when computing overhead rates. If provision is made in this manner, normal spoilage cost is distributed to all production, even though in a particular lot, less than normal spoilage has occurred. The abnormal spoilage, whether positive or negative, is the difference between the actual and normal spoilage. The cost accountant customarily shows the amount of abnormal spoilage as an expense of the income period, thereby calling upper management's attention to the matter. To avoid including in good units a double charge for lost units (once for actual and once by way of overhead rate), the accountant must charge the normal loss to an overhead expense account. As an inferior alternative to providing for spoilage in over-head rates, the accountant may segregate such costs as they occur.

For purposes of discussion, let us assume both that no provision for lost unit costs is reflected in the overhead rate, and that all units lost are normally

---

[2] Most cost accounting problems confuse the reader by presenting input quantities in terms of the preceding department's unit of measure, as well as output data for the present department regarding units transferred, in ending inventory, and lost. The input data is redundant when one has the output data to work with.

lost. Then, unless management decides (erroneously, from a theoretical standpoint) to treat all lost unit costs as expenses of the income period, these costs require reallocation to good units produced. In the circumstances stipulated, those costs appearing in the third column of matrix R, the cost report, require reallocation to either or both ending inventory or units transferred to the next department. What is needed to guide the reallocation are some criteria that recognize (1) amount of loss and (2) "beneficiaries" of the loss.

The point of loss determines how much the lost units cost. To illustrate, consider a process wherein metal is poured into molds, then the molds are cooled and treated further, and, finally, all molds are subjected to a "torture" test. When the metal is poured, some can be expected to spill; this shrinkage has occurred at the very beginning of processing and involves only material costs. When the molds are cooled and treated further, some can be expected to crack or chip; this spoilage has happened gradually during the process and involves materials and some conversion costs. Finally, when the "torture" tests are performed, more molds can be expected to crack or chip; this spoilage has taken place at the end of the process and similarly involves both material and conversion costs, but, at this point, the conversion costs as well as the material costs are complete.

What causes lost units? When we ask what brings the service input known as lost units into existence, we are dealing with the acquisition rather than the allocation phase of the problem. Other than destructive torture testing, lost units are caused by defective inputs, that is, either defective materials, or defective production received from the preceding department(s), or deficient labor, or defective equipment, or any or all of these in combination. Perhaps the most important point to grasp is that lost units embody expectations; the loss is repetitive and normal, and hence it is another input similar to other overhead services and yet distinct from them in that it embodies, or aggregates, the department's own materials, labor, and overhead. It may help intuitively to conceive of these lost units as offering a "practice" service, which benefits good production.

This brings us to the question of which "good" output benefits from or uses the lost units input. Different viewpoints lead to different interpretations. Theoretically, all units produced after the lost units benefit from the errors and practice that have taken place; hence, there is a good argument for spreading these intangible benefits over the production of ensuing periods. On the other hand, one could adopt the view that the good units preceding the lost units were responsible for the loss. In order for these units to be "good," others had to be "lost." This is the view ordinarily adopted if for no other reason than that it is easier and more practical to work with. Let us see how this viewpoint is implemented.

If loss takes place at the very end of processing, then only the units that have reached that point, that is, transferred units, have benefited. If loss takes place at the very start of processing or while the materials are awaiting processing (as in the case of an evaporation loss), all good units put into production have benefited. If loss takes place during processing, the units that benefit are those that have passed the point of loss. Here it is customary to use an average fraction of completion to determine how many units have passed this point. This is an expedient but inaccurate procedure, because such an average would only coincidently reflect the number of units that had actually passed the critical point.

As an interesting aside, consider the following question. What output has benefited from a loss detected during processing or at the very end of processing that is attributable to either defective materials or to defective production received from a preceding department? The curious observation here is that the point of detection is not the point of loss. These faulty inputs existed before processing began in this department, and the loss (to the point of detection) should be distributed to units transferred and units in ending inventory just as if the lost units were discovered at the very start of processing. It is not customary, however, to ascertain the cause of loss when reallocating, probably because it is not deemed practical to do so.

The equivalent productions determined under the average method, although used in practice, are not suited to measuring and distributing the "benefits" of lost unit costs. Under the average method, the work done last period on ending inventory enters the computation of not only last period's equivalent productions but also this period's by way of being included in the units transferred. Now, this "double counting" is necessary to obtain average unit costs, but it is theoretically wrong as a measure of work done this period. Therefore, to distribute lost unit costs properly, the equivalent productions should be adjusted to an FIFO basis by subtracting from each the equivalent units pertaining to the previous period.

The accepted rules for reallocating lost unit costs are listed below. In view of the "double counting" built into the computation of equivalent production under the average method, the rules should be modified to require the use of FIFO equivalent production figures. It would be easy and inexpensive to make this change.

Stage of loss[3]	*Means of reallocating lost unit costs*
Beginning of processing	Use "good" equivalent production of materials for the first production department in sequence; all subsequent departments should use "good" equivalent production of units-received-from-preceding-department (assuming that the present department puts these

---

[3] It is usually assumed that loss occurs at some one of these three stages, rather than a combination of them. If it were desired to recognize a combination of stages, it would be necessary to determine how much equivalent production was lost at each stage and then to apportion the lost cost for each stage, according to the criterion of reallocation at that stage.

Chapter 7: Matrix Algebra and Accounting

units into processing at the very beginning of its operations). (It should be observed that if units-received-from-preceding-department are mixed with departmental materials at the start of processing, their equivalent productions will be the same.)

During processing — Use "good" equivalent production of conversion.

End of processing — Distribute loss to units transferred.

Exhibit 7 presents a problem illustrating the generalized matrix computations of Exhibit 6 in addition to illustrating the reallocating of lost unit costs. Exhibit 7, however, does not illustrate the suggested use of FIFO basis equivalent production for allocating input costs. It employs instead the average basis equivalent production in keeping with established practice.

For comparison purposes, Exhibit 8 presents a conventional cost report for the problem solved in Exhibit 7. The conventional report is not easily understood, because it obscures the process of allocating inputs to outputs; furthermore, it does not accord the lost unit destination its full status as a data output, because it buries lost unit costs as a unit cost adjustment to the costs of the "good" output designations.

EXHIBIT 7
Problem Data

(m, c, p) = portion of production done during present period for m (materials), c (conversion), and p (preceding department's costs). **KEY**

QUANTITY DATA

Opening inventory $(0, \frac{2}{3}, 0)$		30,000
Transferred in (converted to units of current department)		150,000
Put into process		20,000
	Total	200,000
Transferred out		158,000
Ending inventory $(\frac{3}{4}, \frac{1}{2}, 1)$		40,000
Lost units (lost gradually during processing, $\frac{1}{2}$ complete)		2,000
	Total	200,000

COST DATA

Opening inventory:

Preceding department's costs	$10,000
Departmental material costs	3,780
Departmental conversion costs	5,370

Selected Accounting Applications of Matrix Algebra

171

During period:

Preceding department's costs	$110,000
Departmental material costs	34,020
Departmental conversion costs	48,330
Total	$211,500

NOTE All units lost are "normal" losses; furthermore, no provision for lost units has been made in the overhead rate.

Solution *Equivalent production:*

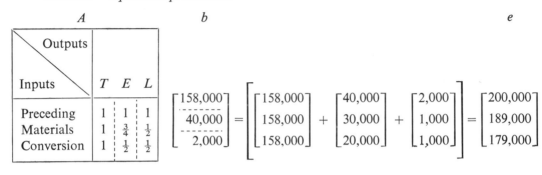

Unit costs:

$u_P = (\$10,000 + \$110,000) \div 200,000 = \$0.60$

$u_M = (\$3,780 + \$34,020) \div 189,000 = \$0.20$

$u_C = (\$5,370 + \$48,330) \div 179,000 = \$0.30$

Cost allocation:

$$
\begin{matrix} U \\ \begin{bmatrix} 0.60 & & \\ & 0.20 & \\ & & 0.30 \end{bmatrix} \end{matrix}
\begin{matrix} D \\ \begin{bmatrix} 158,000 & 40,000 & 2,000 \\ 158,000 & 30,000 & 1,000 \\ 158,000 & 20,000 & 1,000 \end{bmatrix} \end{matrix}
= R \text{ (Cost report)}
$$

R (Cost Report)

Costs	Transferred	Ending Inventory	Lost	Costs to be Accounted for
Preceding department's	$ 94,800	$24,000	$1,200	$120,000
Departmental material	31,600	6,000	200	37,800
Departmental conversion	47,400	6,000	300	53,700
Totals	$173,800	$36,000	$1,700	$211,500
Reallocation	1,498	202	(1,700)	0
Costs accounted for:	$175,298	$36,202	0	$211,500

Reallocation: $1,700\left(\dfrac{148,000}{168,000}; \dfrac{20,000}{168,000}\right) = (1,498; 202)$

("Good" FIFO equivalent production of conversion is 148,000 for T and 20,000 for E. Practice prefers using 158,000 for T and 20,000 for E.)

The totals surrounding matrix R have been obtained merely by adding and cross-adding. The multiplication UD did not produce these totals. Also, UD had nothing to do with reallocation.

NOTE

EXHIBIT 8

Conventional Cost Report

COSTS TO BE ACCOUNTED FOR

Opening inventory:

Preceding department's costs	$ 10,000	$ ——
Departmental material costs	3,780	——
Departmental conversion costs	5,370	——

Costs during period:

Preceding department's costs	110,000	0.600000
Departmental material costs	34,020	0.200000
Departmental conversion costs	48,330	0.300000
Totals	$211,500	$1.100000

Adjustment for lost units (see Note)	——	$0.010119
Totals	$211,500	

COSTS ACCOUNTED FOR

Transferred [158,000($1.10) + 148,000($0.010119)]: $175,298

Ending inventory:

Preceding department's costs [40,000($0.60)]	$24,000	
Departmental material costs [30,000($0.20)]	6,000	
Departmental conversion costs [20,000($0.30)]	6,000	
Adjustment for lost units [20,000($0.010119)]	202	36,202
Totals		$211,500

NOTE
Adjustment for lost units

$$\frac{\text{Lost unit costs}}{\begin{array}{c}\text{"Good" equivalent}\\ \text{production of conversion}\end{array}} = \frac{2,000(\$0.60) + 1,000(\$0.20) + 1,000(\$0.30)}{168,000} = \$0.010119$$

(Once again, practice would favor reallocating using an average (178,000), not an FIFO (168,000) figure.)

In the process of determining overhead rates, the accountant is concerned with, among other matters,

1. the primary (or direct) allocation of itemized overhead costs to various service and production departments, and

2. the secondary allocation of individual service department (or better, service *rendering* department) primary overhead costs to service *consuming* departments (i.e., other service departments and production departments).

The criterion governing secondary allocation is that of usage. How much of a given service will each consuming department use? Here usage is meant in two senses: actual usage and potential usage. Given some measurement indices, such as number of employees, floor area, man hours, and kilowatt hours, actual usage is measured by estimating consuming department responsibility (in terms of a specific index) for increasing rendering department variable costs. Potential usage is measured (again in terms of a specific index) by calculating consuming department responsibility for bringing about the fixed costs of the rendering departments. In either case, consuming department usage may be expressed as a set of percentages, each percentage weighted according to rendering department proportions of fixed and variable costs.

Let us see how matrices may be applied to secondary overhead allocation. Following are the data for an example. It is assumed that the percentages in the table have been determined by observing the usage criterion.

KEY S_i = service department i
P_j = production department j

Consuming department / Rendering department	S_1	S_2	P_1	P_2	P_3
S_1	0	40%	10%	30%	20%
S_2	25%	0	45%	20%	10%

	S_1	S_2	P_1	P_2	P_3
Primary overhead allocation totals (000 omitted)	$90	$180	$377	$307	$246
Standard machine hours (estimated, 000 omitted)			200	50	150

The system of equations requiring solution is

$S_1 = 90 + 0.25S_2$
$S_2 = 180 + 0.40S_1$

The system may be stated in matrices as follows:

$$
\begin{matrix} A & x & b \end{matrix}
$$

$$
\begin{bmatrix} 1 & -0.25 \\ -0.40 & 1 \end{bmatrix} \begin{bmatrix} S_1 \\ S_2 \end{bmatrix} = \begin{bmatrix} 90 \\ 180 \end{bmatrix}
$$

$$
\text{Total} = 270
$$

The solution is

$$
\begin{matrix} x & A^{-1} & b & x \end{matrix}
$$

$$
\begin{bmatrix} S_1 \\ S_2 \end{bmatrix} = \begin{bmatrix} 1/0.9 & 0.25/0.9 \\ 0.40/0.9 & 1/0.9 \end{bmatrix} \begin{bmatrix} 90 \\ 180 \end{bmatrix} = \begin{bmatrix} 150 \\ 240 \end{bmatrix}
$$

The amounts in vector x must be allocated to the production departments. Accordingly, we form matrix P by transposing the percentages shown under P_i and use this matrix to obtain our ultimate amounts for redistribution (shown in vector r).

$$
\begin{matrix} P & x & r \end{matrix}
$$

$$
\begin{bmatrix} 0.10 & 0.45 \\ 0.30 & 0.20 \\ 0.20 & 0.10 \end{bmatrix} \begin{bmatrix} 150 \\ 240 \end{bmatrix} = \begin{bmatrix} 123 \\ 93 \\ 54 \end{bmatrix}
$$

$$
\text{Total} = 270
$$

The amounts in vector r must then be added to the primary allocation amounts for the production departments (say, vector d) to obtain the total overhead costs (vector t).

$$
\begin{matrix} r & d & t \end{matrix}
$$

$$
\begin{bmatrix} 123 \\ 93 \\ 54 \end{bmatrix} + \begin{bmatrix} 377 \\ 307 \\ 246 \end{bmatrix} = \begin{bmatrix} 500 \\ 400 \\ 300 \end{bmatrix}
$$

Because matrices may be multiplied and added, it is possible to "link up" several stages of allocation. In our secondary overhead allocation example, for instance, we could proceed as follows:

$$
t = d + PA^{-1}b
$$

Let us first form PA^{-1}. It would always make sense to do this where the departmental interrelationships can be expected to remain stable, as they might for planning purposes.

$$
\begin{matrix} P & A^{-1} & PA^{-1} \end{matrix}
$$

$$
\begin{bmatrix} 0.10 & 0.45 \\ 0.30 & 0.20 \\ 0.20 & 0.10 \end{bmatrix} \begin{bmatrix} 1/0.9 & 0.25/0.9 \\ 0.40/0.9 & 1/0.9 \end{bmatrix} = \begin{bmatrix} 0.3111 & 0.5278 \\ 0.4222 & 0.3055 \\ 0.2667 & 0.1667 \end{bmatrix}
$$

Note that PA^{-1} is an "effective" matrix (the columns total 1; see Exhibit 3 in Chapter 6).

We see that the equation for t holds.[4]

$$
\begin{array}{ccccccc}
t & & d & & PA^{-1} & & b \\
\begin{bmatrix} 500 \\ 400 \\ 300 \end{bmatrix} & = & \begin{bmatrix} 377 \\ 307 \\ 246 \end{bmatrix} & + & \begin{bmatrix} 0.3111 & 0.5278 \\ 0.4222 & 0.3055 \\ 0.2667 & 0.1667 \end{bmatrix} \begin{bmatrix} 90 \\ 180 \end{bmatrix} & = & \begin{bmatrix} 377 \\ 307 \\ 246 \end{bmatrix} + \begin{bmatrix} 123 \\ 93 \\ 54 \end{bmatrix}
\end{array}
$$

The overhead rates are, therefore,

$$\frac{\$500}{200} \text{ for } P_1, \quad \frac{\$400}{50} \text{ for } P_2, \quad \text{and} \quad \frac{\$300}{150} \text{ for } P_3$$

Variance Analysis

Matrices may be helpful in price level work and traditional variance analysis. Let us consider the analysis of labor variances. Here the inputs involve wage rates for different categories of labor; transformation involves labor hours; and the outputs are the standard costs and variances.

EXAMPLE

Given Data

Labor type A:
  Standard = 600 hours at $3 per hour
  Actual   = 640 hours at $2.75 per hour

Labor B:
  Standard = 1,000 hours at $4 per hour
  Actual   =   900 hours at $5 per hour

Labor type C:
  Standard =   800 hours at $2 per hour
  Actual   = 1,000 hours at $2.50 per hour

Matrix Solution

KEY

P = standard wage rate
ΔP = change in wage rate
$P + \Delta P$ = actual wage rate
Q = standard hours
ΔQ = change in standard hours
$Q + \Delta Q$ = actual hours

---

[4] Further discussion of this type of transformation may be found in Neil Churchill, "Linear Algebra and Cost Allocation: Some Examples," *The Accounting Review*, October, 1964.

$$P\begin{bmatrix} A & B & C \\ 3 & 4 & 2 \end{bmatrix} \quad \Delta P\begin{bmatrix} -0.25 & 1 & 0.50 \end{bmatrix} \begin{array}{c} A \\ B \\ C \end{array}\begin{bmatrix} Q & \Delta Q \\ 600 & 40 \\ 1{,}000 & -100 \\ 800 & 200 \end{bmatrix} =$$

	Standard	Net Efficiency Variance
	$7,400	$120
	$1,250	−$10
	Net Wage Variance	Net Mixed Variance

NOTE

1. The signs attached to the net variance may be interpreted as follows: − indicates a favorable variance; + indicates an unfavorable variance.

2. The percentage change in prices and quantities of each type of labor may easily be shown below the left-hand matrix or alongside the right-hand matrix. In this way, further investigation of variances could be limited to only those types that varied significantly from some predetermined figures (or better, from some predetermined acceptable range of figures, assuming each labor type has its own range).

Eliminating Intercompany Profit in Consolidated Financial Statements

Whenever one company acquires a controlling interest in another company in either the same or a related industry, the need for consolidated financial statements arises. A controlling company is known as a parent, and a controlled company is known as a subsidiary. A subsidiary may, in turn, be a parent of another subsidiary, or may even reciprocally own a noncontrolling interest in its parent.

Frequently the companies in a consolidated group transact business with one another. These transactions when viewed from the over-all consolidated position should have no more effect on profits than a man's switching money from one trouser pocket to another has on increasing the total money he has on his person. Yet when the intercompany transactions occur, elements of profit are usually present. Consequently, when consolidating the separate financial statements of the constituent companies, these intercompany profits must be eliminated.

In what types of transactions do intercompany profits arise? Basically only three types of transactions involve intercompany profits:

1. transactions wherein one affiliated company transfers merchandise to another at some price other than cost;

2. transactions wherein one affiliated company sells fixed assets to or constructs them for another at a price that differs from cost; and

Selected Accounting Applications of Matrix Algebra   **177**

3. transactions wherein one affiliated company acquires some of the outstanding long-term obligations (such as bonds payable) of another at some price that differs from the carrying value shown by the ledger of the issuing affiliate.

The extent of complications depends on whether the equity (the method under which a parent augments the balance in its Investment-in-Subsidiary Account by the undistributed net profits of its subsidiary that have accrued since acquisition) or cost (the method under which no changes in the Investment-in-Subsidiary Account are recorded, other than for subsequent purchases and sales of stock of the subsidiary) method is employed in keeping affiliate records.

The cost method of maintaining affiliate ledgers merely requires the elimination of 100% of intercompany profits against the retained earnings account of the selling affiliate. The equity method requires the elimination of the parent's effective interest in the selling subsidiary's profits against the parent's retained earnings; the remaining percentage is eliminated against the selling subsidiary's retained earnings, thereby reducing the minority interest. The rules below are followed:

1. *Sale by parent to wholly owned subsidiary:* eliminate 100% of the profit against the parent's retained earnings.

2. *Sale by parent to partially owned subsidiary:* eliminate 100% of the profit against the parent's retained earnings.

3. *Sale by wholly owned subsidiary to parent:* eliminate 100% of the profit against the parent's retained earnings.

4. *Sale by partially owned subsidiary to parent:* eliminate parent's effective interest in the profits of the selling subsidiary against the parent's retained earnings and the balance of profits against the selling subsidiary's earnings.

5. *Sale by one partially owned subsidiary to another partially owned subsidiary:* eliminate the parent's effective interest in the profits of the selling subsidiary against the parent's retained earnings and the balance of profits against the selling subsidiary's retained earnings.

Actually, all five rules are summarized in the fifth rule. To prevent misunderstanding, the expression "parent's effective interest" refers to parent in the global sense, that is, not in the minor-parent sense. "Parent" in the global sense is synonymous with the majority interest, and the externally held interests in the subsidiaries are known as the minority interests. Let us see how this rule may be implemented in terms of matrices.

Exhibit 9 presents the matrix approach to eliminating intercompany profits under the equity method. Matrix P is an effective interests matrix, which eliminates intercompany profits (vector p) against majority and minority retained earnings (vector r). Schedule P in Exhibit 9 serves to calculate the net amounts of intercompany profits (p_i) made by each affiliate in its selling capacity. The exhibit also presents the compound journal entry that may be formulated from Schedule P and vector r.

Schedule P lists those intercompany profits made by each selling affiliate that, at the date of the balance sheet, still constitute part of the asset balances of the purchasing affiliates. Note that, as far as Schedule P is concerned, it does not matter which affiliate *purchases* which asset. The intercompany profit is what is removed from the consolidated asset balances, and matrix P provides for subtracting the majority effective interest (in the selling affiliate) percentage of these profits from consolidated retained earnings and the residual percentage of the profits from the minority (selling subsidiary) retained earnings. The contents of the various columns are as follows:

Inventory profits Inventory profits are entered individually in the first money column of Schedule P. Note that the inventories of a manufacturer may contain intercompany net fixed asset profits arising through the depreciation and overhead absorption mechanisms.

Net fixed asset profits Profits in fixed assets are entered in the second column of Schedule P, and the accumulated excess depreciation on these overvalued fixed assets is entered in the third column. The two figures are netted when cross-adding to arrive at the amount of p_i.

Net bond financing profits Net bond financing profits occur when one company acquires some of the outstanding bonds of an affiliated company and the bonds have been issued and purchased at either premium or discount prices or both. In essence, the issuing company sells the bonds to a purchasing affiliate, and profits (or losses) arise when the applicable discount or premium or both are eliminated as if these bonds had been retired.

Exhibit 10 presents data for a problem that illustrates the use of the matrices in Exhibit 9. The solution to this problem is shown in Exhibit 11. The problem deals with eliminating intercompany profits from the opening balances of the period. The transactions during the period could then be treated as illustrated and summarized in Exhibit 12.

EXHIBIT 9
Intercompany Profit Matrices

$$\begin{array}{ccc} P & p & r \\ [P_{ji}] & [p_i] & = [r_j] \\ (n \times n) & (n \times 1) & (n \times 1) \end{array}$$

KEY

P_{ji} = the effective interest of company j in company i: $i, j = A, B, \ldots, N$

p_i = an element in vector p that shows the total amount of intercompany profit made by company i

r_j = the change to be made in retained earnings of company j as the result of eliminating intercompany profit when consolidating

Schedule P

Seller	Inventory	Fixed Assets		Bonds				Cross Totals
				Owned		Payable		
		Cost	Acc. Depn.	Discount	Premium	Discount	Premium	
	I	FA	$\sum_{k=1}^{a} D_k$	D_{bo}	P_{bo}	D_{bp}	P_{bp}	P_i
A								
B								
$\vdots$								
N								
Consolidated account totals	$\sum I$	$\sum FA$	$(\sum\sum_{k=1}^{a} D_k)$	$(\sum D_{bo})$	$\sum P_{bo}$	$\sum D_{bp}$	$(\sum P_{bp})$	$\sum P_i$

NOTE

1. Parentheses indicate subtraction.
2. The upper limit, a, in $\sum D_k$ is either $t - 1$ (balance at beginning of current year), where a consolidated profit and loss statement is to be prepared, or t (balance at end of current year), where a consolidated balance sheet only is to be prepared.

Chapter 7: Matrix Algebra and Accounting

EXHIBIT 9
(cont.)

Debits:

r_A

r_B

$\vdots$

r_N

$\sum P_{bp}$

$\sum D_{bo}$

$\sum \sum_{k=1}^{a} D_k$

Credits:

$\sum I$

$\sum FA$

$\sum P_{bo}$

$\sum D_{bp}$

EXHIBIT 10
Illustrative Problem

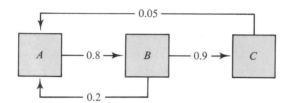

Company A has two subsidiaries, B and C. The nominal ownership relationships are shown above. Arrows indicate which company owns what, and the decimals correspond to the percentages of the voting capital stock that are owned; thus, for example, B owns 20% of A and 90% of C.

Consolidated financial statements (including both income statement and balance sheet) are to be prepared. Data concerning intercompany profits in the account balances at the beginning of the year are shown in the following table.

	Profit	Seller	Purchaser
Opening inventories:	$ 24,000	A	B
	18,000	B	C
	10,000	A	C
	40,000	A	B
	6,000	C	A
Fixed assets:			
Cost	120,000⎫	A	B
Accumulated depreciation	80,000⎭		
Intercompany held bonds:			
Portion of premium on issuer's books	6,000⎫	A	B
Discount on purchaser's books	2,000⎭		

Selected Accounting Applications of Matrix Algebra

EXHIBIT 11

Schedule P

Seller	Inventory	Fixed Assets		Bonds		Cross Totals
				Owned	Payable	
		Cost	Acc. Depn.	Discount	Premium	p_i
A	$\begin{cases}24{,}000 \\ 10{,}000 \\ 40{,}000\end{cases}$	120,000	(80,000)	(2,000)	(6,000)	106,000
B	18,000					18,000
C	6,000					6,000
Consolidated account totals	98,000	120,000	(80,000)	(2,000)	(6,000)	130,000

See note.

$$
\begin{array}{ccc}
P & p & r \\
\begin{bmatrix} 0.93284 & 0.74626 & 0.67164 \\ 0.06095 & 0.24876 & 0.22388 \\ 0.00621 & 0.00498 & 0.10448 \end{bmatrix} & \begin{bmatrix} 106{,}000 \\ 18{,}000 \\ 6{,}000 \end{bmatrix} & = \begin{bmatrix} 116{,}343 \\ 12{,}282 \\ 1{,}375 \end{bmatrix}
\end{array}
$$

$$
\begin{array}{ccc}
 & \text{Totals} \quad 130{,}000 & 130{,}000
\end{array}
$$

Intercompany profits elimination entry:

Retained earnings A	$116,343	
Retained earnings B	12,282	
Retained earnings C	1,375	
Accumulated depreciation	80,000	
Bonds owned (or unamortized bond discount if such separate account exists)	2,000	
Unamortized bond premium	6,000	
Opening inventory		$ 98,000
Fixed assets		120,000

NOTE The calculation of matrix P has been illustrated in Exhibits 2 and 3 in the preceding chapter. Matrix P is designated E in Exhibit 3.

EXHIBIT 12

Journal Entries During Period

CGS_j = cost of goods sold of Company j; $j = A$ (selling affiliate), B (purchas-   **KEY**
    ing affiliate)
I_j = inventory of Company j
AR_j = accounts receivable of Company j
AP_j = accounts payable of Company j
F_j = net fixed assets of Company j
S_j = sales of Company j
D_j = depreciation of j
P_B = purchases of B
EI_k = ending inventory for $k = 1$ (balance sheet), 2 (income statement)

Affiliate A uses perpetual inventory system; B uses a periodical system.   **ASSUME**

Intercompany bonds acquired during the period may be treated in the same   **NOTE**
manner as they would have been had they been on hand at the beginning of
the period. Any entries for realization (amortization, cost of sales, depreciation) of part of intercompany profits would merely be reversed.

	Inventory			Fixed Assets		
Entry for cost of	I_A	20,000		I_A	20,000	
items that will be	AP_A		20,000	AP_A		20,000
sold intercompany						
Entries for sale	AR_A	25,000		AR_A	25,000	
	S_A		25,000	S_A		25,000
	CGS_A	20,000		CGS_A	20,000	
	I_A		20,000	I_A		20,000
Entries recording	P_B	25,000		F_B	25,000	
acquisition	AP_B		25,000	AP_B		25,000
Entry recording	EI_1	25,000				
ending inventory	EI_2		25,000			
Elimination entries	AP_B	25,000		AP_B	25,000	
	AR_A		25,000	AR_A		25,000
	S_A	25,000		S_A	25,000	
	CGS_A		20,000	CGS_A		20,000
	EI_1		5,000	F_B		5,000

Matrix Algebra and Its Accounting Applications

Objectives

This chapter has actually been addressed to a broader objective than illustrating some matrix applications in accounting. A. C. Littleton put his finger on this objective when, in 1953, he observed:

> ...In actual historical evolution, accounting principles have been slowly distilled out of accounting actions. That is to say, accounting rules, having first been the fruits of tentative actions, grew in significance until they became guides to predetermined actions. As these accounting particulars grew increasingly diverse and complex, so did accounting actions and the accompanying rules, customs, practices. And as this diversity of particulars falls under more and more critical consideration, it becomes increasingly advisable to decide whether there are elements of order, sequence, interrelation within the mass.[5]

And as the body of accounting literature continues to expand, there is a growing need to interrelate diverse accounting areas. The interrelation of diverse accounting areas is the broad objective of this chapter. Let us see how matrix algebra may accomplish such interrelation.

The Logical Structure of Accounting Processes

Much of traditional accounting procedure involves the acquisition, valuation, and allocation of input data. By concentrating on these processes, diverse accounting areas may be interrelated. Let us illustrate this notion by referring to two accounting areas that perhaps, at first glance, seem related only in that money and accounting are concerned. These areas are the preparation of process cost reports and the preparation of liquidation statements. These areas may be viewed in terms of their acquisition, valuation, and allocation phases as follows:

Process cost reports		*Liquidation statement*
The listing of material, labor, and overhead components	Acquisition	The listing of all available assets
The determining of historical cost outlays of components	Valuation	The determining of realizable values of assets
The distributing of valued cost components to output designations	Allocation	The distributing of valued assets to various types of creditors and owners

The similarities between these areas are now more apparent. Both involve

---

[5] A. C. Littleton, "Structure of Accounting Theory," Monograph No. 5, American Accounting Association, 1953, p. 123.

listing a set of inputs (acquisition phase), determining appropriate values for these inputs (valuation phase), and distributing the valued inputs to output destinations (allocation phase). Likewise, the differences between the two areas are evident: The inputs in process costing are data on materials, labor, and overhead, whereas those involved in liquidation are data on all available assets; the values assigned to inputs in process costing are historical cost outlays, whereas those in liquidation are realizable values; the output destinations in process costing are product costs, whereas those in liquidation are claimants' equities.

Now, I believe that the interrelationship of diverse accounting areas can best be accomplished by concentrating on allocation processes. The inputs and outputs in the various accounting areas differ, as do the methods of input valuation. Consequently, the acquisition and valuation processes are apt not to lead to extensive interrelation, and this leaves us with allocation processes as the most promising avenue. We seek, therefore, the answer to the question, "Can the allocation of inputs to outputs be standardized in order that diverse accounting areas may be interrelated?"

Note that we are dealing with a procedural issue, which, if resolved, can lay the basis for a host of theoretical and pedagogical considerations.

To facilitate discussion, let us introduce some "matrix shorthand." We will need the following.

Matrix Shorthand

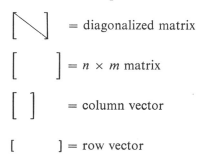

Let us use this shorthand and return now to comparing the allocation phases of process cost reports and liquidation statements. The cost allocation matrices of Exhibit 6 may be summarized as follows:

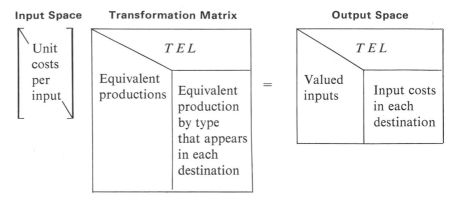

where T = units transferred
      E = units in ending inventory
      L = units lost in processing

The liquidation matrices shown in Exhibit 4 are summarized as follows:

Input Space   Transformation Matrix   Output Space

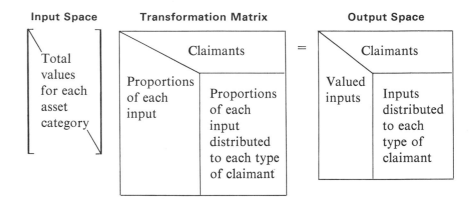

How well have matrices succeeded in further interrelating the process costing and statement of affairs areas? The matrix approach in both cases employed diagonalized matrices. The transformation matrices were composed of either quantities or proportions, depending on whether the nonzero elements in the diagonalized matrices were dollars per unit or total dollars. Hence, the allocation procedures in these areas are very similar under the matrix approach. The reports that resulted from matrix allocation are identical in format, and this is very significant, pedagogically speaking. When process costing and statements of affairs are taught, perhaps the single most time-consuming chore is to memorize (and understand) the separate report formats. Under the matrix approach, only one, easy-to-understand report format is necessary. This matrix format arrays inputs according to outputs, and, after all, this is what allocation is all about. I contend that no other format for reporting allocations is as appealing as the input-output format. No other report format shows correspondence of inputs to outputs as well. No other report format is easier to understand. No other report format is as simple.

Many accounting areas can be approached in exactly the same manner, that is, by the formulation of a diagonalized matrix and a transformation matrix to obtain an input-output matrix report.[6] The trick is to recognize data inputs and outputs as such and to determine the accounting criteria that govern the allocation. Usually, the accounting criteria can be reduced to simply reflecting ownership or to measuring usage. If any difficulty is encountered, it is apt to be not so much in recognizing inputs as it is in recognizing output designations.[7]

Uses of Matrix Inversion

Anytime a set of simultaneous equations is to be solved, an inverse matrix may be used to obtain the solution, provided that the solution exists. In the problem section of the previous chapter, matrix inversion was used in the determination of a multiple regression line such as might be needed in budgetary analysis. In this chapter, matrix inversion was applied to secondary overhead allocation, eliminating intercompany profits, and calculating bonus and taxes. And as we shall see in Chapter 8, matrix inversion lies at the heart of linear programing procedures.

Secondary allocation (using PA^{-1}) may be summarized with matrix shorthand as follows:

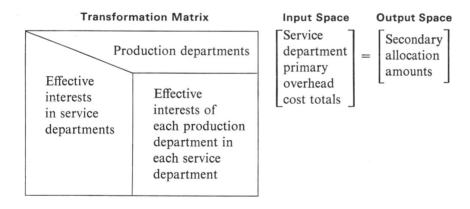

[6] Some of the other accounting areas that can be treated this way include job order costing, standard costing, period budgeting, primary overhead allocation, and responsibility accounting.

[7] Some typical data output designations include products, departments, time periods, uses of funds, creditors, partners, and companies.

The matrices for eliminating intercompany profits are summarized as follows:

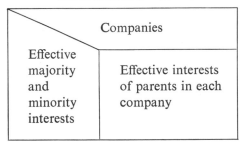

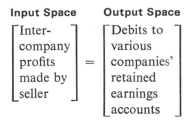

Observe that effective interests were necessary in these cases because it was desired to allocate inputs to outputs without changing the total amount of the inputs. In computing bonus and taxes, on the other hand, there is no restriction on keeping input and output totals equal. Here we start with "preliminary" shares in profits and adjust them to reflect interrelationships. The bonus-tax matrices are summarized as follows:

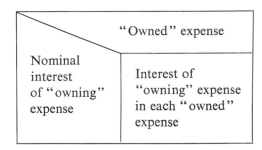

Other Uses of Matrices Two allocations other than those involving diagonalized matrices or inverted matrices were introduced in this chapter. The computation of a depreciation lapse schedule was treated essentially as follows:

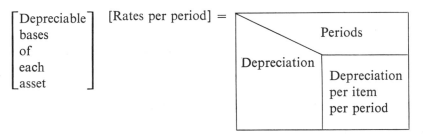

Note that the input-output format here resulted from the multiplication of two vectors, rather than from the use of a diagonalized matrix.

The last matrix allocation to be summarized involved calculation of variances. The procedures were

Input Space	Transformation Matrix		Output Space	
$\begin{bmatrix} \text{Standard costs per input} \\ \hline \text{Changes in standard costs} \end{bmatrix}$	$\begin{bmatrix} \text{Standard quantities per input} \end{bmatrix}$	$\begin{bmatrix} \text{Changes in standard quantities} \end{bmatrix}$	$=$ $\begin{bmatrix} \text{Standard cost} \\ \hline \text{Price variance} \end{bmatrix}$	$\begin{bmatrix} \text{Quantity variance} \\ \hline \text{Mixed variance} \end{bmatrix}$

This formulation made use of the fact that a vector of actual costs can be decomposed into a vector of standard costs plus a vector of differences or changes. In addition to summarizing the respective labor and material variances, this approach permits rapid calculation of percentages of changes to aid in determining the significance of each change.

Now what is the message in all this? It is simply that

Summary and Conclusions

1. One or two simple matrix manipulations may be employed instead of a vast number of existing accounting procedures.
2. Matrices are a means of expressing accounting problems concisely.
3. Matrices add cohesiveness to the body of diverse accounting knowledge.
4. The input-output form of report may be recognized as being superior to other forms not only because it is readily understood, but also because it would significantly help in the interrelation of diverse accounting areas.

To some extent, the procedures of acquiring, valuing, and allocating are present in every accounting area. In general terms, the logical accounting procedures have the following mathematical analogs:

Logical procedure	*Mathematical analog*
1. Separate identification of inputs	Use of a set of unit vectors
2. Aggregation of inputs	Formation of linear combinations of basis vectors to express interior points in input space
3. Valuation of inputs	Use of scalars to reflect values determined outside accounting space
4. Combination and allocation of inputs to outputs in order to observe criteria peculiar to each area	Choice of elements in transformation matrix to reflect criteria, and use of matrices to accomplish combination and allocation

In the matrix approach, decisions must be made outside the system as to which inputs should be recognized, what values should be assigned, and which outputs should be observed. The matrix system reflects these decisions but does not formulate them. The decisions involving inputs and values are made in accordance with accounting criteria, whereas the decision as to outputs depends on the particular accounting area. Transformation is similar in each area; all that is necessary is to determine the percentages or totals (depending on whether input data is in terms of total values or unit values, respectively) that effect the proper linear combinations of input space data.

The foregoing all suggests the following tentative redefinition, for accounting purposes, of the term "allocation":

> Allocation is the distributing of inputs to outputs according to accounting criteria that reflect ownership and measure usage. Allocation is best accomplished by forming linear combinations of input variables.

Suggestions for Further Study

Among the articles in accounting that involve matrices are the following:

N. Churchill, "Linear Algebra and Cost Allocations: Some Examples," *The Accounting Review*, October, 1964.

R. M. Cyert, H. J. Davidson, and G. L. Thompson, "Estimation of the Allowance for Doubtful Accounts by Markov Chains," *Management Science*, Vol. 8, 1962, pp. 287–303.

N. Dopuch, "Mathematical Programming and Accounting Approaches to Incremental Cost Analysis," *The Accounting Review*, October, 1963.

N. Dopuch and D. Drake, "Accounting Implications of a Mathematical Programming Approach to the Transfer Price Problem," *Journal of Accounting Research*, Spring, 1964.

A. Drebin, "The Inventory Calculus," *Journal of Accounting Research*, Spring, 1966.

Y. Ijiri, "A Linear Programming Model for Budgeting and Financial Planning," *Journal of Accounting Research*, Autumn, 1963.

R. K. Jaedicke, "Improving Break-even Analysis by Linear Programming Techniques," *N.A.A. Bulletin*, March, 1961.

R. Manes, "Using Computers to Improve Distribution of Service Costs," *The Journal of Accountancy*, March, 1963.

R. Mattessich, "Towards a General and Axiomatic Foundation of Accountancy; with an Introduction to the Matrix Formulation of Accounting Systems," *Accounting Research* (England), October, 1957.

Mohamed Onsi, "Linear Programming: An Accounting Information Model," *Management Accounting*, December, 1966.

A. Richards, "Input-Output Accounting for Business," *The Accounting Review*, July, 1960.

T. Williams and C. Griffin, "Matrix Theory and Cost Allocation," *The Accounting Review*, July, 1964.

Problems

1. Prepare a depreciation lapse schedule for the assets below using the sum-of-the-years'-digits method and a five-year life.

    Depreciation schedule

	Cost	Salvage
Grinder	$50,000	10%
Welder	20,000	25%
Drill press	80,000	25%
Polisher	10,000	10%

2. Compute executive bonus, franchise taxes, and federal income taxes given that

    Bonus-tax problem

    (a) Bonus is 20% of profits after all taxes.

    (b) Franchise tax is 5% of net profits before all taxes.

    (c) Federal income tax is 40% of net profits.

    (d) Profits before bonus, franchise tax, and federal income tax are $500,000.

3. Prepare a statement of affairs in input-output format from the following data.

    Statement of affairs Balance Sheet

Cash	$ 12,000	Accounts payable	$ 40,000
Accounts receivable	15,000	Accrued wages	2,000
Inventory	32,000	Notes payable	10,000
Bonds	6,000	Mortgage payable	80,000
Property, plant, and		Owners' equity	58,000
equipment (net)	125,000		
	$190,000		$190,000

Additional data:

1. $13,000 can be collected on accounts receivable.

2. The inventory can be sold for $35,000.

3. The bonds, which have been pledged as security for the notes payable, have a market value of $5,000.

4. A buyer has offered $100,000 for the property, plant, and equipment. These assets, however, have been used for collateral in obtaining the mortgage.

Process cost **4.** Prepare an equivalent production schedule and a cost report from the following data. Use the weighted average method.

	Units
Opening inventory (three-fourths done as far as departmental materials are concerned, two-fifths as far as conversion)	20,000
Received from preceding department (converted to units of this department)	400,000
Put into process	180,000
Transferred to finished goods	530,000
Ending inventory (two-thirds departmental materials; two-fifths conversion)	60,000
Lost units (lost gradually during processing; 60% departmental materials, 50% conversion)	10,000

Note The process is such that the materials from the preceding department are the base to which departmental materials are added.

COST DATA *Opening inventory:*

Materials from preceding department	$ 200,000
Departmental materials	124,000
Departmental conversion costs	50,000

Cost of materials received from preceding department during the month	5,800,000

Departmental costs during month:

Materials	4,484,000
Conversion costs	3,304,000

Process cost **5.** From the following data, prepare a cost report on an average costing basis.

Key (P, M, C) = portion of production done during present month for P (goods received from preceding department), M (departmental materials), C (departmental conversion costs).

QUANTITY DATA

Opening inventory $(0, \frac{1}{4}, \frac{1}{2})$	40,000
Received from preceding department during period	360,000
Units added by present department	100,000
	500,000
Transferred out	320,000
Ending inventory $(1, \frac{2}{3}, \frac{1}{2})$	150,000

Lost units (normal loss occurring gradually during processing; no provision in overhead rate: 1, $\frac{2}{3}$, $\frac{1}{4}$)		30,000
		500,000

COST DATA Opening inventory:

Preceding department's costs	$ 120,000
Departmental material costs	60,000
Departmental conversion costs	60,160

Costs during month:

Preceding department's costs	1,380,000
Departmental material costs	804,000
Departmental conversion costs	1,187,240
Total	$3,611,400

6. Compute net wage, efficiency, and mixed variances from the following labor statistics.

Variance analysis

	Standard		Actual	
Labor Type	Wage/Hour	Hours	Wage/Hour	Hours
A	$3.00	1,000	$2.80	800
B	2.50	1,500	2.75	1,600
C	4.25	200	4.00	250
D	5.00	500	5.50	600

7. Compute overhead absorption rates from the following data.

Secondary allocation

Rendering \ Consuming	S_1	S_2	P_1	P_2	P_3	P_4
S_1	0	0.25	0.1	0.15	0.3	0.2
S_2	0.2	0	0.2	0.1	0.1	0.4

	S_1	S_2	P_1	P_2	P_3	P_4
Primary allocation totals (000 omitted)	$190	$285	$104	$226	$137	$208
Direct labor hours (000 omitted)			20	60	50	50

Answer: Overhead rates per direct labor hour: $10, $5, $5, $8

8. Parent (P) Company owns 80% of Affiliate (A) Company and 90% of Subsidiary (S) Company, which in turn owns 20% of Parent Company. Consolidated financial statements (including both balance sheet and income statement) are to be prepared. Data concerning intercompany profits in the beginning-of-the-year account balances appear below. Prepare an intercompany profit elimination entry.

Eliminating intercompany profits

	Profit	Seller	Purchaser
Opening inventories:	$30,000	A	P
	20,000	P	S
	18,000	S	A
	40,000	A	S
Fixed assets:			
Cost	90,000 ⎫	P	S
Accumulated depreciation	(20,000) ⎭		
Intercompany bonds:			
Portion of discount on issuer's books	(5,000) ⎫	A	S
Premium on purchaser's books	(1,000) ⎭		

Answer:

Retained earnings		
P	220,000	
A	8,200	
S	17,800	
Accumulated depreciation	20,000	
Bonds owned		1,000
Unamortized bond discount		5,000
Opening inventory		170,000
Fixed assets		90,000

8

Linear Programing:
Graphs and Simplex Algorithm

Developing Intuitions for Linear Programing

Linear programing is a dynamic tool the accountant can use to help management make better decisions.

The concept of programing has many intuitive counterparts. Its essence consists of procedures for "doing the best with what you've got." More formally, programing is the process of optimizing subject to restrictions or constraints. In linear programing, the function to be optimized and the constraints may be stated in linear form, for example, $a_1x_1 + a_2x_2 + \cdots + a_nx_n$.

Let us see what is meant by "constraints." A man *maximizes* his happiness subject to restrictions of imperfect knowledge, limited time, limited money, etc. A student *maximizes* his knowledge subject to the constraints of limited time, maintenance of social position, attainment of minimum grade point average, parental pressure, aspiration level, I.Q., etc. A golfer *minimizes* his score subject to pangs of conscience, basic coordination, knowledge of the game, limited time, social acceptability, etc. Similarly, linear programing is constrained optimization; its applicability seems extremely broad. And it is very appealing; imagine "doing the best with what you've got"! This is a soothing thought, for once you have done your best, you may as well relax—by definition, you could not have done better!

But the "worry-wart" and the perfectionist respond, "Yes I could, just by improving on or eliminating some constraint." The questions then arise: Which constraint or constraints? If one is improved, won't some other worsen? If one is eliminated, won't some other be imposed? Consider our student, for example. Suppose he decides to spend more time on studying and less on sleeping. Obviously this procedure cannot be guaranteed to improve his knowledge, because he may need a certain amount of sleep to make the studying fruitful. Not all constraints may have been considered originally; for example, his minimum sleeping time constraint may not have been stated. Similarly, a man who in maximizing his happiness eliminates his limited money constraint by robbing a bank will find that his happiness is now constrained by fear of detection. And a golfer who, by seeing a golf professional, seeks to improve his knowledge of the game constraint may well find that his basic coordination constraint worsens. Then, too, some constraints may not really pertain. For example, the man maximizing his happiness may find that his money is so limited that time is not a consideration, or vice versa. (This is known as a redundant constraint in linear programing.)

Accounting is also concerned with determining those constraints affecting management's objectives and with ascertaining the most promising alterations in the constraints. The accountant is not finished once an optimal solution to a problem is determined. He must then consider constraints and cost data to see whether some changes are desirable.

A partial list of possible constraints that might enter a management decision problem would include

Capacity of machines
Number of men available
Quantity of output demanded
Quantity of output that may be supplied
Time
Capital
Various managerial policies, such as
  Making at least a given quantity of an item
  Using certain types of labor or equipment
  Making at least a given quantity of every item in the product line

Which constraints pertain to a problem depends, of course, on the problem. Whether all the pertinent constraints are considered depends not only on the mathematical proficiency of the programer, but also on the keenness of his imagination. Here, then, a division of labor becomes possible: An expert mathematician could be complemented by an imaginative accountant, provided, of course, the two can communicate.

A Graphical View of Linear Programing and Definitions of Its Terms

Although the solution techniques of linear programing rely on matrix algebra and something called the simplex algorithm, it may be best to study first a

Figure 34

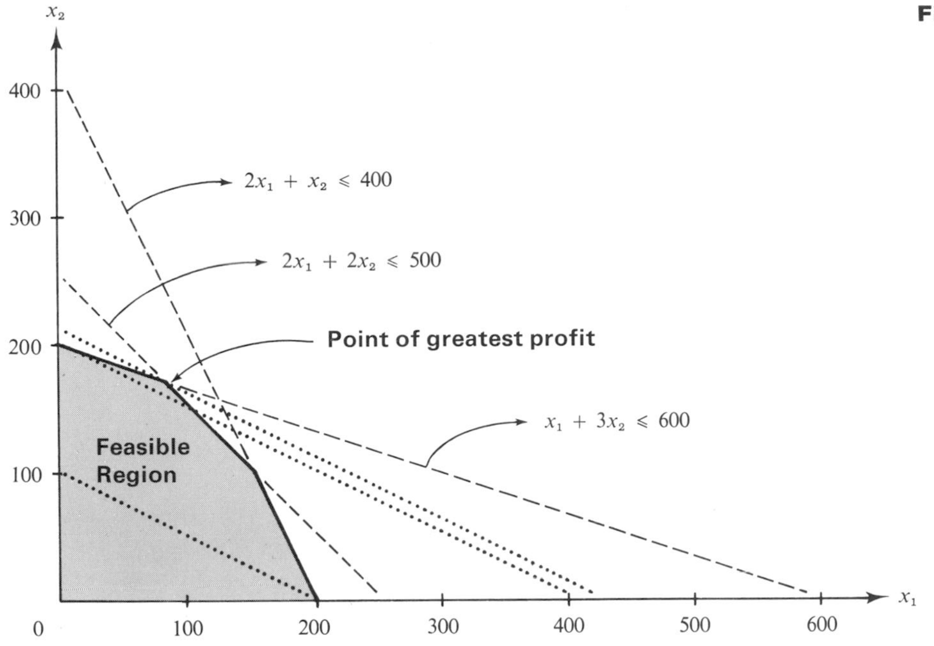

linear programing problem in graphical form, as shown in Figure 34.

Objective function:	Maximize profit:	$Z = \$2x_1 + \$4x_2$
	Constraints:	$2x_1 + x_2 \leq 400$
		$2x_1 + 2x_2 \leq 500$
		$x_1 + 3x_2 \leq 600$
	Non-negativity restrictions:	$x_i \geq 0$

The problem is stated mathematically beneath the figure. We start with something known as an objective function, which is an equation that expresses the profit (Z in Figure 34) to be maximized or the cost to be minimized. Profits are defined as the number of units of product sold, multiplied by the contribution margin of each product; contribution margin is the selling price minus the variable costs of production, distribution, and administration. This is usually stated in the following mathematical form:

KEY

c_i = the contribution margin of the ith product
x_i = the number of units sold of the ith product
Z = profits

$$Z = \sum c_i x_i$$

The constraints are shown under the objective function. Let us assume that the scarce quantity that constrains or limits us is the time available in each of the three departments. The coefficients then represent the amount of time (measured, say, in hours) needed to produce one unit of each product. For example, it takes two hours to produce a unit of product x_1 and one hour to produce a unit of x_2 in department 1. The totality of constraints is the following system of equations:

KEY

a_{ji} = the quantity of the jth scarce factor required to make the ith product

$x_j^{(1)}$ = the total quantity available of the jth scarce factor; the superscript distinguishes the original capacity available from the product variable, x_i

$$\sum a_{1i}x_i \le x_1^{(1)}$$
$$\vdots \qquad \vdots$$
$$\sum a_{ni}x_i \le x_n^{(1)}$$

A desirable solution to the problem must satisfy *all* the constraints. Hence, the solution lies in the feasible region, or that region bounded by all of the constraints, including the non-negativity restrictions.

The non-negativity restrictions ($x_i \ge 0$) shown in Figure 34 merely require what is intuitively obvious: either some or none of each product must be made; the plant cannot manufacture negative quantities.

The shaded area in the graph is the feasible region. The solid lines and their dashed extensions are the graphs of the constraints obtained by first setting one variable in a constraint equal to zero, solving the resulting expression for the other variable, repeating the process (switching the roles of the variables), and then drawing the connecting line. The dotted lines are iso-revenue lines; that is, any point on a dotted line yields the same profit. These lines are drawn parallel to one another with each line in succession being moved farther from the origin. The optimal solution occurs at that point on the iso-revenue (profit) line which lies farthest from the origin and which touches the boundary of the feasible region. The slope of the profit lines may be determined by setting Z equal to zero and solving for x_1:

$$0 = 2x_1 + 4x_2$$
$$x_2 = -\tfrac{2}{4}x_1$$

Consequently, the slope is falling at a rate of $-\tfrac{1}{2}$.

The graphing technique for solving linear programing problems is efficient so long as we are considering only two variables. Problems involving more than two variables are solved by using Dantzig's simplex algorithm.[1]

---

[1] A description of this algorithm first appeared in G. B. Dantzig, "Maximization of a Linear Function of Variables Subject to Linear Inequalities," contained in *Activity Analysis of Production and Allocation*, T. C. Koopmans, Ed., Cowles Commission Monograph No. 13 (New York: John Wiley & Sons, 1951), ch. 21.

Let us see how the simplex method proceeds using the problem graphed in Figure 34. At the first stage (hereafter referred to as "tableau") of the simplex, it is assumed that nothing is produced, that all facilities are idle. This corresponds to the origin of the feasible region. It is then determined, according to criteria that will be discussed later, which product best increases profits. Because the contribution margin of x_2 is \$4 and that of x_1 is only \$2, the second tableau determines the profit when the maximum amount of x_2 is made. This amount is determined by solving for the intersection of the x_2 axis [this is the non-negativity restriction, $x_1 = 0$ (observe that in graphing inequalities, the expressions are treated as equations; i.e., $x_1 \leq 0$ becomes $x_1 = 0$)] and the constraint, $x_1 + 3x_2 \leq 600$. We have

$$x_1 + 3x_2 \leq 600$$
$$x_1 = 0$$

Therefore,

$$x_2 = 200$$

At this point, we make profits of 200(\$4) = \$800.

The criteria is then applied again to determine a new program (if one exists) in which the profit would be at least as great as it was when 200 x_2 and no x_1 are made. In this case, the next tableau determines the profit at the intersection of the constraint, $2x_1 + 2x_2 \leq 500$ and $x_1 + 3x_2 \leq 600$. We have

$$
\begin{aligned}
2x_1 + 2x_2 &= 500 \\
-2(x_1 + 3x_2 &= 600) \\
\hline
-4x_2 &= -700 \\
x_2 &= 175
\end{aligned}
$$

By substitution we determine x_1:

$$x_1 + 3(175) = 600$$
$$x_1 = 600 - 525 = 75$$

Our profit at this point is 75(\$2) plus 175(\$4) or \$850.

Under the simplex method, the criteria are again applied to see if there is some other point at which at least \$850 could be earned. The criteria show, however, that no such point exists and that the maximum profits occur at $x_1 = 75$, $x_2 = 175$.

The purpose of the last few paragraphs has been to show that the simplex algorithm determines the profits at adjacent constraint intersections on the boundary of the feasible region in such a way that only those intersections which yield the same or greater levels of profit are considered (mathematically it could be said that profits increase monotonically from one stage to the next). If, by chance, the slope of the profit line coincides with the slope of a constraint (i.e., if both lines have the same slope or slant), the condition of alternative optima occurs. Where alternative optima exist, there is, theoretically, an infinity of different programs that yield the same profit. Any point on the constraint border coincident with the profit line will determine a different program in terms of the quantities of the variables selected, but when the quantities are multiplied by their respective profits, the resulting total profits will be the same.

In terms of the vector space[2] concepts described in Chapter 6, the simplex algorithm consists of applying criteria to select a new set of basis vectors at each iteration (i.e., for each new tableau), expressing all vectors not in the basis as linear combinations of the basis vectors, and determining the profits (or costs where minimization of costs is the objective) associated with the vectors (products) in the basis.[3] Let us make this more concrete.

The Simplex Algorithm

Procedurally, the simplex method consists of (1) selecting the membership of the basis set of vectors by applying entering and exiting criteria, and (2) using the Gauss-Jordan (or some other) method of inversion to restate all vectors as linear combinations of the basis vectors.

Entering and Exiting Criteria   As one proceeds from one corner of the feasible region to another, it is reassuring to know that the solution is improving, or, at least, not getting worse. Fortunately, two criteria have been developed that give us this assurance by designating one vector to enter the basis matrix in the next iteration and one vector to remove.

We shall need more symbols to state these criteria.

KEY $(z_j - c_j)$ = the opportunity cost per unit if vector j gets put into the basis in the next iteration

$x_i^{(p)}$ = the quantity of product i produced at iteration p

$\lambda_{ij}^{(p)}$ = the value of the coefficient a_{ij} after p iterations. These are the scalars needed to express vector j at stage p as a linear combination of the vectors in the basis (indicated $i \in B$, where $\in$ is read "is a member of"). In one criterion, the subscript j will become k

---

[2] The remainder of this chapter will discuss linear programing in terms of vector spaces and matrices. It is assumed that the reader has command of Chapter 6 or its equivalent and is familiar with matrix inversion using the Gauss-Jordan technique (this technique is also presented in Chapter 6).

[3] A basis set of vectors is a set of n vectors that may be used to express any other point (vector) in n-space. The process of forming linear combinations permits expressing any given vector in terms of the addition of scalar (i.e., integers or fractions) multiples of the basis vectors. For more detailed discussion, see Chapter 6.

to indicate the column vector that is chosen to enter the basis in the next iteration.

$z_j = \sum_{i \in B} c_i \lambda_{ij}^{(p)}$, that is, the summation of the products of the contribution margins of the vectors in the basis, multiplied by the linear combination scalars for vector j

The criteria may be formally stated as follows:

ENTERING VECTOR CRITERION: Choose minimum $(z_j - c_j) \leq 0$

EXITING VECTOR CRITERION: Choose minimum $\dfrac{x_i^{(p)}}{\lambda_{ik}^{(p)}}$; $\lambda_{ik}^{(p)} > 0$

These criteria have been stated with maximizing profits in mind; however, in a cost minimization problem, the "dollar" criterion (i.e., the entering vector criterion) changes to: maximum $(z_j - c_j) \geq 0$. The "quantity" criterion stays the same in either case. Actually, any minimization problem may be changed to a maximization problem by changing the c_j to $-c_j$. If this translation is performed, the criteria are applied as in a maximization problem.

NOTE

Observe that if all $(z_j - c_j) > 0$, there is no way to improve profit, although if any $(z_j - c_j) = 0$ other than for vectors in the basis, there are alternative ways of generating the same profit.

The algebraic proof of the validity of these criteria is involved but interesting. At one point in the proof, $(z_j - c_j)$ (which is a negative quantity according to the entering criterion) is preceded by a minus sign; hence, the greatest addition to profit comes from the most negative $(z_j - c_j)$. The exiting criterion selects a minimum value because if some value other than the minimum is chosen, at least one x_i quantity in the next iteration becomes negative in violation of the non-negativity restrictions.

The Gauss-Jordan method for obtaining an inverse was presented in Chapter 6. In essence, this technique starts with the expression

Gauss-Jordan Inversion

$[A \vdots I]$ and replaces it with $[I \vdots A^{-1}]$

Usually in the Gauss-Jordan method the identity matrix is arrayed alongside the matrix to be inverted merely as a procedural device; that is, no special significance is attached to the identity matrix. In the simplex algorithm, the identity matrix is the matrix of the slack variables. Slack variables are best described in terms of an example.

Consider the following problem. A manufacturer wishes to know how much he should make of each of three products, x_1, x_2, and x_3, to maximize his profits. His accountants have determined that the contribution margins for these products in the light of existing market conditions are $6, $7, and $8, respectively. The times it takes to produce each product in each of the plant's three departments and the capacities of these departments are shown in Table 7.

Table 7

Departments	Production Times (hours)			Departmental Capacities (hours)
	x_1	x_2	x_3	
Machining	1	2	1	100,000
Assembling	3	4	2	120,000
Finishing	2	6	4	200,000

The problem may be formulated mathematically as follows:

Maximize profit: $\quad Z = \$6x_1 + \$7x_2 + \$8x_3$

Constraints:
$$
\begin{aligned}
1x_1 + 2x_2 + 1x_3 &\le 100{,}000 \\
3x_1 + 4x_2 + 2x_3 &\le 120{,}000 \\
2x_1 + 6x_2 + 4x_3 &\le 200{,}000
\end{aligned}
\tag{1}
$$

Non-negativity
restrictions: $\quad x_i \ge 0$

The inequality signs in (1) are bothersome; to incorporate matrix algebra into the analysis we need equations. To accomplish this, "slack" variables, s_i, are introduced. Thus, the first inequality becomes

$$1x_1 + 2x_2 + 1x_3 + 1s_1 = 100{,}000 \tag{2}$$

Equation (2) states, in essence, that if the quantities of x_i to be produced together fall short of the 100,000 hours capacity, the idle capacity will appear as a reading of s_1. Therefore, s_1 takes up any slack in the machining department.

Because idle capacity generates no profit, the contribution margins associated with the slack variables are all zero. By introducing slack variables in all departments (1) may now be restated:

Maximize profit: $\quad Z = \$6x_1 + \$7x_2 + \$8x_3 + \$0 \sum_{i=1}^{3} s_i$

Constraints:
$$
\begin{aligned}
1x_1 + 2x_2 + 1x_3 + 1s_1 + 0s_2 + 0s_3 &= 100{,}000 \\
3x_1 + 4x_2 + 2x_3 + 0s_1 + 1s_2 + 0s_3 &= 120{,}000 \\
2x_1 + 6x_2 + 4x_3 + 0s_1 + 0s_2 + 1s_3 &= 200{,}000
\end{aligned}
\tag{3}
$$

Non-negativity
restrictions: $\quad x_i, s_i \ge 0$

The first tableau in the simplex method selects the slack vectors as the basis set of vectors. This guarantees a feasible solution, as we shall see. The slack vectors are so chosen precisely because they are unit vectors, which together form an identity matrix. Then, because an identity matrix is its own inverse $(I = I^{-1})$, the other vectors may simply be written down as their coefficients appear in the original inequalities. This idea may be generalized for all tableaus by saying that any tableau may be generated by using the inverse of the basis matrix at that stage to multiply the original tableau. Mathematically,

$$B^{(p)-1}(x^{(1)}|A|I)_1 = (x^{(p)}|\lambda_{ij}^{(p)}|B^{(p)-1})$$ (4)

NOTE

1. The subscript 1 designates the first tableau, and A designates the original coefficient matrix.

2. $B^{(p)-1}$ is the inverse of the basis matrix at tableau (p).

3. Because the identity matrix is its own inverse, $B^{(p)-1} = I$ in the first tableau, and we have

$$I(x^{(1)}|A|I)_1 = (x^{(1)}|A|I)_1.$$

Study (4) carefully. Not only does it interrelate the notations employed so far, but it also

1. shows the positioning of the matrices at work in the simplex method (especially keep in mind that the inverse matrix appears at iteration p in the position originally occupied by the matrix of the slack variables, I);

2. presents a matrix approach to solutions [actually the simplex method does not return each iteration to the original tableau in order to compute tableau p; instead, simplex modifies the $(p - 1)$ tableau, i.e., proceeds recursively, and thereby avoids having to go through the entire inversion routine from scratch].

The flow chart in Figure 35 summarizes the simplex procedures, and Exhibit 1 considers the same problem we have been studying.

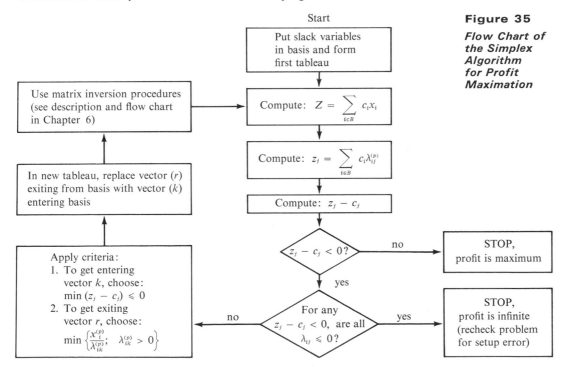

Figure 35

Flow Chart of the Simplex Algorithm for Profit Maximation

EXHIBIT 1
Procedural Comments

1. Observe column headings carefully, because they indicate contents of the tableaus. Trace the setup of Tableau 1 to the statement of the problem. Contribution margins are labeled c_j in general and c_i when the vectors are in the basis. Vectors in the basis appear under the heading $(i \in B)$. $x^{(p)}$ indicates the quantity to be made at stage p of each variable in the basis. In Tableau 1, the slack vectors s_i are in the basis, and idle time is the order of the day (we are, in fact, at the origin in the feasible region). Also in Tableau 1, we see the matrix (A) of the coefficients of the variables.

2. We see the value of Z beneath the $x^{(p)}$ column at every stage. Z is calculated by multiplying the respective contribution margins for the vectors (variables) in the basis by the corresponding values of these variables; that is, $Z = \sum c_i x_i^{(p)}$. For example, Z in Tableau 2 is $[0(50{,}000) + 0(20{,}000) + 8(50{,}000)] = 400{,}000$.

3. We also see the label $z_j - c_j$ for the row beneath each tableau. The z_j for each separate column j is gotten by multiplying the respective contribution margins for the variables in the basis by the corresponding values appearing in column j; that is, $z_j = \sum c_j \lambda_{ij}^{(p)}$. The value of c_j appearing in the column heading is then subtracted from z_j to get $z_j - c_j$. For example, the computation of $z_j - c_j$ for x_1 in Tableau 2 is as follows: $[0(\frac{1}{2}) + 0(2) + 8(\frac{1}{2})] - 6 = -2$. $z_j - c_j$ for x_2 in Tableau 3 is $[0(\frac{1}{4}) + 6(\frac{1}{2}) + 8(\frac{5}{4})] - 7 = 6$. The most negative $z_j - c_j$ at stage p is the entering vector at stage n. (p = present; n = next.)

4. The exiting vector criterion appears as the last column heading. According to this criterion, the value of $x^{(p)}$ appearing in the ith row (i.e., $x_i^{(p)}$) is divided by the value appearing in the entering vector column (Column k) in the ith row. The minimum quotient is the exiting vector. The element appearing in the entering column and exiting row is circled to designate it as the "pivot element." In the next tableau (Tableau n), the contribution margin and the variable designation of the vector chosen to enter (by applying the criterion to Tableau p) are inserted in the $(i \in B)$ position formerly occupied by the vector chosen to exit (by applying the criterion to Tableau p).

5. The Gauss-Jordan elementary row operations are then applied (once only, not the complete inversion routine), treating the circled element as the "pivot" row and the remaining rows as "other" rows.

6. The increase in profit (Z) from one tableau to the next is merely a multiplication of the quantity of the entering product to be produced at the next stage [this equals the $x_i^{(p)}/\lambda_{ik}^{(p)}$ amount opposite the exiting vector] by the negative of its opportunity cost $(z_k - c_k)$.

EXHIBIT 1
Problem

Maximize profit: $Z = \$6x_1 + \$7x_2 + \$8x_3$

Constraints:

$$1x_1 + 2x_2 + 1x_3 \le 100{,}000 \quad \text{(Machining Department capacity)}$$
$$3x_1 + 4x_2 + 2x_3 \le 120{,}000 \quad \text{(Assembling Department capacity)}$$
$$2x_1 + 6x_2 + 4x_3 \le 200{,}000 \quad \text{(Finishing Department capacity)}$$

Non-negativity
restrictions: $x_i, s_i \ge 0$

$c_j \rightarrow$			6	7	8	0	0	0	
$c_i \downarrow$	$(i \in B)$	$x^{(p)}$	x_1	x_2	x_3	s_1	s_2	s_3	$x_i^{(p)}/\lambda_{ik}^{(p)}$

Tableau 1

0	s_1	100,000	1	2	1	1	0	0	$100{,}000/1 = 100{,}000$
0	s_2	120,000	3	4	2	0	1	0	$120{,}000/2 = 60{,}000$
0	s_3	200,000	2	6	(4)	0	0	1	$200{,}000/4 = 50{,}000 \rightarrow$ (exiting vector)

$z_j - c_j$		$(Z=0)$	-6	-7	-8	0	0	0	Increase in profit at next stage:

$\uparrow$
(entering
vector)

$$\frac{200{,}000}{4}\,(8) = \$400{,}000$$

Tableau 2

0	s_1	50,000	$\tfrac{1}{2}$	$\tfrac{1}{4}$	0	1	0	$-\tfrac{1}{4}$	$50{,}000/\tfrac{1}{2} = 100{,}000$
0	s_2	20,000	(2)	1	0	0	1	$-\tfrac{1}{2}$	$20{,}000/2 = 10{,}000 \rightarrow$ (exiting vector)
\$8	x_3	50,000	$\tfrac{1}{2}$	$\tfrac{3}{2}$	1	0	0	$\tfrac{1}{4}$	$50{,}000/\tfrac{1}{2} = 100{,}000$

$z_j - c_j$		$(Z = \$400{,}000)$	-2	5	0	0	0	2	Increase in profit at next stage:

$\uparrow$
(entering
vector)

$$\frac{20{,}000}{2}\,(2) = \$20{,}000$$

Tableau 3

0	s_1	45,000	0	$\tfrac{1}{4}$	0	1	$-\tfrac{1}{4}$	$-\tfrac{1}{8}$
\$6	x_1	10,000	1	$\tfrac{1}{2}$	0	0	$\tfrac{1}{2}$	$-\tfrac{1}{4}$
\$8	x_3	45,000	0	$\tfrac{5}{4}$	1	0	$-\tfrac{1}{4}$	$\tfrac{3}{8}$

$z_j - c_j$		$(Z = \$420{,}000)$	0	6	0	0	1	$\tfrac{3}{2}$

Profits at the optimum are \$420,000. 10,000 units of x_1 and 45,000 units of x_3
should be produced. Idle capacity in Machining Department = 45,000 hours.

Let us see how Tableau 3 in Exhibit 1 could be generated in terms of the matrices of (4).

Tableau 1

$i \in B^{(3)}$ ↓	$B^{(3)-1}$			$x^{(1)}$	A			I		
s_1	1	$-\frac{1}{4}$	$-\frac{1}{8}$	100,000	1	2	1	1	0	0
x_1	0	$\frac{1}{2}$	$-\frac{1}{4}$	120,000	3	4	2	0	1	0
x_3	0	$-\frac{1}{4}$	$\frac{3}{8}$	200,000	2	6	4	0	0	1

Tableau 3

	$x^{(3)}$	$\lambda_{ij}^{(3)}$			$B^{(3)-1}$		
=	45,000	0	$\frac{1}{4}$	0	1	$-\frac{1}{4}$	$-\frac{1}{8}$
	10,000	1	$\frac{1}{2}$	0	0	$\frac{1}{2}$	$-\frac{1}{4}$
	45,000	0	$\frac{5}{4}$	1	0	$-\frac{1}{4}$	$\frac{3}{8}$

Importance of the Inverse Matrix

We are given a basis matrix B and must rewrite other vectors in the space as linear combinations of the basis vectors. The coefficients necessary to effect these linear combinations appear in the Tableau 3 matrix above. We seek the set of λ_{ij} in the expression $x_j = \sum \lambda_{ij} b_j$, where b_j is the set of basis vectors (or what is the same thing, matrix B). To illustrate, assume we know that s_1, x_1, and x_3 are in the basis B and we wish to find λ_{ij} in order to express x_2 as a linear combination of these basis vectors. The problem and its solution are as follows.

Problem

$$
\begin{array}{c}
\begin{array}{ccc} s_1 & x_1 & x_3 \end{array} \\
B \\
\begin{bmatrix} 1 & 1 & 1 \\ 0 & 3 & 2 \\ 0 & 2 & 4 \end{bmatrix}
\end{array}
\begin{array}{c} \lambda \\ \begin{bmatrix} \lambda_{12} \\ \lambda_{22} \\ \lambda_{32} \end{bmatrix} \end{array}
=
\begin{array}{c} x_2 \\ \begin{bmatrix} 2 \\ 4 \\ 6 \end{bmatrix} \end{array}
$$

Solution

$$
\begin{array}{c} B^{-1} \\ \begin{bmatrix} 1 & -\frac{1}{4} & -\frac{1}{8} \\ 0 & \frac{1}{2} & -\frac{1}{4} \\ 0 & -\frac{1}{4} & \frac{3}{8} \end{bmatrix} \end{array}
\begin{array}{c} x_2 \\ \begin{bmatrix} 2 \\ 4 \\ 6 \end{bmatrix} \end{array}
=
\begin{array}{c} \lambda_{i2} \\ \begin{bmatrix} \frac{1}{4} \\ \frac{1}{2} \\ \frac{5}{4} \end{bmatrix} \end{array}
$$

Proof

$$
\begin{array}{c} x_2 \\ \begin{bmatrix} 2 \\ 4 \\ 6 \end{bmatrix} \end{array}
=
\frac{1}{4}
\begin{array}{c} s_1 \\ \begin{bmatrix} 1 \\ 0 \\ 0 \end{bmatrix} \end{array}
+
\frac{1}{2}
\begin{array}{c} x_1 \\ \begin{bmatrix} 1 \\ 3 \\ 2 \end{bmatrix} \end{array}
+
\frac{5}{4}
\begin{array}{c} x_3 \\ \begin{bmatrix} 1 \\ 2 \\ 4 \end{bmatrix} \end{array}
$$

Conclusion B^{-1} may be used to determine the set of scalars λ_{ij} necessary to express vectors not in the basis in terms of the basis vectors. This is perfectly general; given the times of a new product, say x_4, it would be necessary only to multiply these times by the inverse matrix $(B^{(3)-1})$ to obtain the linear combination scalars,

Chapter 8: Graphs and Simplex Algorithm

λ_{i4}, at Tableau 3. Then, if $z_4 - c_4 < 0$, x_4 enters the basis and we continue the process until a new optimum solution is reached.

Thus far, the discussion has focussed on the $\leq$ type of inequality. Slack variables with zero unit contribution margins were introduced to convert the inequalities to equations. If the inequality is of the $\geq$ type, two new variables are used to generate equations: a surplus variable (which has a coefficient of -1 and a unit contribution margin of zero), and an artificial variable (which has a coefficient of 1 and a unit contribution margin of $-M$ in a profit maximization problem and M in a cost minimization problem). Frequently the word "slack" is used to refer to both slack and surplus variables. The -1 coefficient of a surplus variable serves to reduce the $\geq$ to $=$, and the artificial variable is introduced to provide a unit vector to complete the identity matrix in the first tableau. The $-M$ associated with the artificial variable in a maximization problem is intended to represent a very large negative number in order to drive this vector from the basis as soon as possible. It may help to think in the following terms: $-M = -10,000$ or, if that is not negative enough, try $-M = -10,000,000$. The point is that M is considerably larger than (and has an opposite sign to) any other contribution margin c_j in the particular problem. If an artificial vector remains in the basis in the final tableau, it means that no solution to the problem will satisfy all the constraints.

By convention and because it assures completion of the identity matrix for the first tableau, constraints that are already equations are nevertheless altered by appending artificial variables a_i. Here the artificials have $+1$ coefficients and prices of either $-M$ (in a maximization problem) or M (in a minimization problem).

Exhibit 2 illustrates the restatement of all types of linear constraints in its first tableau. The objective function could be restated as

$$\text{maximize } Z = \$6x_1 + \$7x_2 + \$8x_3 + \$0 \sum s_i - M \sum a_i$$

If there is a feasible solution, the a_i will each have a zero value (i.e., they will not appear in the optimal basis). Note that this problem is the same as the preceding one except for the signs in the constraints. To give the revised problem some new managerial significance, assume that management has imposed a "full employment" policy for the Finishing Department and an "at least full employment" policy for the Assembling Department. The astute reader immediately senses that something is amiss; he thinks: Is there no limit to how far the company will go in its "at least full employment" policy? In answer to this question, it may be said that if an upper limit, say a hours, were known, it would be necessary to introduce an additional constraint: $3x_1 + 4x_2 + 2x_3 \leq a$. For simplicity we shall assume that any figure, however large, is permissible (actually a limit will be imposed by both the first and third constraints).

EXHIBIT 2

Problem

Maximize profit: $\qquad Z = \$6x_1 + \$7x_2 + \$8x_3$

Constraints:
$$1x_1 + 2x_2 + 1x_3 \le 100{,}000$$
$$3x_1 + 4x_2 + 2x_3 \ge 120{,}000$$
$$2x_1 + 6x_2 + 4x_3 = 200{,}000$$

Non-negativity restrictions: $\qquad x_i,\ s_i \ge 0$

$c_j \rightarrow$			6	7	8	0	0	$-M$	$-M$	
c_i	$(i \in B)$	$x^{(p)}$	x_1	x_2	x_3	s_1	s_2	a_2	a_3	$x_i^{(p)}/\lambda_{ik}^{(p)}$

Tableau 1

c_i	$(i\in B)$	$x^{(p)}$	x_1	x_2	x_3	s_1	s_2	a_2	a_3	$x_i^{(p)}/\lambda_{ik}^{(p)}$
0	s_1	100,000	1	2	1	1	0	0	0	100,000/2 = 50,000
$-M$	a_2	120,000	3	(4)	2	0	-1	1	0	120,000/4 = 30,000 →
$-M$	a_3	200,000	2	6	4	0	0	0	1	200,000/6 = 33,333
$z_j - c_j$	$(Z = -320{,}000M)$		$-5M-6$	$-10M-7$	$-6M-8$	0	M	0	0	

↑ (under x_2)

Tableau 2

c_i	$(i\in B)$	$x^{(p)}$	x_1	x_2	x_3	s_1	s_2	a_2	a_3	$x_i^{(p)}/\lambda_{ik}^{(p)}$
0	s_1	40,000	$-\frac{1}{2}$	0	0	1	$\frac{1}{2}$	$-\frac{1}{2}$	0	40,000/$\frac{1}{2}$ = 80,000
7	x_2	30,000	$\frac{3}{4}$	1	$\frac{1}{2}$	0	$-\frac{1}{4}$	$\frac{1}{4}$	0	------------
$-M$	a_3	20,000	$-\frac{5}{2}$	0	1	0	$(\frac{3}{2})$	$-\frac{3}{2}$	1	20,000/$\frac{3}{2}$ = 13,333$\frac{1}{3}$ →
$z_j - c_j$	$(Z = -20{,}000M + \$210{,}000)$		$\frac{5}{2}M-\frac{3}{4}$	0	$-M-\frac{9}{2}$	0	$-\frac{3}{2}M-\frac{7}{4}$	$\frac{3}{2}M+\frac{7}{4}$	0	

↑ (under s_2)

Tableau 3

c_i	$(i\in B)$	$x^{(p)}$	x_1	x_2	x_3	s_1	s_2	a_2	a_3	$x_i^{(p)}/\lambda_{ik}^{(p)}$
0	s_1	100,000/3	$\frac{1}{3}$	0	$-\frac{1}{3}$	1	0	0	$-\frac{1}{3}$	$\frac{100{,}000}{3}/\frac{1}{3} = 100{,}000$
7	x_2	100,000/3	$(\frac{1}{3})$	1	$\frac{2}{3}$	0	0	0	$\frac{1}{6}$	$\frac{100{,}000}{3}/\frac{1}{3} = 100{,}000$ →
0	s_2	40,000/3	$-\frac{5}{3}$	0	$\frac{2}{3}$	0	1	-1	$\frac{2}{3}$	------------
$z_j - c_j$	$(Z = \$700{,}000/3)$		$-11/3$	0	$-10/3$	0	0	M	$M+\frac{7}{6}$	

↑ (under x_1)

Tableau 4

c_i	$(i\in B)$	$x^{(p)}$	x_1	x_2	x_3	s_1	s_2	a_2	a_3
0	s_1	0	0	-1	-1	1	0	0	$-\frac{1}{2}$
6	x_1	100,000	1	3	2	0	0	0	$\frac{1}{2}$
0	s_2	180,000	0	5	4	0	1	-1	$\frac{3}{2}$
$z_j - c_j$	$(Z = \$600{,}000)$		0	11	4	0	0	M	$3+M$

Profits at the optimum are $600,000. 100,000 units of x_1 should be produced. 180,000 additional hours of capacity must be obtained for the Assembling Department to achieve the optimum profits. Actually, the solution is degenerate, since s_1 is in the basis at a zero level. More will be said about degeneracy shortly. INDICATIONS

The inverse is still found under the slacks if slacks are taken in a broader sense to include artificials. To wit, NOTE

$$
\begin{array}{ccccccc}
 & B & & & B^{-1} & & I \\
s_1 & x_1 & s_2 & s_1 & a_2 & a_3 & \\
\begin{bmatrix} 1 & 1 & 0 \\ 0 & 3 & -1 \\ 0 & 2 & 0 \end{bmatrix} & & & \begin{bmatrix} 1 & 0 & -\frac{1}{2} \\ 0 & 0 & \frac{1}{2} \\ 0 & -1 & \frac{3}{2} \end{bmatrix} & & & = \begin{bmatrix} 1 & 0 & 0 \\ 0 & 1 & 0 \\ 0 & 0 & 1 \end{bmatrix}
\end{array}
$$

It is well to note a few additional facts about the simplex algorithm: Further Remarks About Simplex

1. It has been said that the solution is optimal (and the iterations are finished) when $z_j - c_j \geq 0$ for all vectors not in the basis. The iterations are also completed, however, if all $\lambda_{ij} \leq 0$ for any $z_j - c_j < 0$. In such a case, the solution is said to be unbounded, and the profit Z becomes infinite. It is well to reconsider the constraints in such an instance to see if an important one has been omitted.

2. If there are ties in values in either the entering or the exiting criterion at any stage, arbitrarily select one of the tied candidate vectors. Where ties exist in exiting vectors, the problem is degenerate. In the next tableau, one of the tied vectors (the one left in the basis) will be in the basis at a zero level. However, in general, this does not create any procedural problems; continue the simplex technique in the ordinary way.

Sensitivity and Applications

Let us briefly review simplex procedures. Exhibit 3 contains a short problem you should solve before reading the printed solution. A Review Problem

In Tableau 3 of Exhibit 3, the $z_j - c_j$ values under the slack variables have been labeled "dual evaluators." The dual evaluators or "shadow prices," as they are often called, indicate the opportunity cost of using each of the respective departments for one hour. These are opportunity costs in the true sense of the word, because they are measured in terms of foregoing the next best alternative. They answer the question, "What does it cost to use facilities?" The answer to this question is meaningful only when the facilities Dual Evaluators are already optimally employed. You would expect, for instance, that the opportunity cost would be zero for using the facilities of a department that has idle capacity and no other means of turning the idle capacity into revenue. The dual evaluator for such a department will be zero. For a demonstration of this fact, see Exhibit 1, Tableau 3. There the Machining Department has idle capacity, and we find $z_j - c_j = 0$ under the s_1 column.

The potential uses of dual evaluators are indeed great, and we shall shortly investigate one suggested accounting use of them. However, first we should recognize certain limitations, because, just as opportunity costs generally change when alternatives change, a given set of shadow prices pertain only for specified ranges of contribution margins, capacities, and capacity utilization coefficients (i.e., the a_{ij} previously described).

Sensitivity   These last thoughts bring us to the subject of sensitivity analysis. Here we are concerned with the question, "How much can the parameters $[c_j, a_{ij}, x_i^{(1)}]$ of the system change without changing the membership of the set of basis vectors in the optimal solution and without changing the dual evaluators?" Space restrictions prevent the complete development of the answer to the question. It can be observed, however, that the inverse matrix plays a central role in sensitivity analysis, and we can illustrate this fairly simply with the capacity parameters.

Capacities may change without removing a vector from the basis, although this may change the quantities produced. For simplicity of notation, let $x^{(1)}$, the original capacities, be represented by b. In the general case,

$$B^{(p)^{-1}} b = x^{(p)}$$

Then introduce new capacities $\hat{b}$, where $\hat{b} = b + \Delta b$ and Δb stands for the positive or negative change introduced. Our basis vectors need not be changed so long as

$$B^{(p)^{-1}} \hat{b} = \hat{x}^{(p)}, \quad \text{and} \quad \hat{x}^{(p)} \text{ is } \geq 0$$

(This is the non-negativity restriction.) But this is tantamount to saying that

$$B^{(p)^{-1}}(b + \Delta b) = B^{(p-1)}b + B^{(p)^{-1}} \Delta b = x^{(p)} + B^{(p)^{-1}} \Delta b$$

Consequently, so long as

$$x^{(p)} + B^{(p)^{-1}} \Delta b \geq 0$$

the vectors that were in the optimal basis remain in the basis but at different values.

We must be careful as to what it is that we want to do; we do not wish to drive all the vectors out of the basis. If all vectors were to be driven out simultaneously, we would choose $\Delta b = -b$ to make $\hat{x}^{(p)} = 0$. Exceed this point [i.e., select $\Delta b = -(b + \epsilon)$, where ϵ is a very small quantity], and we will

EXHIBIT 3
Problem

Maximize profit: $\quad Z = \$20x_1 + \$16x_2 + \$25x_3$

Constraints: $\qquad\qquad x_1 + 2x_2 + x_3 \leq 40$ (Department 1 capacity)

$\qquad\qquad\qquad\qquad 5x_1 + x_2 + 6x_3 \leq 60$ (Department 2 capacity)

Non-negativity
restrictions: $\qquad\qquad x_i, s_i \geq 0$

$c_j \rightarrow$			20	16	25	0	0	
c_i $\downarrow$	$(i \in B)$	$x^{(p)}$	x_1	x_2	x_3	s_1	s_2	$x_i^{(p)}/\lambda_{ik}^{(p)}$

Tableau 1

0	s_1	40	1	2	1	1	0	$40/1 = 40$
0	s_2	60	5	1	⑥	0	1	$60/6 = 10 \rightarrow$
$z_j - c_j$		$(Z = 0)$ -20		-16	-25	0	0	

Expected increase in profits:
$$\frac{60}{6}(\$25) = \$250 = \frac{\$2,750}{11}$$

Tableau 2

0	s_1	30	$\frac{1}{6}$	$\frac{11}{6}$	0	1	$-\frac{1}{6}$	$30/\frac{11}{6} = 180/11 \rightarrow$
25	x_3	10	$\frac{5}{6}$	$\frac{1}{6}$	1	0	$\frac{1}{6}$	$10/\frac{1}{6} = 60$
$z_j - c_j$		$(Z = \$250)$	$\frac{5}{6}$	$-\frac{71}{6}$	0	0	$\frac{25}{6}$	

Expected increase in profits:
$$\left(30 \div \frac{11}{6}\right)\left(\frac{71}{6}\right) = \frac{\$2,130}{11}$$

Tableau 3

16	x_2	180/11	$\frac{1}{11}$	1	0	$\frac{6}{11}$	$-\frac{1}{11}$	
25	x_3	80/11	$\frac{9}{11}$	0	1	$-\frac{1}{11}$	$\frac{2}{11}$	
$z_j - c_j$		$\left(Z = \dfrac{\$4,880}{11}\right)$	$\frac{21}{11}$	0	0	$\frac{71}{11}$	$\frac{34}{11}$	$\leftarrow$ Dual evaluators

$B^{(3)} \qquad B^{(3)-1} = I$

Optimal profit $= \dfrac{\$4,880}{11}$

Optimal program: produce $180/11 \, x_2$ and $80/11 \, x_3$.

Also: $B^{(3)-1}$ times Tableau 1 yields Tableau 3.

violate the non-negativity restrictions. What we want to do is to drive some one vector from the basis. Let us make this notion concrete by working with the problem of Exhibit 3.

Initially, our goal will be to drive x_2 out of the basis and leave x_3 in at some quantity k. How must we select $\hat{b}$ to accomplish our purpose? Recall that

$$B^{(3)-1} = \begin{bmatrix} \frac{6}{11} & -\frac{1}{11} \\ -\frac{1}{11} & \frac{2}{11} \end{bmatrix}$$

and that

$$B^{(3)} = \begin{bmatrix} 2 & 1 \\ 1 & 6 \end{bmatrix}$$

Then we may determine $\hat{b}$ as follows:

Goal:

$$\overset{B^{(3)-1}}{\begin{bmatrix} \frac{6}{11} & -\frac{1}{11} \\ -\frac{1}{11} & \frac{2}{11} \end{bmatrix}} \overset{\hat{b}}{\begin{bmatrix} \hat{b}_1 \\ \hat{b}_2 \end{bmatrix}} = \overset{x^{(3)}}{\begin{bmatrix} 0 \\ k \end{bmatrix}}$$

Solution:

$$B^{(3)}B^{(3)-1}\hat{b} = \hat{b} = B^{(3)}\hat{x}^{(3)} = \begin{bmatrix} 2 & 1 \\ 1 & 6 \end{bmatrix}\begin{bmatrix} 0 \\ k \end{bmatrix} = \begin{bmatrix} k \\ 6k \end{bmatrix}$$

Implication:

$$\overset{\hat{b}}{\begin{bmatrix} k \\ 6k \end{bmatrix}} - \overset{b}{\begin{bmatrix} 40 \\ 60 \end{bmatrix}} = \overset{\Delta b}{\begin{bmatrix} k - 40 \\ 6k - 60 \end{bmatrix}}$$

Consequently, if capacities change as shown under Δb, x_2 will leave the basis.

Demonstration:

Let $k = 10$; then

$$\Delta b = \begin{bmatrix} -30 \\ 0 \end{bmatrix}$$

and the new value of $\hat{x}^{(3)}$ would be

$$\begin{bmatrix} \frac{6}{11} & -\frac{1}{11} \\ -\frac{1}{11} & \frac{2}{11} \end{bmatrix}\overset{b}{\begin{bmatrix} 10 \\ 60 \end{bmatrix}} = \overset{x^{(3)}}{\begin{bmatrix} 0 \\ 10 \end{bmatrix}}$$

Similarly, x_3 can be driven out instead of x_2 if

$$\Delta b = \begin{bmatrix} 2k - 40 \\ k - 60 \end{bmatrix}$$

To summarize, if

$$\Delta b = \begin{bmatrix} 2k - 40 \\ k - 60 \end{bmatrix} \quad \text{or} \quad \begin{bmatrix} k - 40 \\ 6k - 60 \end{bmatrix}$$

for any k whatever, then our optimal production program changes regarding both which products are produced and the quantity produced of each product. Any changes in capacity (Δb) not occurring in these proportions only cause alterations in the optimal quantities of the products presently produced. For example, let

$$\Delta b = \begin{bmatrix} 10 \\ 20 \end{bmatrix}$$

By using the present inverse, we may compute our new quantities as follows:

$$\begin{matrix} B^{(3)-1} & b & \Delta b & \hat{x}^{(3)} \end{matrix}$$

$$\begin{bmatrix} \frac{6}{11} & -\frac{1}{11} \\ -\frac{1}{11} & \frac{2}{11} \end{bmatrix} \left(\begin{bmatrix} 40 \\ 60 \end{bmatrix} + \begin{bmatrix} 10 \\ 20 \end{bmatrix} \right) = \begin{bmatrix} 22 \\ 10 \end{bmatrix}$$

Professor J. M. Samuels made a most interesting observation:

Dual Evaluators and Variance Analysis

> In the normal accounting procedures, if one department...does not produce its budgeted output, a certain amount of the overheads will not be absorbed. The real loss, however, is the amount of profit that the business has failed to obtain, or the difference between what could have been achieved with the optimal plan and what was achieved.[4]

Acting on this viewpoint, Samuels developed an LP approach to variance analysis that relies on the use of shadow prices. Essentially, the system he devised can be reduced to

1. determining the optimal production program, its profit and shadow prices,
2. setting a "budget," say, in hours based on this optimal program,
3. calculating the differences between actual and "budget,"
4. multiplying the differences by the shadow prices, and
5. assigning responsibility for the foregone profits (or extra earnings) to the appropriate department(s).

Let us use the problem of Exhibit 3 to illustrate a shadow price approach to variance analysis. Assume that the departments are linked in series with Department 2 using the output of Department 1. First let us fix the

---

[4] J. M. Samuels, "Opportunity Costing: An Application of Mathematical Programming," *Journal of Accounting Research*, Autumn, 1965, p. 185.

relationship between the shadow prices and the contribution margins firmly in mind. We note the following equations:

FOR x_2: $2\left(\dfrac{\$71}{11}\right) + 1\left(\dfrac{\$34}{11}\right) = \dfrac{\$176}{11} = \$16$

FOR x_3: $1\left(\dfrac{\$71}{11}\right) + 6\left(\dfrac{\$34}{11}\right) = \dfrac{\$275}{11} = \$25$

If the optimal quantities ($x_2 = \frac{180}{11}$, $x_3 = \frac{80}{11}$) are made, the optimal profits, \$4,880/11, will be generated and each department will "make budget."

Shadow prices [$\sum$ (Times)(Optimal quantities)] = "Budget"

DEPARTMENT 1: $\dfrac{\$71}{11}$ $\left[2\left(\dfrac{180}{11}\right) + 1\left(\dfrac{80}{11}\right)\right]$ $=$ $\dfrac{\$2,840}{11}$

DEPARTMENT 2: $\dfrac{\$34}{11}$ $\left[1\left(\dfrac{180}{11}\right) + 6\left(\dfrac{80}{11}\right)\right]$ $=$ $\dfrac{\$2,040}{11}$

Total Profit $\dfrac{\$4,880}{11}$

Now suppose Department 1 makes $\frac{187}{11}$ units of x_2 and only $\frac{66}{11}$ of x_3. This results in the department equaling "budget":

$$\frac{\$71}{11}\left[2\left(\frac{187}{11}\right) + \left(\frac{66}{11}\right)\right] = \frac{\$2,840}{11}$$

However, it also results in Department 2 falling short of its budget because it must then produce off-optimum quantities. Because, in our example, Department 2 is limited to the units it receives from Department 1, we have

Available capacity $=$ 60
Time required for x_3 $= [6(\frac{66}{11})] =$ 36
Time remaining for x_2 = 24 (of which only 17 $= \frac{187}{11}$ are used)

Profits generated by Department 2:

$$\frac{\$34}{11}\left[1\left(\frac{187}{11}\right) + 6\left(\frac{66}{11}\right)\right] = \frac{\$1,802}{11}$$

Consequently, the action taken by Department 1 in disrupting the optimal combination has led to Department 2 being idle 7 hours (because it had no units to work on) and to a reduction in profits of \$238/11 [i.e., 7(\$34/11)].

Suppose further that Department 2 made only $\frac{176}{11}x_2$ and $\frac{66}{11}x_3$. Then, Department 2 would be held for the difference between what it actually made and what it could have made from the quantities it received from Department 1; that is,

$$\frac{\$34}{11}\left(\frac{187}{11} - \frac{176}{11}\right) = \frac{\$34}{11}$$

Chapter 8: Graphs and Simplex Algorithm

An interesting issue arises under this approach when a department has idle capacity and, hence, a shadow price of $0. Here, control would probably have to be achieved by comparison of input and output times (and pertinent costs) as is done in traditional variance analysis, unless this department were also responsible for some other department failing to "make budget."

An important advantage of the Samuel's approach over traditional variance analysis would seem to lie in its appeal. It seems much more dynamic to hold someone responsible for foregone profits than for unabsorbed costs.

Problems

1. The statement of a linear programing problem having to do with the optimal selection of products for production in two departments is as follows:

    Maximize profits: $\quad Z = \$15X_1 + \$18X_2 + \$24X_3$

    Constraints: $\qquad\qquad\quad 2X_1 + \quad 3X_2 + \quad 2X_3 \le 120$
    $\qquad\qquad\qquad\qquad\quad 3X_1 + \quad X_2 + \quad 4X_3 \le 180$

    Non-negativity
    restrictions: $\qquad\qquad X_i \ge 0$

    The inverse matrix for the vectors in the basis in the optimal tableau is

    $$B^{-1}$$
    $$\begin{bmatrix} \frac{2}{5} & -\frac{1}{5} \\ -\frac{1}{10} & \frac{3}{10} \end{bmatrix}$$

    (a) Use B^{-1} to generate the optimal tableau and determine the optimal program and its profits.

    (b) Determine whether product X_4 should be manufactured, given that its contribution margin C_4 is $30 and that it takes 2 units of time in Department 1 and 5 units of time in Department 2.

    (c) If X_4 is to be produced, compute the new program.

2. Maximize: $\quad Z = \$0.60x_1 + \$0.70x_2 + \$0.50x_3$

    Constraints: $\qquad\quad 2.4x_1 + \quad 3.0x_2 + \quad 2.0x_3 \le 1,200$
    $\qquad\qquad\qquad\qquad\quad 2.5x_2 + \quad 1.5x_3 \le \quad 600$
    $\qquad\qquad\quad 5.0x_1 \qquad\qquad\quad + \quad 2.5x_3 \le 1,500$

    Answer: $\quad Z = \$295.20; \ x_1 = 180, \ x_2 = 96, \ x_3 = 240$

3. Maximize: $Z = 5A - 2B + 3C$

   Constraints:
   $$2A + 2B - C \geq 2$$
   $$3A - 4B \qquad \leq 3$$
   $$B + 3C \leq 5$$

   Answer: $Z = 85/3$; $A = 23/3$, $B = 5$

4. Consider the problem presented in Exhibit 1. Suppose a new product, x_4, which requires 2 hours of machining, 3 hours of assembling, and 2 hours of finishing, can be made. What minimum contribution margin must x_4 have to cause the company to consider seriously its adoption?

5. A company can manufacture any one of three products on its four pieces of equipment. The market for these products is such that any amount the company sells will not affect market prices. Determine the company's monthly profit and its optimal production program from the following data. (Try to solve the problem without consulting the hint.)

		Unit material costs	Net unit selling price
PRODUCT	A	$20	$ 50
	B	40	125
	C	50	150

Note   The unit selling price is the net of variable selling and administrative expenses.

		Machine times (hours)			Machine capacity (hours)	Variable costs of labor and overhead per hour of machine time
		A	B	C		
MACHINE	(1)	2	1.5	4	7,000	$10
	(2)	3	2	0	4,000	8
	(3)	0	3	0	3,000	20
	(4)	0	3	2	6,000	15

Machines (1) and (2) are similar; so are machines (3) and (4). A product is made on either (1) or (2) and then may go on to either (3) or (4) if necessary.

Other monthly manufacturing, selling, and administrative expenses that are either fixed in amount or joint to one or more products amount to $25,000.

Hint   The contribution margin per product cannot be stated as a single figure for every product, because a unit of product may be made on different machines at a different cost. It is necessary, therefore, to consider products in terms of variables that reflect the variety of production processes; to wit,

P_{ijk} = product i ($i = A, B, C$) begun on machine j ($j = 1, 2$) and finished on machine k ($k = 0, 3, 4$, where $k = 0$ indicates a product not requiring further processing beyond the first operation).

6. There is a famous linear programing model known as "The Warehousing
Model." In its basic form, the model addresses the buying, selling, and storage
problems of a warehouse manager.

K = warehouse capacity
S = initial stock of inventory in the warehouse
p_j = units to be purchased (or made) in period j ($j = 1, 2, \ldots, n$)
s_j = units to be sold in period j
m_j = market price per unit sold in j
c_j = cost per unit purchased (or made) in j

It is assumed that sales in period i must be made from inventory available at
the start of the period; consequently, sales may be expressed as follows:

$$\sum_{j=1}^{i} s_j \leq S + \sum_{j=1}^{i-1} p_j$$

Purchases during period i are limited to available storage capacity; therefore,
we have

$$\sum_{j=1}^{i} p_j \leq K - S + \sum_{j=1}^{i} s_j$$

Since the manager seeks to maximize profit, the complete statement of the
problem is

Maximize profits: $\quad \sum_{j=1}^{n} m_j s_j - \sum_{j=1}^{n} c_j p_j$

Constraints: $\quad \sum_{j=1}^{i} p_j - \sum_{j=1}^{i} s_j \leq K - S; \quad -\sum_{j=1}^{i-1} p_j + \sum_{j=1}^{i} s_j \leq S$

Non-negativity
  restrictions: $\quad p_j, s_j \geq 0$

When viewed in terms of the original tableau, the problem appears as
shown below.

$c_j \rightarrow$		c_1	c_2	$\ldots$	c_{n-1}	c_n	m_1	m_2	m_3	$\ldots$	m_n	
	$x^{(p)}$	p_1	p_2	$\ldots$	p_{n-1}	p_n	s_1	s_2	s_3	$\ldots$	s_n	"slacks"
	$K - S$	1					1					1
	$K - S$	1	1				1	1				1
	$\vdots$											
	$K - S$	1	1	$\ldots$	1	1	1	1	1	$\ldots$	1	$\ldots 1$
	S	0					1					1
	S	-1					1	1				1
	S	-1	-1				1	1	1			1
	$\vdots$											
	S	-1	-1	$\ldots -1$		0	1	1	1	$\ldots$	1	$\ldots 1$

Parameter values are estimated for c_j and m_j, and values for K and S are known. The simplex algorithm solves for values of p_j and s_j.

(a) What meaning should be attached to the shadow prices?

(b) Suppose we substituted "receipts" and "disbursements" or "incomes" and "expenses" for "sales" and "purchases" in the warehousing problem. What other accounting areas might be studied in this context?

Answer: Some excellent answers to these questions may be found in:

A. Charnes, W. W. Cooper, and M. H. Miller, "Application of Linear Programming to Financial Budgeting and the Costing of Funds," *J. Business of Univ. of Chicago*, January, 1959.

These answers are repeated and developed further in:

A. Charnes and W. W. Cooper, *Management Models and Industrial Applications of Linear Programming*, vol. II (New York: John Wiley & Sons, 1961), ch. 17.

Linear Programing:
The Transportation Problem

Procedures

The problems we have dealt with so far have been concerned with supply. No limitations on production have been imposed by way of demand constraints. The transportation problem, however, considers both demand and supply constraints simultaneously.

Exhibit 1 presents a problem in which four customers, *A*, *B*, *C*, and *D*, require 11, 20, 10, and 14 truckloads (or, more generally, "units"), respectively. There are three warehouses, Warehouse 1, Warehouse 2, and Warehouse 3, that can supply these four customers subject to the quantities they have available (25 truckloads, 12 truckloads, and 18 truckloads, respectively). The cost per truckload from each source (supply) warehouse to each customer destination (demand) is also known. Note that the total truckloads demanded equals the total truckloads available. The problem is then to minimize the total cost of shipping.

Five tableaus are presented in Exhibit 1, and, though they look formidable, many people find them considerably easier to work with than simplex tableaus. A typical cell and its contents are as follows:

c_{ij} is the cost to ship from warehouse *i* to customer *j*　　　　**KEY**

219

$x_{ij}^{(p)}$ is the quantity shipped in tableau p from warehouse i to customer j. If no quantity appears, it is an unused route.

$z_j - c_j$ has the same meaning as heretofore (it is the unit cost, which will be multiplied by $x_{ij}^{(n)}$ and the total subtracted from $Z^{(p)}$ to obtain $Z^{(n)}$, where p = present tableau and n = next tableau).

EXHIBIT 1

Problem

Minimize: $Z = C^T x = \$(3, 1, 3, 5, 2, 3, 4, 3, 1, 4, 2, 6)^T x$

Constraints:
$$x_{11} + x_{12} + x_{13} + x_{14} = 25$$
$$x_{21} + x_{22} + x_{23} + x_{24} = 12$$
$$x_{31} + x_{32} + x_{33} + x_{34} = 18$$
$$x_{11} + x_{21} + x_{31} \quad\quad = 11$$
$$x_{12} + x_{22} + x_{32} \quad\quad = 20$$
$$x_{13} + x_{23} + x_{33} \quad\quad = 10$$
$$x_{14} + x_{24} + x_{34} \quad\quad = 14$$

Non-negativity restrictions: $x_i \geq 0$

Tableau 1

$K_1 = 3 \quad K_2 = 1 \quad K_3 = 2 \quad K_4 = 6$

S_i \ D_j		A	B	C	D	TOTAL
$R_1 = 0$	①	3 11	1 14	3 -1	5 1	25
$R_2 = 2$	②	2 3	3 6	4 $6 - x$	3 x 5	12
$R_3 = 0$	③	1 2	4 -3	2 $4 + x$	6 $14 - x$	18
TOTAL		11	20	10	14	55

$Z^{(1)} = \$181$

$$K_1 = 3 \quad K_2 = 1 \quad K_3 = -3 \quad K_4 = 1$$

Tableau 2

S_i \ D_j		A	B	C	D	TOTAL
$R_1 = 0$	①	3 $11 - x$	1 $14 + x$	3 -6	5 -4	25
$R_2 = 2$	②	2 3	3 $6 - x$	4 -5	3 $6 + x$	12
$R_3 = 5$	③	1 x 7	4 2	2 10	6 $8 - x$	18
	TOTAL	11	20	10	14	55

$Z^{(2)} = \$151$

$$K_1 = 3 \quad K_2 = 1 \quad K_3 = 4 \quad K_4 = 8$$

Tableau 3

S_i \ D_j		A	B	C	D	TOTAL
$R_1 = 0$	①	3 $5 - x$	1 20	3 1	5 x 3	25
$R_2 = -5$	②	2 -4	3 -7	4 -5	3 12	12
$R_3 = -2$	③	1 $6 + x$	4 -5	2 10	6 $2 - x$	18
	TOTAL	11	20	10	14	55

$Z^{(3)} = \$109$

Procedures

Tableau 4

$$K_1 = 3 \quad K_2 = 1 \quad K_3 = 4 \quad K_4 = 5$$

S_i \ D_j	A	B	C	D	TOTAL
$R_1 = 0$ ①	3 $3 - x$	1 20	3 x 1	5 2	25
$R_2 = -2$ ②	2 -1	3 -4	4 -2	3 12	12
$R_3 = -2$ ③	1 $8 + x$	4 -5	2 $10 - x$	6 -3	18
TOTAL	11	20	10	14	55

$$Z^{(4)} = \$103$$

Tableau 5

$$K_1 = 2 \quad K_2 = 1 \quad K_3 = 3 \quad K_4 = 5$$

S_i \ D_j	A	B	C	D	TOTAL
$R_1 = 0$ ①	3 -1	1 20	3 3	5 2	25
$R_2 = -2$ ②	2 -2	3 -4	4 -3	3 12	12
$R_3 = -1$ ③	1 11	4 -4	2 7	6 -2	18
TOTAL	11	20	10	14	55

Chapter 9: The Transportation Problem

$$Z^{(5)} = \$(3, 1, 3, 5, 2, 3, 4, 3, 1, 4, 2, 6) \overset{x}{\begin{bmatrix} 0 \\ 20 \\ 3 \\ 2 \\ 0 \\ 0 \\ 0 \\ 12 \\ 11 \\ 0 \\ 7 \\ 0 \end{bmatrix}} = [\$100]$$

Because $z_j - c_j$ for any vector (cell in this case) in the basis is zero, it follows that

$$R_i^{(p)} + K_j^{(p)} = z_j - c_j = 0$$

for any $x_{ij}^{(p)}$ (i.e., for any used cell). For any unused cell,

$$z_j - c_j = [R_i^{(p)} + K_j^{(p)}] - c_{ij}$$

Because we are minimizing cost, we select as entering vector (cell) the maximum $(z_j - c_j) \geq 0$.

To avoid a "cart pulling the donkey" situation, let us study how the $x_{ij}^{(p)}$ got in the basis in the first tableau in Exhibit 1. The tableau follows the "northwest corner" rule, whereby customer A gets as much of his requirements from Warehouse 1 as possible (i.e., A's entire requirements of 11 truckloads). The remainder of Warehouse 1's supply (i.e., $25 - 11 = 14$) is then assigned to customer B, because this remainder does not exceed B's needs (if it did, we would satisfy B and give the remainder to C). We then have the remainder of B's needs (i.e., $20 - 14 = 6$) supplied by Warehouse 2 (Warehouse 2 has more than enough available to satisfy B's remaining requirements). The remainder of Warehouse 2's supply is then assigned to customer C. The remainder of C's needs is filled by Warehouse 3. And, finally, the remainder of Warehouse 3's supply is assigned to customer D, and this exactly fills D's requirements.

The cost at this stage, $Z^{(1)}$, may be computed by multiplying the $x_{ij}^{(1)}$ by their corresponding c_{ij}; that is,

$$Z^{(1)} = \sum_{i,j \in B^{(1)}} c_{ij}x_{ij}^{(1)} = \$3(11) + \$1(14) + \$3(6) + \$4(6) + \$2(4) + \$6(14) = \$181$$

The notation used in Exhibit 1, except for $R_i^{(p)}$ and $K_j^{(p)}$, should be familiar from studying simplex. $R_i^{(p)}$ and $K_j^{(p)}$ are known as keys; the R stands for row

Procedures   **223** and the K for column. Here is how their values are obtained.[1] For any used cell, c_{ij}, $c_{ij} = R_i + K_j$. Arbitrarily, set $R_1^{(p)} = 0$, and for each used cell in row 1, insert its c_{ij} as $K_j^{(p)}$ (because $c_{ij} = 0 + K_j$). Continue in the same way until row 1 is finished. Thus, in Tableau 1 in Exhibit 6, $K_1 = 3$ because $c_{11} = 3$ (i.e., $R_1 + K_1 = c_{11}$, or $0 + K_1 = 3$), and, similarly, $K_2 = 1$ because $c_{12} = 1$. Continue in row 1 and solve for any other K_j's that have assignments. Observe what has happened. Because $x_{11}^{(1)}$ is in the basis, $z_1 - c_1$ must equal zero, and so it does:

$$R_1 + K_1 - c_{11} = 0 + 3 - 3 = 0$$

Similarly,

$$R_1 + K_2 - c_{12} = 0 + 1 - 1 = 0$$

Next, scan column 1 (customer A) to see whether there are any other used cells (i.e., vectors in the basis). There are none. Proceed to column 2; $x_{22}^{(1)}$ is in use. We know

$$R_2 + K_2 - c_{22} = 0$$

Filling in known figures, we obtain

$$R_2 + 1 - 3 = 0$$

therefore, $R_2 = 2$.

Now in row 2, consider the next filled-in cell, $x_{23}^{(1)}$. We know

$$R_2 + K_3 - c_{23} = 0$$

Filling in known figures, we obtain

$$2 + K_3 - 4 = 0$$

therefore, $K_3 = 2$.

We continue in this fashion until we have all our keys. Because $z_j - c_j$ for used cells $= 0$, we do not put a zero in the lower right corner of each $x_{ij}^{(p)}$.

We must next determine the $z_j - c_j$ values for unused cells; for example, row 1, columns 3 and 4:

$$R_i^{(p)} + K_j^{(p)} - c_{ij} = z_j - c_j$$
$$R_1 + K_3 - c_{13} = 0 + 2 - 3 = -1$$
$$R_1 + K_4 - c_{14} = 0 + 6 - 5 = 1$$

Another example is row 2, columns 1 and 4:

$$R_2 + K_1 - c_{21} = 2 + 3 - 2 = 3$$
$$R_2 + K_4 - c_{24} = 2 + 6 - 3 = 5$$

---

[1] There are other ways of proceeding, but knowing a variety of these alternate approaches is of little importance. One good way, well understood, is all that is needed.

Chapter 9: The Transportation Problem

Inspect the $z_j - c_j$ values we have calculated. Locate maximum $z_j - c_j > 0$ (row 2, column 4; the value is 5). This cell (vector) is the entering vector, and, as in the simplex algorithm, we know that the improvement in the objective function in the next tableau will be $\$5x_{24}^{(2)}$. We obtain $x_{24}^{(2)}$ in such a way that we do not violate the non-negativity restrictions. That is, we cannot ship negative units. Because the rim requirements (the constraints in the right-hand column and the bottom row, excluding the common total, 55) must be observed, we are forced to indulge in a little "stealing from Peter to pay Paul." This process is known as determining the loop.

The body of Tableau 1 is reproduced below.

11	14			
	6	$6 - x$	x	12
		$4 + x$	$14 - x$	18
		10	14	

We place an x in the cell with the maximum $z_j - c_j > 0$ (i.e., in row 2, column 4). We then place $+x$ and $-x$ in the most convenient manner *that involves only used cells and that will satisfy the rim requirements*. Thus, if we add x to row 2, we must subtract it elsewhere in row 2 in order that the total of the used cells in row 2 of the next tableau will equal 12. Therefore, we subtract x from cell $(2, 3)$ (ordered pairs will be used to indicate location of a cell: the first number is the row number, the second is the column number). However, when we subtract x from $(2, 3)$, we force ourselves to add x to some other cell in column 3 in order to satisfy the 10 truckloads customer C wants. Therefore, we add x to cell $(3, 3)$, and this, in turn, forces us to subtract x from cell $(3, 4)$. This closes the loop, because we had already added x to cell $(2, 4)$. The rim requirements are now satisfied; any row that has a $+x$ also has a $-x$, and any column that has a $-x$ also has a $+x$. The appropriate loops for the other tableaus are

Tableau 2

$-x$	$+x$		
	$-x$		$+x$
$\widehat{x}$			$-x$

Tableau 3

$-x$			$\widehat{x}$
$+x$			$-x$

Tableau 4

$-x$		$\widehat{x}$	
$+x$		$-x$	

where $\widehat{x}$ = starting point.

The non-negativity restriction tells us how much to choose for x each time. We cannot take away more than the cell with the smallest value opposite a

$-x$ has to give. Hence, in Tableau 1, cell (2, 3) has the smallest value (6) opposite a $-x$, and the value of x is, therefore, 6. Tableau 2 is then prepared from Tableau 1 by adjusting the latter program by the amount $x = 6$, wherever x appears.

The basic transportation problem procedures may be summarized as follows:

1. Determine a shipping program.

2. Compute R_i and K_j values.

3. Determine $z_j - c_j$ values for all unused cells.

4. Determine a suitable loop where some $z_j - c_j > 0$.

5. Select the value of x.

6. Prepare the next tableau by repeating the process.

These steps have been inserted in the flow chart in Figure 36.

Figure 36

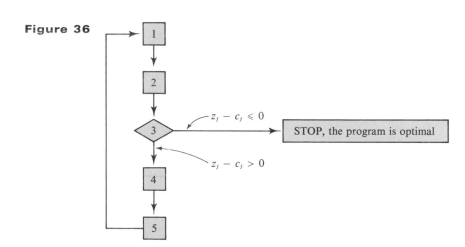

There is no necessity to use the "northwest corner" rule for a starting program. Cautious selection of minimum and "next best" row and column costs may save many iterations.

Transportation Problem Complications

The transportation problem requires that the total supplied equals the total demanded. Often demand exceeds supply or vice versa. To restore equality in such instances, "dummy" sources (demand exceeds supply and back ordering takes place) or "dummy" destinations (supply exceeds demand) are used. In concept, this is similar to introducing slack variables in the simplex algorithm; however, instead of zero costs, very large (M) costs are used to discourage the cells from being used for the "real" part of the program. Exhibit 2 illustrates the use of a "dummy" destination. The same procedures would also apply for a "dummy" source problem (it is even permissible to transpose the tableaus so that destinations are in the rows and sources are in the columns; then the "dummy" source problem would appear exactly like the "dummy" destination problem).

A transportation problem becomes "degenerate" whenever there are fewer than $m + n - 1$ (where m and n are the number of rows and columns, respectively, of the tableau) variables in the basis. The problem will become apparent when we try to solve for the $R_i K_j$. If the solution is degenerate, one or more of these values cannot be determined. To remedy the problem, an artificial, small amount ϵ is inserted in the tableau wherever needed for determining the values of the keys, R_i and K_j. This process is known as "perturbing." ϵ is treated as if it were zero. Exhibit 3 illustrates perturbing and degeneracy.

Another interesting complication occurs whenever in the optimal tableau there exists some z_j (not $z_j - c_j$) that is negative. Then, if additional units were demanded in that column and were available from that source (row), the additional units could be shipped along with the former units for less than the previous total cost. Curiously enough, the additional units are not shipped from the cell in question. Refer to the optimal solution in Exhibit 1. Close examination reveals that z_j for cell (2, 2) equals $\$-1$. If customer B demands 1 unit more and if Warehouse 2 has the additional unit to send, the new program is as follows:

EXHIBIT 2

Use of a "Dummy" Destination

	D_j	$D_1 = 8$	$D_2 = 3$	$D_3 = M - 2$	
S_i		A	B	DUMMY	TOTAL
$R_1 = 0$	①	8 $20 - x$	3 $20 + x$	M -2	40
$R_2 = 2$	②	2 x 8	5 $10 - x$	M 15	25
	TOTAL	20	30	15	65

$Z^{(1)} = 270 + 15M$

$$D_1 = 8 \qquad D_2 = 3 \qquad D_3 = M + 6$$

S_i \\ D_j		A	B	DUMMY	TOTAL
$R_1 = 0$	①	8 10 − x	3 30	M x 6	40
$R_2 = -6$	②	2 10 + x	5 −8	M 15 − x	25
	TOTAL	20	30	15	65

$$Z^{(2)} = 190 + 15M$$

$$D_1 = 2 \qquad D_2 = 3 \qquad D_3 = M$$

S_i \\ D_j		A	B	DUMMY	TOTAL
$R_1 = 0$	①	8 −6	3 30	M 10	40
$R_2 = 0$	②	2 20	5 −2	M 5	25
	TOTAL	20	30	15	65

"*Real*" *part of the program:*

Total Cost $= Z^{(3)} = \$3(30) + \$2(20) = \$130$

"*Inventory*" *part of the program:*

Warehouse 1 has 10 truckloads in inventory.
Warehouse 2 has 5 truckloads in inventory.

EXHIBIT 3

Resolving Degeneracy by Perturbing

$$K_1 = 2 \quad K_2 = 1 \quad K_3 = 1 \quad K_4 = -1$$

D_j / S_i	A	B	C	D	TOTAL
$R_1 = 0$ ①	2 $15 - x$	1 $5 + x$	3 -2	3 -4	20
$R_2 = 1$ ②	3 0	2 $35 - x$	2 $\epsilon + x$	3 -3	35
$R_3 = 3$ ③	3 x 2	5 -1	4 $20 - x$	2 12	32
$R_4 = 2$ ④	4 0	2 1	2 1	1 10	10
TOTAL	15	40	20	22	97

1. An ϵ is needed in cell (2,3) to complete the keys.   NOTE
2. To be nondegenerate, $m + n - 1$ (m and n are dimensions of matrix) variables must appear in the basis. Here, $m + n - 1 = 4 + 4 - 1 = 7$, and before ϵ there were 6.

The tableau is no longer degenerate, because 7 variables are in the basis.

D_j / S_i	A	B	C	D	TOTAL
①		20			20
②		20	15		35
③	15		5	12	32
④				10	10
TOTAL	15	40	20	22	97

S_i \\ D_j	A	B	C	D	TOTAL
①	3	1 21	3 3	5 1	25
②	2	3	4	3 13	13
③	1 11	4	2 7	6	18
TOTAL	11	21	10	14	56

$$Z = \$1(21) + \$3(3) + \$5(1) + \$3(13) + \$1(11) + \$2(7) = \$99$$

We see that 56 units have now been shipped for $99, whereas 55 units had previously cost $100! Furthermore, no shipment was made from cell (2, 2). Actually, another additional unit could be shipped with a consequent reduction to $98. This is the limit, because cell (1, 4) would become negative were another unit so treated. To see how the limit comes in, mentally form a loop for cell (2, 2), but reverse the signs of the x's and treat the resultant $-x$ in (2, 2) as if it were nonexistent, because an x cannot enter (2, 2) (if it did, it would render the program suboptimal). The smallest value opposite a $-x$ appears in cell (1, 4), and this is the limit of change that could be made.

Concluding Suggestions

If you understand and have command of all the material presented in these LP chapters, you have made a good beginning in linear programing. Great challenge and reward await you in more advanced study of linear programing. More and more areas of accounting and other aspects of management are being recast in linear programing terms. Any area formerly approached from a *ceteris paribus* (change one thing while holding all others constant) position is apt to have its foundations shaken when it is brought under a *mutatis mutandis* (change all things simultaneously, i.e., in combination) scrutiny. Many assumptions previously considered necessary before progress could be made in the study of a problem are no longer needed. As a result, reality replaces sterility, and important new insights are gained.

The accountant who recognizes the need for further linear programing knowledge will find articles on the subject in many accounting journals. However, for a thorough knowledge of its many applications to management problems, there is no more authoritative work presently available than

A. Charnes and W. W. Cooper, *Management Models and Industrial Applications of Linear Programming*, vols. I and II (New York: John Wiley & Sons, Inc., 1961).

Another book of special importance to accountants is

Yuji Ijiri, *Management Goals and Accounting for Control* (Amsterdam: North-Holland Publishing Company, 1965) (distributed by Rand McNally & Company, Chicago).

Problems

1. A trucking company has three terminals, any of which can serve any of four cities. Terminal 1 has 20 trucks, terminal 2 has 9, and terminal 3 has 14. City 1 requires 7 truckloads, City 2 requires 15, City 3 requires 10, and City 4 requires 11. The distances in miles from each terminal to each city are as follows: *Transportation*

Terminal	City 1	City 2	City 3	City 4
1	200	100	200	400
2	100	300	400	300
3	100	300	200	500

Assuming costs to be proportional to mileage, how should the company program its service to minimize cost?

2. Determine the optimal shipping program and its cost from the following data: *Demand > supply*

Customer	Quantity demanded (units)
A	30
B	20
C	15
D	40

Factory	Quantity available (units)
(1)	32
(2)	24
(3)	39

Costs to ship units:

	Customers			
	A	B	C	D
Factories (1)	20	4	8	13
(2)	7	9	2	12
(3)	14	8	15	6

3. Complete the problem below.

Origin \ Destination	D_1	D_2	D_3	D_4	D_5	TOTAL
O_1	10 / 4	20 / 6	5 / 2	9	8	12
O_2	4	15	8 / 5	25 / 2	5 / x	7
O_3	2	14	7	10 / 6	3 / 2	8
TOTAL	4	6	7	8	2	27

Answer: Note the appearance (and treatment) of degeneracy.

$$k_1 = 10 \quad k_2 = 20 \quad k_3 = 5 \quad k_4 = 22 \quad k_5 = 2$$

	Origins \ Destinations	D_1	D_2	D_3	D_4	D_5	TOTAL
$R_1 = 0$	O_1	10 / 4	20 / 6	5 / $2-x$	9 / x / 13	8 / -6	12
$R_2 = 3$	O_2	4 / 9	15 / 8	8 / $5+x$	25 / $\epsilon - x$	5 / 2	7
$R_3 = -12$	O_3	2 / -4	14 / -6	7 / -14	10 / 8	3 / -13	8
	TOTAL	4	6	7	8	2	27

$$k_1 = 10 \quad k_2 = 20 \quad k_3 = 5 \quad k_4 = 9 \quad k_5 = 2$$

Origins \ Destinations	D_1	D_2	D_3	D_4	D_5	TOTAL
$R_1 = 0$ O_1	10 $4 - x$	20 6	5 2	9 $\epsilon + x$ -6	8	12
$R_2 = 3$ O_2	4 9	15 8	8 5	25 -13	5 2	7
$R_3 = 1$ O_3	2 x 9	14 7	7 -1	10 $8 - x$	3 0	8
TOTAL	4	6	7	8	2	27

Degeneracy has now disappeared. The ordinary procedures should be con- **Note** tinued until the optimal solution is obtained.

Origins \ Destinations	D_1	D_2	D_3	D_4	D_5	TOTAL
O_1	10	20 6	5 2	9 4	8	12
O_2	4	15	8 5	25	5 2	7
O_3	2 4	14	7	10 4	3	8
TOTAL	4	6	7	8	2	27

Appendix

Table A.1 $f_{\overline{n}|r\%} = (1 + r)^n$ f = future value of a single sum

$N \downarrow$ $\% \rightarrow$	$\frac{1}{3}$	$\frac{1}{2}$	1	2
1	1.0033	1.0050	1.0100	1.0200
2	1.0067	1.0100	1.0201	1.0404
3	1.0100	1.0151	1.0303	1.0612
4	1.0134	1.0202	1.0406	1.0824
5	1.0168	1.0253	1.0510	1.1041
6	1.0201	1.0304	1.0615	1.1262
7	1.0235	1.0355	1.0721	1.1487
8	1.0270	1.0407	1.0829	1.1717
9	1.0304	1.0459	1.0937	1.1951
10	1.0338	1.0511	1.1046	1.2190
11	1.0372	1.0564	1.1157	1.2434
12	1.0407	1.0617	1.1268	1.2682
13	1.0442	1.0670	1.1381	1.2936
14	1.0476	1.0723	1.1495	1.3195
15	1.0511	1.0777	1.1610	1.3459
16	1.0546	1.0831	1.1726	1.3728
17	1.0581	1.0885	1.1843	1.4002
18	1.0617	1.0939	1.1961	1.4282
19	1.0652	1.0994	1.2081	1.4568
20	1.0687	1.1049	1.2202	1.4859
30	1.1049	1.1614	1.3478	1.8114
40	1.1422	1.2208	1.4889	2.2080
50	1.1808	1.2832	1.6446	2.6916

3	4	5	6	8	10
1.0300	1.0400	1.0500	1.0600	1.0800	1.1000
1.0609	1.0816	1.1025	1.1236	1.1664	1.2100
1.0927	1.1249	1.1576	1.1910	1.2597	1.3310
1.1255	1.1699	1.2155	1.2625	1.3605	1.4641
1.1593	1.2167	1.2763	1.3382	1.4693	1.6105
1.1941	1.2653	1.3401	1.4185	1.5869	1.7716
1.2299	1.3159	1.4071	1.5036	1.7138	1.9487
1.2668	1.3686	1.4775	1.5938	1.8509	2.1436
1.3048	1.4233	1.5513	1.6895	1.9990	2.3579
1.3439	1.4802	1.6289	1.7908	2.1589	2.5937
1.3842	1.5395	1.7103	1.8983	2.3316	2.8531
1.4258	1.6010	1.7959	2.0122	2.5182	3.1384
1.4685	1.6651	1.8856	2.1329	2.7196	3.4523
1.5126	1.7317	1.9799	2.2609	2.9372	3.7975
1.5580	1.8009	2.0789	2.3966	3.1722	4.1772
1.6047	1.8730	2.1829	2.5404	3.4259	4.5950
1.6528	1.9479	2.2920	2.6928	3.7000	5.0545
1.7024	2.0258	2.4066	2.8543	3.9960	5.5599
1.7535	2.1068	2.5270	3.0256	4.3157	6.1159
1.8061	2.1911	2.6533	3.2071	4.6610	6.7275
2.4273	3.2434	4.3219	5.7435	10.0627	17.4494
3.2620	4.8010	7.0400	10.2857	21.7245	45.2592
4.3839	7.1067	11.4674	18.4201	46.9016	117.3908

Appendix

Table A.2 $p_{\overline{n}|r\%} = (1 + r)^{-n}$ $p = $ present value of a single sum

N ↓ \ %→	$\frac{1}{3}$	$\frac{1}{2}$	1	2
1	0.9967	0.9950	0.9901	0.9804
2	0.9934	0.9901	0.9803	0.9612
3	0.9901	0.9851	0.9706	0.9423
4	0.9868	0.9802	0.9610	0.9238
5	0.9835	0.9754	0.9515	0.9057
6	0.9803	0.9705	0.9420	0.8880
7	0.9770	0.9657	0.9327	0.8706
8	0.9738	0.9609	0.9235	0.8535
9	0.9705	0.9561	0.9143	0.8368
10	0.9673	0.9513	0.9053	0.8203
11	0.9641	0.9466	0.8963	0.8043
12	0.9609	0.9419	0.8874	0.7885
13	0.9577	0.9372	0.8787	0.7730
14	0.9545	0.9326	0.8700	0.7579
15	0.9514	0.9279	0.8613	0.7430
16	0.9482	0.9233	0.8528	0.7284
17	0.9451	0.9187	0.8444	0.7142
18	0.9419	0.9141	0.8360	0.7002
19	0.9388	0.9096	0.8277	0.6864
20	0.9357	0.9051	0.8195	0.6730
30	0.9051	0.8610	0.7419	0.5521
40	0.8755	0.8191	0.6717	0.4529
50	0.8469	0.7793	0.6080	0.3715

N ↓ \ %→	12	14	15	16
1	0.8929	0.8772	0.8696	0.8621
2	0.7972	0.7695	0.7561	0.7432
3	0.7118	0.6750	0.6575	0.6407
4	0.6355	0.5921	0.5718	0.5523
5	0.5674	0.5194	0.4972	0.4761
6	0.5066	0.4556	0.4323	0.4104
7	0.4523	0.3996	0.3759	0.3538
8	0.4039	0.3506	0.3269	0.3050
9	0.3606	0.3075	0.2843	0.2630
10	0.3220	0.2697	0.2472	0.2267
11	0.2875	0.2366	0.2149	0.1954
12	0.2567	0.2076	0.1869	0.1685
13	0.2292	0.1821	0.1625	0.1452
14	0.2046	0.1597	0.1413	0.1252
15	0.1827	0.1401	0.1229	0.1079
16	0.1631	0.1229	0.1069	0.0930
17	0.1456	0.1078	0.0929	0.0802
18	0.1300	0.0946	0.0808	0.0691
19	0.1161	0.0829	0.0703	0.0596
20	0.1037	0.0728	0.0611	0.0514
30	0.0334	0.0196	0.0151	0.0116
40	0.0107	0.0053	0.0037	0.0026
50	0.0035	0.0014	0.0009	0.0006

3	4	5	6	8	10
0.9709	0.9615	0.9524	0.9434	0.9259	0.9091
0.9426	0.9246	0.9070	0.8900	0.8573	0.8264
0.9151	0.8890	0.8638	0.8396	0.7938	0.7513
0.8885	0.8548	0.8227	0.7921	0.7350	0.6830
0.8626	0.8219	0.7835	0.7473	0.6806	0.6209
0.8375	0.7903	0.7462	0.7050	0.6302	0.5645
0.8131	0.7599	0.7107	0.6651	0.5835	0.5132
0.7894	0.7307	0.6768	0.6274	0.5403	0.4665
0.7664	0.7026	0.6446	0.5919	0.5002	0.4241
0.7441	0.6756	0.6139	0.5584	0.4632	0.3855
0.7224	0.6496	0.5847	0.5268	0.4289	0.3505
0.7014	0.6246	0.5568	0.4970	0.3971	0.3186
0.6810	0.6006	0.5303	0.4688	0.3677	0.2897
0.6611	0.5775	0.5051	0.4423	0.3405	0.2633
0.6419	0.5553	0.4810	0.4173	0.3152	0.2394
0.6232	0.5339	0.4581	0.3936	0.2919	0.2176
0.6050	0.5134	0.4363	0.3714	0.2703	0.1978
0.5874	0.4936	0.4155	0.3503	0.2502	0.1799
0.5703	0.4746	0.3957	0.3305	0.2317	0.1635
0.5537	0.4564	0.3769	0.3118	0.2145	0.1486
0.4120	0.3083	0.2314	0.1741	0.0994	0.0573
0.3066	0.2083	0.1420	0.0972	0.0460	0.0221
0.2281	0.1407	0.0872	0.0543	0.0213	0.0085

20	25	30	40	50
0.8333	0.8000	0.7692	0.7143	0.6667
0.6944	0.6400	0.5917	0.5102	0.4444
0.5787	0.5120	0.4552	0.3644	0.2963
0.4823	0.4096	0.3501	0.2603	0.1975
0.4019	0.3277	0.2693	0.1859	0.1317
0.3349	0.2621	0.2072	0.1328	0.0878
0.2791	0.2097	0.1594	0.0949	0.0585
0.2326	0.1678	0.1226	0.0678	0.0390
0.1938	0.1342	0.0943	0.0484	0.0260
0.1615	0.1074	0.0725	0.0346	0.0173
0.1346	0.0859	0.0558	0.0247	0.0116
0.1122	0.0687	0.0429	0.0176	0.0077
0.0935	0.0550	0.0330	0.0126	0.0051
0.0779	0.0440	0.0254	0.0090	0.0034
0.0649	0.0352	0.0195	0.0064	0.0023
0.0541	0.0281	0.0150	0.0046	0.0015
0.0451	0.0225	0.0116	0.0033	0.0010
0.0376	0.0180	0.0089	0.0023	0.0007
0.0313	0.0144	0.0068	0.0017	0.0005
0.0261	0.0115	0.0053	0.0012	0.0003
0.0042	0.0012	0.0004	0.0000	0.0000
0.0007	0.0001	0.0000	0.0000	0.0000
0.0001	0.0000	0.0000	0.0000	0.0000

Table A.3 $F_{\overline{n}|r\%} = \sum\limits_{i=0}^{n-1} (1 + r)^i$ F = future value of an annuity

$N \downarrow$ $\% \rightarrow$	$\frac{1}{3}$	$\frac{1}{2}$	1	2
1	1.0000	1.0000	1.0000	1.0000
2	2.0033	2.0050	2.0100	2.0200
3	3.0100	3.0150	3.0301	3.0604
4	4.0200	4.0301	4.0604	4.1216
5	5.0334	5.0503	5.1010	5.2040
6	6.0502	6.0755	6.1520	6.3081
7	7.0703	7.1059	7.2135	7.4343
8	8.0939	8.1414	8.2857	8.5830
9	9.1208	9.1821	9.3685	9.7546
10	10.1512	10.2280	10.4622	10.9497
11	11.1850	11.2792	11.5.68	12.1687
12	12.2222	12.3356	12.6825	13.4121
13	13.2629	13.3972	13.8093	14.6803
14	14.3071	14.4642	14.9474	15.9739
15	15.3547	15.5365	16.0969	17.2934
16	16.4059	16.6142	17.2579	18.6393
17	17.4605	17.6973	18.4304	20.0121
18	18.5187	18.7858	19.6147	21.4123
19	19.5803	19.8797	20.8109	22.8406
20	20.6455	20.9791	22.0190	24.2974
30	31.4946	32.2800	34.7849	40.5681
40	42.7104	44.1588	48.8864	60.4020
50	54.3053	56.6451	64.4632	84.5794

3	4	5	6	8	10
1.0000	1.0000	1.0000	1.0000	1.0000	1.0000
2.0300	2.0400	2.0500	2.0600	2.0800	2.1000
3.0909	3.1216	3.1525	3.1836	3.2464	3.3100
4.1836	4.2465	4.3101	4.3746	4.5061	4.6410
5.3091	5.4163	5.5256	5.6371	5.8666	6.1051
6.4684	6.6330	6.8019	6.9753	7.3359	7.7156
7.6625	7.8983	8.1420	8.3938	8.9228	9.4872
8.8923	9.2142	9.5491	9.8975	10.6366	11.4359
10.1591	10.5828	11.0266	11.4913	12.4876	13.5795
11.4639	12.0061	12.5779	13.1808	14.4866	15.9374
12.8078	13.4864	14.2068	14.9716	16.6455	18.5312
14.1920	15.0258	15.9171	16.8699	18.9771	21.3843
15.6178	16.6268	17.7130	18.8821	21.4953	24.5227
17.0863	18.2919	19.5986	21.0151	24.2149	27.9750
18.5989	20.0236	21.5786	23.2760	27.1521	31.7725
20.1569	21.8245	23.6575	25.6725	30.3243	35.9497
21.7616	23.6975	25.8404	28.2129	33.7502	40.5447
23.4144	25.6454	28.1324	30.9056	37.4502	45.5992
25.1169	27.6712	30.5390	33.7600	41.4463	51.1591
26.8704	29.7781	33.0660	36.7856	45.7620	57.2750
47.5754	56.0849	66.4388	79.0582	113.2832	164.4940
75.4012	95.0255	120.7998	154.7619	259.0565	442.5925
112.7968	152.6670	209.3480	290.3358	573.7701	1163.9082

Table A.4 $\quad P_{\overline{n}|r\%} = \sum_{i=1}^{n} p_{\overline{i}|r\%} = \sum_{i=1}^{n} (1 + r)^{-i} \qquad P = \text{present value of an annuity}$

N ↓ / %→	$\frac{1}{3}$	$\frac{1}{2}$	1	2
1	0.9967	0.9950	0.9901	0.9804
2	1.9901	1.9851	1.9704	1.9416
3	2.9801	2.9702	2.9410	2.8839
4	3.9669	3.9505	3.9020	3.8077
5	4.9504	4.9259	4.8534	4.7135
6	5.9307	5.8964	5.7955	5.6014
7	6.9077	6.8621	6.7282	6.4720
8	7.8814	7.8230	7.6517	7.3255
9	8.8520	8.7791	8.5660	8.1622
10	9.8193	9.7304	9.4713	8.9826
11	10.7834	10.6770	10.3676	9.7868
12	11.7442	11.6189	11.2551	10.5753
13	12.7019	12.5562	12.1337	11.3484
14	13.6565	13.4887	13.0037	12.1062
15	14.6078	14.4166	13.8651	12.8493
16	15.5560	15.3399	14.7179	13.5777
17	16.5011	16.2586	15.5623	14.2919
18	17.4430	17.1728	16.3983	14.9920
19	18.3818	18.0824	17.2260	15.6785
20	19.3175	18.9874	18.0456	16.3514
30	28.5051	27.7941	25.8077	22.3965
40	37.3923	36.1722	32.8347	27.3555
50	45.9889	44.1428	39.1961	31.4236

N ↓ / %→	12	14	15	16
1	0.8929	0.8772	0.8696	0.8621
2	1.6901	1.6467	1.6257	1.6052
3	2.4018	2.3216	2.2832	2.2459
4	3.0373	2.9137	2.8550	2.7982
5	3.6048	3.4331	3.3522	3.2743
6	4.1114	3.8887	3.7845	3.6847
7	4.5638	4.2883	4.1604	4.0386
8	4.9676	4.6389	4.4873	4.3436
9	5.3282	4.9464	4.7716	4.6065
10	5.6502	5.2161	5.0188	4.8332
11	5.9377	5.4527	5.2337	5.0286
12	6.1944	5.6603	5.4206	5.1971
13	6.4235	5.8424	5.5831	5.3423
14	6.6282	6.0021	5.7245	5.4675
15	6.8109	6.1422	5.8474	5.5755
16	6.9740	6.2651	5.9542	5.6685
17	7.1196	6.3729	6.0472	5.7487
18	7.2497	6.4674	6.1280	5.8178
19	7.3658	6.5504	6.1982	5.8775
20	7.4694	6.6231	6.2593	5.9288
30	8.0552	7.0027	6.5660	6.1772
40	8.2438	7.1050	6.6418	6.2335
50	8.3045	7.1327	6.6605	6.2463

3	4	5	6	8	10
0.9709	0.9615	0.9524	0.9434	0.9259	0.9091
1.9135	1.8861	1.8594	1.8334	1.7833	1.7355
2.8286	2.7751	2.7232	2.6730	2.5771	2.4869
3.7171	3.6299	3.5460	3.4651	3.3121	3.1699
4.5797	4.4518	4.3295	4.2124	3.9927	3.7908
5.4172	5.2421	5.0757	4.9173	4.6229	4.3553
6.2303	6.0021	5.7864	5.5824	5.2064	4.8684
7.0197	6.7327	6.4632	6.2098	5.7466	5.3349
7.7861	7.4353	7.1078	6.8017	6.2469	5.7590
8.5302	8.1109	7.7217	7.3601	6.7101	6.1446
9.2526	8.7605	8.3064	7.8869	7.1390	6.4951
9.9540	9.3851	8.8633	8.3838	7.5361	6.8137
10.6350	9.9856	9.3936	8.8527	7.9038	7.1034
11.2961	10.5631	9.8986	9.2950	8.2442	7.3667
11.9379	11.1184	10.3797	9.7122	8.5595	7.6061
12.5611	11.6523	10.8378	10.1059	8.8514	7.8237
13.1661	12.1657	11.2741	10.4773	9.1216	8.0216
13.7535	12.6593	11.6896	10.8276	9.3719	8.2014
14.3238	13.1339	12.0853	11.1581	9.6036	8.3649
14.8775	13.5903	12.4622	11.4699	9.8181	8.5136
19.6004	17.2920	15.3724	13.7648	11.2578	9.4269
23.1148	19.7928	17.1591	15.0463	11.9246	9.7790
25.7298	21.4822	18.2559	15.7619	12.2335	9.9148

20	25	30	40	50	
0.8333	0.8000	0.7692	0.7143	0.6667	
1.5278	1.4400	1.3609	1.2245	1.1111	
2.1065	1.9520	1.8161	1.5889	1.4074	
2.5887	2.3616	2.1662	1.8492	1.6049	
2.9906	2.6893	2.4356	2.0352	1.7366	
3.3255	2.9514	2.6427	2.1680	1.8244	
3.6046	3.1611	2.8021	2.2628	1.8829	
3.8372	3.3289	2.9247	2.3306	1.9220	
4.0310	3.4631	3.0190	2.3790	1.9480	
4.1925	3.5705	3.0915	2.4136	1.9653	
4.3271	3.6564	3.1473	2.4383	1.9769	
4.4392	3.7251	3.1903	2.4559	1.9846	
4.5327	3.7801	3.2233	2.4685	1.9897	
4.6106	3.8241	3.2487	2.4775	1.9931	
4.6755	3.8593	3.2682	2.4839	1.9954	
4.7296	3.8874	3.2832	2.4885	1.9970	
4.7746	3.9099	3.2948	2.4918	1.9980	
4.8122	3.9279	3.3037	2.4941	1.9986	
4.8435	3.9424	3.3105	2.4958	1.9991	
4.8696	3.9539	3.3158	2.4970	1.9994	
4.9789	3.9950	3.3321	2.4999	2.0000	
4.9966	3.9995	3.3332	2.5000	2.0000	
4.9994	3.9999	3.3333	2.5000	2.0000	

Table A.5   Four-Place Common Logarithms

N	0	1	2	3	4	5	6	7	8	9	1	2	3	4	5	6	7	8	9
															Proportional Parts				
10	0000	0043	0086	0128	0170	0212	0253	0294	0334	0374	4	8	12	17	21	25	29	33	37
11	0414	0453	0492	0531	0569	0607	0645	0682	0719	0755	4	8	11	15	19	23	26	30	34
12	0792	0828	0864	0899	0934	0969	1004	1038	1072	1106	3	7	10	14	17	21	24	28	31
13	1139	1173	1206	1239	1271	1303	1335	1367	1399	1430	3	6	10	13	16	19	23	26	29
14	1461	1492	1523	1553	1584	1614	1644	1673	1703	1732	3	6	9	12	15	18	21	24	27
15	1761	1790	1818	1847	1875	1903	1931	1959	1987	2014	3	6	8	11	14	17	20	22	25
16	2041	2068	2095	2122	2148	2175	2201	2227	2253	2279	3	5	8	11	13	16	18	21	24
17	2304	2330	2355	2380	2405	2430	2455	2480	2504	2529	2	5	7	10	12	15	17	20	22
18	2553	2577	2601	2625	2648	2672	2695	2718	2742	2765	2	5	7	9	12	14	16	19	21
19	2788	2810	2833	2856	2878	2900	2923	2945	2967	2989	2	4	7	9	11	13	16	18	20
20	3010	3032	3054	3075	3096	3118	3139	3160	3181	3201	2	4	6	8	11	13	15	17	19
21	3222	3243	3263	3284	3304	3324	3345	3365	3385	3404	2	4	6	8	10	12	14	16	18
22	3424	3444	3464	3483	3502	3522	3541	3560	3579	3598	2	4	6	8	10	12	14	15	17
23	3617	3636	3655	3674	3692	3711	3729	3747	3766	3784	2	4	6	7	9	11	13	15	17
24	3802	3820	3838	3856	3874	3892	3909	3927	3945	3962	2	4	5	7	9	11	12	14	16
25	3979	3997	4014	4031	4048	4065	4082	4099	4116	4133	2	3	5	7	9	10	12	14	15
26	4150	4166	4183	4200	4216	4232	4249	4265	4281	4298	2	3	5	7	8	10	11	13	15
27	4314	4330	4346	4362	4378	4393	4409	4425	4440	4456	2	3	5	6	8	9	11	13	14
28	4472	4487	4502	4518	4533	4548	4564	4579	4594	4609	2	3	5	6	8	9	11	12	14
29	4624	4639	4654	4669	4683	4698	4713	4728	4742	4757	1	3	4	6	7	9	10	12	13
30	4771	4786	4800	4814	4829	4843	4857	4871	4886	4900	1	3	4	6	7	9	10	11	13
31	4914	4928	4942	4955	4969	4983	4997	5011	5024	5038	1	3	4	6	7	8	10	11	12
32	5051	5065	5079	5092	5105	5119	5132	5145	5159	5172	1	3	4	5	7	8	9	11	12
33	5185	5198	5211	5224	5237	5250	5263	5276	5289	5302	1	3	4	5	6	8	9	10	12
34	5315	5328	5340	5353	5366	5378	5391	5403	5416	5428	1	3	4	5	6	8	9	10	11
35	5441	5453	5465	5478	5490	5502	5514	5527	5539	5551	1	2	4	5	6	7	9	10	11
36	5563	5575	5587	5599	5611	5623	5635	5647	5658	5670	1	2	4	5	6	7	8	10	11
37	5682	5694	5705	5717	5729	5740	5752	5763	5775	5786	1	2	3	5	6	7	8	9	10
38	5798	5809	5821	5832	5843	5855	5866	5877	5888	5899	1	2	3	5	6	7	8	9	10
39	5911	5922	5933	5944	5955	5966	5977	5988	5999	6010	1	2	3	4	5	7	8	9	10
40	6021	6031	6042	6053	6064	6075	6085	6096	6107	6117	1	2	3	4	5	6	8	9	10
41	6128	6138	6149	6160	6170	6180	6191	6201	6212	6222	1	2	3	4	5	6	7	8	9
42	6232	6243	6253	6263	6274	6284	6294	6304	6314	6325	1	2	3	4	5	6	7	8	9
43	6335	6345	6355	6365	6375	6385	6395	6405	6415	6425	1	2	3	4	5	6	7	8	9
44	6435	6444	6454	6464	6474	6484	6493	6503	6513	6522	1	2	3	4	5	6	7	8	9
45	6532	6542	6551	6561	6571	6580	6590	6599	6609	6618	1	2	3	4	5	6	7	8	9
46	6628	6637	6646	6656	6665	6675	6684	6693	6702	6712	1	2	3	4	5	6	7	7	8
47	6721	6730	6739	6749	6758	6767	6776	6785	6794	6803	1	2	3	4	5	5	6	7	8
48	6812	6821	6830	6839	6848	6857	6866	6875	6884	6893	1	2	3	4	4	5	6	7	8
49	6902	6911	6920	6928	6937	6946	6955	6964	6972	6981	1	2	3	4	4	5	6	7	8
50	6990	6998	7007	7016	7024	7033	7042	7050	7059	7067	1	2	3	3	4	5	6	7	8
51	7076	7084	7093	7101	7110	7118	7126	7135	7143	7152	1	2	3	3	4	5	6	7	8
52	7160	7168	7177	7185	7193	7202	7210	7218	7226	7235	1	2	2	3	4	5	6	7	7
53	7243	7251	7259	7267	7275	7284	7292	7300	7308	7316	1	2	2	3	4	5	6	6	7
54	7324	7332	7340	7348	7356	7364	7372	7380	7388	7396	1	2	2	3	4	5	6	6	7
N	0	1	2	3	4	5	6	7	8	9	1	2	3	4	5	6	7	8	9

N	0	1	2	3	4	5	6	7	8	9	1	2	Proportional Parts 3	4	5	6	7	8	9
55	7404	7412	7419	7427	7435	7443	7451	7459	7466	7474	1	2	2	3	4	5	5	6	7
56	7482	7490	7497	7505	7513	7520	7528	7536	7543	7551	1	2	2	3	4	5	5	6	7
57	7559	7566	7574	7582	7589	7597	7604	7612	7619	7627	1	2	2	3	4	5	5	6	7
58	7634	7642	7649	7657	7664	7672	7679	7686	7694	7701	1	1	2	3	4	4	5	6	7
59	7709	7716	7723	7731	7738	7745	7752	7760	7767	7774	1	1	2	3	4	4	5	6	7
60	7782	7789	7796	7803	7810	7818	7825	7832	7839	7846	1	1	2	3	4	4	5	6	6
61	7853	7860	7868	7875	7882	7889	7896	7903	7910	7917	1	1	2	3	4	4	5	6	6
62	7924	7931	7938	7945	7952	7959	7966	7973	7980	7987	1	1	2	3	3	4	5	6	6
63	7993	8000	8007	8014	8021	8028	8035	8041	8048	8055	1	1	2	3	3	4	5	5	6
64	8062	8069	8075	8082	8089	8096	8102	8109	8116	8122	1	1	2	3	3	4	5	5	6
65	8129	8136	8142	8149	8156	8162	8169	8176	8182	8189	1	1	2	3	3	4	5	5	6
66	8195	8202	8209	8215	8222	8228	8235	8241	8248	8254	1	1	2	3	3	4	5	5	6
67	8261	8267	8274	8280	8287	8293	8299	8306	8312	8319	1	1	2	3	3	4	5	5	6
68	8325	8331	8338	8344	8351	8357	8363	8370	8376	8382	1	1	2	3	3	4	4	5	6
69	8388	8395	8401	8407	8414	8420	8426	8432	8439	8445	1	1	2	2	3	4	4	5	6
70	8451	8457	8463	8470	8476	8482	8488	8494	8500	8506	1	1	2	2	3	4	4	5	6
71	8513	8519	8525	8531	8537	8543	8549	8555	8561	8567	1	1	2	2	3	4	4	5	5
72	8573	8579	8585	8591	8597	8603	8609	8615	8621	8627	1	1	2	2	3	4	4	5	5
73	8633	8639	8645	8651	8657	8663	8669	8675	8681	8686	1	1	2	2	3	4	4	5	5
74	8692	8698	8704	8710	8716	8722	8727	8733	8739	8745	1	1	2	2	3	4	4	5	5
75	8751	8756	8762	8768	8774	8779	8785	8791	8797	8802	1	1	2	2	3	3	4	5	5
76	8808	8814	8820	8825	8831	8837	8842	8848	8854	8859	1	1	2	2	3	3	4	5	5
77	8865	8871	8876	8882	8887	8893	8899	8904	8910	8915	1	1	2	2	3	3	4	4	5
78	8921	8927	8932	8938	8943	8949	8954	8960	8965	8971	1	1	2	2	3	3	4	4	5
79	8976	8982	8987	8993	8998	9004	9009	9015	9020	9025	1	1	2	2	3	3	4	4	5
80	9031	9036	9042	9047	9053	9058	9063	9069	9074	9079	1	1	2	2	3	3	4	4	5
81	9085	9090	9096	9101	9106	9112	9117	9122	9128	9133	1	1	2	2	3	3	4	4	5
82	9138	9143	9149	9154	9159	9165	9170	9175	9180	9186	1	1	2	2	3	3	4	4	5
83	9191	9196	9201	9206	9212	9217	9222	9227	9232	9238	1	1	2	2	3	3	4	4	5
84	9243	9248	9253	9258	9263	9269	9274	9279	9284	9289	1	1	2	2	3	3	4	4	5
85	9294	9299	9304	9309	9315	9320	9325	9330	9335	9340	1	1	2	2	3	3	4	4	5
86	9345	9350	9355	9360	9365	9370	9375	9380	9385	9390	1	1	2	2	3	3	4	4	5
87	9395	9400	9405	9410	9415	9420	9425	9430	9435	9440	0	1	1	2	2	3	3	4	4
88	9445	9450	9455	9460	9465	9469	9474	9479	9484	9489	0	1	1	2	2	3	3	4	4
89	9494	9499	9504	9509	9513	9518	9523	9528	9533	9538	0	1	1	2	2	3	3	4	4
90	9542	9547	9552	9557	9562	9566	9571	9576	9581	9586	0	1	1	2	2	3	3	4	4
91	9590	9595	9600	9605	9609	9614	9619	9624	9628	9633	0	1	1	2	2	3	3	4	4
92	9638	9643	9647	9652	9657	9661	9666	9671	9675	9680	0	1	1	2	2	3	3	4	4
93	9685	9689	9694	9699	9703	9708	9713	9717	9722	9727	0	1	1	2	2	3	3	4	4
94	9731	9736	9741	9745	9750	9754	9759	9763	9768	9773	0	1	1	2	2	3	3	4	4
95	9777	9782	9786	9791	9795	9800	9805	9809	9814	9818	0	1	1	2	2	3	3	4	4
96	9823	9827	9832	9836	9841	9845	9850	9854	9859	9863	0	1	1	2	2	3	3	4	4
97	9868	9872	9877	9881	9886	9890	9894	9899	9903	9908	0	1	1	2	2	3	3	4	4
98	9912	9917	9921	9926	9930	9934	9939	9943	9948	9952	0	1	1	2	2	3	3	4	4
99	9956	9961	9965	9969	9974	9978	9983	9987	9991	9996	0	1	1	2	2	3	3	3	4
N	0	1	2	3	4	5	6	7	8	9	1	2	3	4	5	6	7	8	9

Table A.6 Values of e^{-x}

x	0	1	2	3	4	5	6	7	8	9
0.0	1.0000	.9900	.9802	.9704	.9608	.9512	.9418	.9324	.9231	.9139
0.1	.9048	.8958	.8869	.8781	.8694	.8607	.8521	.8437	.8353	.8270
0.2	.8187	.8106	.8025	.7945	.7866	.7788	.7711	.7634	.7558	.7483
0.3	.7408	.7334	.7261	.7189	.7118	.7047	.6977	.6907	.6839	.6771
0.4	.6703	.6636	.6570	.6505	.6440	.6376	.6313	.6250	.6188	.6126
0.5	.6065	.6005	.5945	.5886	.5827	.5770	.5712	.5655	.5599	.5543
0.6	.5488	.5434	.5379	.5326	.5273	.5220	.5169	.5117	.5066	.5016
0.7	.4966	.4916	.4868	.4819	.4771	.4724	.4677	.4630	.4584	.4538
0.8	.4493	.4449	.4404	.4360	.4317	.4274	.4232	.4190	.4148	.4107
0.9	.4066	.4025	.3985	.3946	.3906	.3867	.3829	.3791	.3753	.3716

Values of e^{x}

x	0	1	2	3	4	5	6	7	8	9
0.0	1.0000	1.0101	1.0202	1.0305	1.0408	1.0513	1.0618	1.0725	1.0833	1.0942
0.1	1.1052	1.1163	1.1275	1.1388	1.1503	1.1618	1.1735	1.1853	1.1972	1.2092
0.2	1.2214	1.2337	1.2461	1.2586	1.2712	1.2840	1.2969	1.3100	1.3231	1.3364
0.3	1.3499	1.3634	1.3771	1.3910	1.4049	1.4191	1.4333	1.4477	1.4623	1.4770
0.4	1.4918	1.5068	1.5220	1.5373	1.5527	1.5683	1.5841	1.6000	1.6161	1.6323
0.5	1.6487	1.6653	1.6820	1.6989	1.7160	1.7333	1.7507	1.7683	1.7860	1.8040
0.6	1.8221	1.8404	1.8589	1.8776	1.8965	1.9155	1.9348	1.9542	1.9739	1.9937
0.7	2.0138	2.0340	2.0544	2.0751	2.0959	2.1170	2.1383	2.1598	2.1815	2.2034
0.8	2.2255	2.2479	2.2705	2.2933	2.3164	2.3396	2.3632	2.3869	2.4109	2.4351
0.9	2.4596	2.4843	2.5093	2.5345	2.5600	2.5857	2.6117	2.6379	2.6645	2.6912

x	1	2	3	4	5	6	7	8	9	10
e^{-x}	.36788	.13534	.04979	.01832	.006738	.002479	.000912	.000335	.000123	.000045
e^{x}	2.7183	7.3891	20.086	54.598	148.41	403.43	1096.6	2981.0	8103.1	22026

Note: To obtain values of e^{-x} for values of x other than those listed, use the laws of exponents.

Example: $e^{-6.24} = e^{-6.00}(e^{-.24}) = .002479(.7866) = .00195$

Table A.7 Areas under the Standard Normal Curve from 0 to z

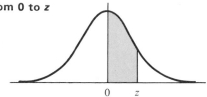

z	0	1	2	3	4	5	6	7	8	9
0.0	.0000	.0040	.0080	.0120	.0160	.0199	.0239	.0279	.0319	.0359
0.1	.0398	.0438	.0478	.0517	.0557	.0596	.0636	.0675	.0714	.0754
0.2	.0793	.0832	.0871	.0910	.0948	.0987	.1026	.1064	.1103	.1141
0.3	.1179	.1217	.1255	.1293	.1331	.1368	.1406	.1443	.1480	.1517
0.4	.1554	.1591	.1628	.1664	.1700	.1736	.1772	.1808	.1844	.1879
0.5	.1915	.1950	.1985	.2019	.2054	.2088	.2123	.2157	.2190	.2224
0.6	.2258	.2291	.2324	.2357	.2389	.2422	.2454	.2486	.2518	.2549
0.7	.2580	.2612	.2642	.2673	.2704	.2734	.2764	.2794	.2823	.2852
0.8	.2881	.2910	.2939	.2967	.2996	.3023	.3051	.3078	.3106	.3133
0.9	.3159	.3186	.3212	.3238	.3264	.3289	.3315	.3340	.3365	.3389
1.0	.3413	.3438	.3461	.3485	.3508	.3531	.3554	.3577	.3599	.3621
1.1	.3643	.3665	.3686	.3708	.3729	.3749	.3770	.3790	.3810	.3830
1.2	.3849	.3869	.3888	.3907	.3925	.3944	.3962	.3980	.3997	.4015
1.3	.4032	.4049	.4066	.4082	.4099	.4115	.4131	.4147	.4162	.4177
1.4	.4192	.4207	.4222	.4236	.4251	.4265	.4279	.4292	.4306	.4319
1.5	.4332	.4345	.4357	.4370	.4382	.4394	.4406	.4418	.4429	.4441
1.6	.4452	.4463	.4474	.4484	.4495	.4505	.4515	.4525	.4535	.4545
1.7	.4554	.4564	.4573	.4582	.4591	.4599	.4608	.4616	.4625	.4633
1.8	.4641	.4649	.4656	.4664	.4671	.4678	.4686	.4693	.4699	.4706
1.9	.4713	.4719	.4726	.4732	.4738	.4744	.4750	.4756	.4761	.4767
2.0	.4772	.4778	.4783	.4788	.4793	.4798	.4803	.4808	.4812	.4817
2.1	.4821	.4826	.4830	.4834	.4838	.4842	.4846	.4850	.4854	.4857
2.2	.4861	.4864	.4868	.4871	.4875	.4878	.4881	.4884	.4887	.4890
2.3	.4893	.4896	.4898	.4901	.4904	.4906	.4909	.4911	.4913	.4916
2.4	.4918	.4920	.4922	.4925	.4927	.4929	.4931	.4932	.4934	.4936
2.5	.4938	.4940	.4941	.4943	.4945	.4946	.4948	.4949	.4951	.4952
2.6	.4953	.4955	.4956	.4957	.4959	.4960	.4961	.4962	.4963	.4964
2.7	.4965	.4966	.4967	.4968	.4969	.4970	.4971	.4972	.4973	.4974
2.8	.4974	.4975	.4976	.4977	.4977	.4978	.4979	.4979	.4980	.4981
2.9	.4981	.4982	.4982	.4983	.4984	.4984	.4985	.4985	.4986	.4986
3.0	.4987	.4987	.4987	.4988	.4988	.4989	.4989	.4989	.4990	.4990
3.1	.4990	.4991	.4991	.4991	.4992	.4992	.4992	.4992	.4993	.4993
3.2	.4993	.4993	.4994	.4994	.4994	.4994	.4994	.4995	.4995	.4995
3.3	.4995	.4995	.4995	.4996	.4996	.4996	.4996	.4996	.4996	.4997
3.4	.4997	.4997	.4997	.4997	.4997	.4997	.4997	.4997	.4997	.4998
3.5	.4998	.4998	.4998	.4998	.4998	.4998	.4998	.4998	.4998	.4998
3.6	.4998	.4998	.4999	.4999	.4999	.4999	.4999	.4999	.4999	.4999
3.7	.4999	.4999	.4999	.4999	.4999	.4999	.4999	.4999	.4999	.4999
3.8	.4999	.4999	.4999	.4999	.4999	.4999	.4999	.4999	.4999	.4999
3.9	.5000	.5000	.5000	.5000	.5000	.5000	.5000	.5000	.5000	.5000

FROM *Outline of Theory and Problems of Statistics* by M. R. Spiegel. Copyright © 1961 by McGraw-Hill, Inc. Used by permission of McGraw-Hill Book Company.

Index

A 8
B 9
C 0
D 1
E 2
F 3
G 4
H 5
I 6
J 7